MOST NOTORIOUS VICTORY

Ben B. Seligman

MOST

NOTORIOUS VICTORY

Man in an Age of Automation

Foreword by Robert L. Heilbroner

The Free Press, New York

Collier-Macmillan Limited, London

Copyright © 1966 by Ben B. Seligman

December 1969

Printed in the United States of America

Collier-Macmillan Canada, Ltd., Toronto, Ontario

Library of Congress Catalog Card Number: 66–23078

Second Printing November 1968

Portions of this work have previously been published as "Auto-mation and the Unions" (now part of Chapter 7) in *Dissent*, Winter 1965; as "Real News and Automated Villains" and as "On Theories of Automation" (both now part of Chapter 10) in *Dissent*, Spring 1965 and May 1966 respectively; as "On Work, Alienation and Leisure" in *The American Journal of Economics and Sociology*, October 1965; as "Automation Comes to the Supermarket", reprinted from the November 1962 issue of *Challenge, The Magazine of Economic Affairs*, a publication of Challenge Communications, Inc.; as "Guaranteed Incomes and Negative Taxes" in *Christianity and Crisis*, January 24, 1966; as "Creating More Jobs: An Anti-Utopian View", reprinted from *American Child*, Nobember 1964, quarterly publication of Na-tional Committee on Employment of Youth, 145 East 32nd Street, New York, New York; and as "Automation and The State", *Commentary*, June 1964; also as "Automation and the Work Force", by Ben B. Seligman, from the book *The Guaranteed Income*, by Robert Theobald, Copyright © 1965, 1966 by Double-day & Company, Inc., reprinted by permission of the publisher. I wish to express my thanks to the editors and publishers for per-mission to use these materials in this book. In addition, I am grate-ful for permission to use e. e. cummings, "pity this busy monster, manunkind", copyright 1944, by E. E. Cummings; reprinted from his volume *Poems 1923–1954*, by permission of Harcourt, Brace & World, Inc., and Faber and Faber Ltd.

B. B. S.

TO THE MEMORY OF

My Father

Foreword

I DON'T think that many people would deny that the differentiating characteristic of the twentieth century is its technological virtuosity or that the most startling contemporary manifestation of that virtuosity is the computer, with its daring infringement of human capabilities. But having gone that far, few people are willing to go much further—least of all, people called "economists." As anyone who reads the current economic literature can testify, our economists are capable of considerable flights of fancy, not to say fantasy. Yet one flight that they seem to be incapable of making is that required to see the technology of our time as fundamentally reshaping the relationships between man and nature, and between man and man, on which present economic society is based. When we compare the fast-changing technological environment with its static economic representation. I am afraid we must declare that *plus ça change, plus c'est la même chose.*

I have had occasion before to wonder about this curious resistance of the economic mind to the implications of science and technology—how astonishing that Lord Keynes and Alfred Marshall, the two greatest architects of modern economic theory, both explicitly excluded technological change from their representations of the economic system! Yet reality does have a way of gradually imposing itself on men's consciousness and eventually of even attaining recognition in their textbooks. We have reached the stage now in the United States at which most of these books assure us that automation is not a "new" problem, that it is not a serious one, and that statements to the contrary are only so many alarums and excursions. This attitude is better than having no opinions at all, but it is not good enough. That is why Ben Seligman's book is peculiarly important. It is the most exhaustive, the most encyclopedic, and certainly the most seriously challenging treatise on the subject that I know of. I cannot foretell how many economists will have crises of faith after examining its detailed panorama, but I would be surprised if there were many whose minds were as firmly made up as before.

That is not to say that I believe an apocalypse of automation threatens us overnight. I suspect that some of the alarms of this book will turn out to be false alarms, that some of the trends it describes may peter out, and that some of the mechanical marvels it cites may simply not work. All that is to be expected in a work of this broad scope and fine texture. What would be the gravest mistake, however, would be to dismiss the main thrust of Ben Seligman's argument because particular instances of it do not materialize. For, with all its focus on the existing state of things, this book is not about today. It is really a book about tomorrow. The central topic of these pages is not the individual machines, the case histories, the theories and countertheories of automation, but the enormous ongoing phenomenon of technological change that is rushing us into the future.

Into what future? A cold and depersonalized vista greets us as the end product of the process so meticulously described in these chapters. No one who has thought through the possibilities for organization and regulation implicit in the technology of cybernation will dismiss that possibility lightly. Yet, in the final analysis, the shape of the future will not be imposed upon us by the wire and glass and electricity of the technology itself. It will reflect, rather, the nature of the social and political and economic system that will install, supervise, and administer the network that will cater to us or be catered to by us.

It is difficult to assert that our present social order is likely to produce the solicitude required for a human use of the powerful techniques of the computer technology. On the other hand, *the new technology is itself changing our social order.* It is too early yet to speak with assurance about its long-run effects, but I would not put aside the chance that it may promote new elites whose outlook, however steeped in science, may yet be more humanist than that of the present business overlordship of technology.

In the meantime we patiently await the changes that we know will overturn our lives. How long must we wait? No question is more important than that of the time span over which the technological transformation of society is apt to take place. The President's Commission on Automation has just completed a thoughtful (if near-sighted) investigation into the impact of automation over the next ten years and has reported that we have nothing to worry about in any fundamental sense. I do not quarrel with that conclusion within the span of another decade. Even at its very worst, technology is not likely to create unemployment on a massive scale in so short a time, *particularly if we follow the Commission's recommendations for the maintenance of a high level of demand.* Nor are the social effects of the new technology likely to change our society unrecognizably within that time.

But what about another *fifty* years of change? Now the shoe seems to me to be on the other foot. It seems impossible that the insinuation of the new technology into the mechanism of the economy half a century from now will *not* have drastically altered its operation. The normal work week, the needed distribution of skills, the levels of reward, and, most of all, the sheer quantity of human labor we shall require are all sure to have changed radically by then. So, too, will much of the intimate texture of life, its established ways, its prevailing social relations, even the conception that men hold of themselves. If one thing is beyond dispute —despite the reluctance of economists to say it aloud—it is that technology is altering life to its existential roots before our very eyes.

Sometime between ten and fifty years hence, then, is the critical period during which we must either find some means of subjecting the technological invasion to responsible public control or during which we must resign ourselves

Foreword

to having it run its course willy-nilly, even if that course runs directly over us. Perhaps it is more meaningful to say that the coming generation—the children who are now in school—will be the last generation able to seize control over technology before technology has irreversibly seized control over it.

A generation is not much time, but it is *some* time. The vast machinery whose potential for social rearrangement is made so explicit in this book is still new, barely installed, only beginning to work its effects on ordinary people in the ordinary round of daily life. We have yet a little while in which to learn, so that we may be in fact the programmers of the future and not the programmed. Let this book be our first lesson.

Robert L. Heilbroner

Preface

THE WRITING of this book, which has absorbed the largest part of my free time during the last three years, represents fundamentally an exercise in what is now called "interdisciplinary research." It is a study not only of the technology of automation but also of its economic, social, psychological, and philosophical implications as well. There was no intent to trespass as a stranger upon the domain of disciplines outside the realms of technology and economics, yet I feel strongly that any social scientist must use the materials of other disciplines if his own analysis is not to flounder. I have therefore searched diligently all the social science literature for guides and insights that might prove useful in grasping what automation is doing to our civilization. I am convinced that, in the study of our new technology, interdisciplinary considerations are essential.

Readers may detect the sources of my own thinking in a group of writers whose common feature is their critical view of contemporary society and all its works — Siegfried Giedion, Clarence E. Ayres, Lewis Mumford, Jacques Ellul, Herbert Marcuse, Norbert Wiener, E. J. Hobsbawm, and Erich Kahler. Except for Ayres and Marcuse, whom I have had the pleasure of meeting briefly in recent years, I have not known these scholars personally, but I have learned much from their many books and articles. Theirs has been a perception of society that impels one to examine carefully the essential aimlessness of our development, an aimlessness that nevertheless moves with an undeniable force toward an end that threatens emptiness or, worse, complete annihilation. It is as though we were behaving like an amoeba, whose pseudopods move in all directions while the whole piece of protoplasm is carried by the tides along a watery surface.

Shortly after I had completed the manuscript of this book, Dr. Kenneth Keniston's study of alienated youth, *The Uncommitted*, came to hand, unfortunately too late for my purposes. Still, it was interesting to note that Keniston's analysis of our alienating society begins with social strains and "historical losses," to employ his own pregnant phrase; and in a fundamental sense these responses stem from the technology of our time. It is technology, argues Keniston, that imposes an "ego dictatorship" in adult life, which, when transmitted to children in a bootless effort to solve the dilemmas of existence, generates what has come to be called "alienation." Keniston's is indeed a fascinating study, for we see how an uncritical acceptance of technology and the values that it has engendered equates the advance of technique with the idea of progress. The consequence is a telescoping of past and future into the present and the destruction of the sense of self that is essential for personal autonomy. All too often "privatization," or an escape from the realm of the public into a closed realm of private fantasy, is confused with autonomy.

The social scientist must deal with such problems as with a palimpsest. He pulls back the upper layers of his subject to expose the fragmentation of work, the rise of the specialist, the final victory of technicism. These developments are reflected in the positive stress that modern science and technology place on process — how a thing is done — rather than on normative criteria. Seldom is the question asked, "Why?" It seems to the practitioner of modern technology an unmeasurable query devoid of meaning, because, in our advanced technological culture, what is relevant can be only something that is measurable, quantifiable. Under such a regime there is no need to inquire after human ends and human purpose.

I call attention to Keniston's book because, though it

views society from a different angle, it appears strongly complementary to my own. For I find also that technology has emptied work of significance and that such a development is bound to create conditions in which a sense of estrangement flourishes. My own study, however, is rooted more consciously in the specifics of technology. My book seeks to analyze the condition of man in an era in which technology has seized control of his fate. It is my thesis that modern technology is by no means a consequence of increments of accident; rather there exists now an internal drive with an independent force that conditions man and his works. This thesis is reviewed in the first chapter, which begins with an overview of the rise of modern technology during the Industrial Revolution of the seventeenth and eighteenth centuries. The significant elements in this upheaval were not only the concatenation of resources, available capital, and an expanded supply of food but also its fortuitous occurrence along a frontier. Britain was a frontier of continental Europe, and the North Country in England was a frontier of the southern commercial centers. Only in such an environment could the explosion of the Industrial Revolution have occurred when it did and in the manner that it did.

The next two chapters pay special attention to the rise of computer technology, tracing its history since World War II and demonstrating how the computer is becoming a major factor in modern life. A feature of this part is a study of the computer-making industry itself, which has been a powerful element in the diffusion and spread of computer techniques. It is in the application of the computer to the broad range of human thought, however, that the threat to man's individuality is revealed. These tendencies are examined in Chapter 3. Although the computer is an extraordinarily useful device in handling the masses of data that modern society demands, it is in its application to productive processes that the most radical impacts are to be expected. With the fully automatic factory not too far off, how does man relate himself to his society, to others about him? A parallel series of questions is explored for the office and white-collar workers. Agencies that might be expected to respond with viable answers are the labor unions and government: In each case a review of the data suggests a less than adequate reply. Does traditional economic and social theory offer suitable analyses for an adequate response to the new technology? This book examines in detail what economists and sociologists have thus far had to say and finds them wanting. For it seems that few face up to the fact that, more than ever, the new technology renders traditional work patterns out of shape and threatens to create a new society in which the control of masses of men may be delivered into the hands of a small number of specialists who believe that only they know what the future ought to be.

I have argued that technology's notorious victory threatens to destroy the essential human qualities that have been thus far characteristic of man. I have contrasted his present condition with the concept of the primitive, a concept that emphasizes man's perennial effort to integrate work, ritual, play, and leisure into a meaningful whole. The charge may be leveled that this contrast resurrects the idea of the "noble savage" and romanticizes the past. Quite the contrary, for neither I nor those who have employed this notion in one way or another — Paul Radin, Stanley Diamond, Kenneth Keniston — seek to return to an unreal Arcadia. Rather the idea of the primitive is employed here as a touchstone by which the inability of man to control himself as he controls his environment may be judged. It serves critics ill to assert that the idea of the primitive implies the idea of savagery, when the latter reaches its apogee of refined perfection only in a technological society.

What then ought to be our objectives? How do we escape the predicament in which we are patently trapped? Ordinary theory — that of the economists, for example — cannot supply useful answers. And why should it, when technical change is conceived to be a mere "given." Robert Solow says that the question of automation is the wrong one, for technology has had no impact on total employment. What is important, he insists, is aggregate demand and something called "capacity output" (but is that not at least a partial function of technical change?). Solow's is an easy escape from the problem, however. Furthermore, it appears to stem from the keen sense of discomfort that economists have always exhibited when confronted by technology. As

Robert Heilbroner says, for most economists, to think of technology as affecting labor utilization is simply too much. But, when social science is constrained by the assumptions and biases of economists, it cannot genuinely flourish. The problem of technology and its impacts requires more than the economist can presently offer for a viable response. It demands the insights that other disciplines can offer as well.

As usual, one must express thanks to a host of friends, relatives, and colleagues, who on reading one or more sections offered comments ranging from irritation to enthusiasm. Their disagreements, suggestions, and qualified approval are deeply appreciated. For their efforts I thank Professors Albert A. Blum, Michigan State University; Lewis A. Coser, Brandeis University; Stanley Diamond, Syracuse University; and John S. Gambs, Hamilton College. I am also grateful to Martin Kessler of *Challenge*; Drs. Sar A. Levitan and Harold L. Sheppard, both of W. E. Upjohn Institute for Employment Research; Ted Silvey of the A.F.L.-C.I.O.; Harvey Swados of Sarah Lawrence College; and Professor Robert S. Weiss of Brandeis University. They will all note that their objections often went unheeded, yet I did listen frequently enough to take advantage of their wisdom. I am especially indebted to Howard Krasnow of the Advanced Systems Division of I.B.M., who kept me from falling into pitholes dug by computer technology and to Israel Gerver of the U.S. Department of Health, Education and Welfare, whose perception of the totality of human affairs lent support to my own dyspeptic views of man's fate. Robert Heilbroner's marvelous sense of balance acted as a welcome restraint; I am grateful for his counsel. The patience of Emanuel Geltman, editor for The Free Press, has been a great comfort. I must also express my thanks to Anita Kupperman, Esther del Grasso, and Barbara Fifield, whose helpfulness at various stages of the book's progress contributed much to its completion. And, once again, as do all authors, I bow to my wife, whose typing skills are an object of continuing admiration.

Ben B. Seligman

Amherst, Massachusetts

MOST NOTORIOUS VICTORY

Shall the axe boast itself against him that
heweth therewith? Or shall the saw magnify
itself against him that shaketh it? ...
Shall the work say of him that made it, He
made me not? Or shall the thing framed say
of him that framed it, He had no understanding?
— Isaiah, X, 15; XXIX, 16

pity this busy monster, manunkind,
not. Progress is a comfortable disease:
your victim (death and life safely beyond)
plays with the bigness of his littleness
— electrons deify one razorblade
into a mountainrange; lenses extend
unwish through curving wherewhen till unwish
returns on its unself.

        A world of made
is not a world of born — pity poor flesh
and trees, poor stars and stones, but never this
fine specimen of hypermagical
ultraomnipotence. We doctors know
a hopeless case if — listen: there's a hell
of a good universe next door; let's go

        — e. e. cummings

Contents

Contents

ONE

Hardware and Software

At First the Wheel   1

Civilized or not, man has always possessed technology. Unceasingly, he has sought to manipulate and control his environment in order to satisfy his needs. In this sense, as C. E. Ayres has said, technology is simply organized skill.[1] Of course, it has been but one part of his heritage – there also were language, social organization, philosophy, religion. All have affected one another, and all have made man what he is, even while man was himself creating them. Yet the most significant set of interactions, if we may employ the sociologist's term, has been that between technology and social organization, for it has determined the manner in which material objects are to be used.[2]

Technology has thus reflected a practical manipulative activity, not a contemplative one. It seldom has been the product of idle curiosity, for it has been used to give man control over nature – or over other men. In large measure, it has been "... the story of the clever people to pass on ... backbreaking work to others less clever than themselves ... "[3] Frequently, technology was employed to make war more deadly, as evident in Leonardo da Vinci's prolific plans for improved machines of terror. Kindly historians have noted how technology reduces the struggle for existence, for by altering the physical environment technology has served man – but under certain prescribed rules, which became in effect its "operational code." When inventions or innovations have occurred, the code has been modified, but often with rather disturbing consequences. Those who are perhaps more critical may have serious questions to pose, for technology has been employed all too often in modes not necessarily inherent in the machine process. (There is much evidence of this fact in some of the contemporary developments that we shall sketch in the following chapters.) When this takes place, the ultimate function of technology is lost to view, as is so often the case today, and it is transformed into unending, senseless activity and a "plundering of life."[4]

Man's unwillingness to accept the limitations of his natural environment first assumed a compulsive thrust in the late fifteenth century, and by the seventeenth century the urge to invent and innovate had become irrepressible. Many of the inventions were extraordinary, but not all were useful—some were nuisances or downright harmful. As Lewis Mumford has demonstrated, gratuitous inventions and negative improvements have been plentiful: Even today certain types of central heating can warp an old bookcase; the elevated toilet seat diminishes the efficiency of the sphincter muscles; and the automobile continues to destroy civilized man with accidents and noxious gases. Not too long ago copious bloodletting was considered a cure for boils, consumption, and old age. But, in the main, inventions were good because, as with the automobile, they gave man motion and a vision of power.[5]

Modern technology is clearly a phenomenon of Western culture. Although the detachable harpoon head of the Eskimo, the bow and arrow of Neolothic man, and the hand loom of ancient Mesopotamia were all artifacts of technology, they did not display the predominant features of modern technique in which complex machines and motive power stemming from sources other than man have molded work and thought. In ancient times men could control their technology and shape their philosophy by the heavens. The capacity to do that today is moot.

Before the rise of the West, technology involved almost exclusively the use of tools. These instruments, generally small in size, were extensions of the hand, and they made

4

the opposable thumb more powerful than it ever could be in a pure state of nature. But man himself supplied the power. (In all probability, man has always had tools, either in single or composite form. Using a bow to activate a drill spindle was a clever application of the latter.)[6] Yet the very flexibility of the hand made tools ill suited to a machine-like process unless they could be torn from the grip of humans. The hand could not work endlessly or with high precision, for, despite the possibilities of limited "automatic" action, as demonstrated in the Taylor and Bedaux methods, hands and arms cannot rotate perpetually.[7] The natural processes of fatigue prevented man from becoming a robot.

Here the machine became a truly revolutionary device, so specialized that it could be made automatic, rotating without pause, as long as energy was fed into its driving mechanism. The striking feature about machines in the twentieth century, however, has been precisely their flexibility, their all-purpose character. Although a hundred years ago the drive was to create single-purpose equipment (and indeed this drive is still prevalent in our own technology), there is a decided tendency now to have an increasing variety of work done by a single or closely related bank of machines. Modular machine tools and numerical control, and indeed the computer itself, demonstrate enough capacity to engage in manifold tasks to suggest that, at least in the sense of flexibility, the machine is again becoming a kind of tool.

FOR THOUSANDS of years technology was relatively static. To be sure, one can always locate an ancestor of a modern device in some classic Greek mechanism, as historians of technology are so fond of doing. Did not Hero of Alexandria describe a steam engine that moved temple doors? Abbot Payson Usher has suggested that what others have described as the industrial mutation of the eighteenth century really had ancient beginnings,[8] and S. Lilley is able to locate the first technological explosion in the third millennium before Christ.[9] Others have asserted that progress has been more linear than exponential. But this discussion ignores the patent fact that the eighteenth century was an axial age. The strategic inventions and innovations of our time have their taproots in that era.

The eighteenth century sharply altered man's social organization, created new sources of power to displace human muscle, and, in the textile industry particularly, provided models for changing a world. What had been done with tools was now done with machines. The machine spun thread, wove and cut cloth, and fabricated cottons. By converting the energies of rushing water or burning coal, other machines supplied power. In the meantime, science developed its own concepts and helped technology perform even greater feats. For example, glass, a discovery of ancient Egypt, made winter indoors more bearable; more important, it lengthened work by allowing the factory to function the year round. But also, glass could be ground to magnify small objects; it could be blown into odd shapes; it made scientific instruments feasible. The knowledge garnered through such instruments helped technology advance still further. Science and technology, once distant cousins, barely on speaking terms, were beginning to have more intimate conversations with each other.

The European continent was quite ready for a technological leap by the eighteenth century. England, destined to outrun everyone, had been lagging behind the other nations for some time. Italian, French, and Dutch industries were fairly well developed. In France the craftsmen were masters of their trades, turning out beautiful furniture and building imposing bridges. Some of the smaller German states like Saxony had begun to industrialize. All the ruling kings and princes sought to foster industry and trade, for that was a prime way to strengthen the state.

Much of the hustle and tumult on the continent, however, had to do with matters of war and articles of luxury. Factories made silks, tapestries, fancy glassware, ornate clocks, pumps for gardens, toys, and automatons for the edification of the rich.[10] Vaucanson, who in 1740 had developed a mechanical loom for figured silks, was required also to entertain the lords and ladies of the French court with automatic drummers and ducks. In Salzburg, a small river was harnessed for water power, but only to play tunes and animate puppets to amuse the Archbishop and his mistresses. Standardization was well known in Germany, but its use was limited to the royal arsenals. Such concern with war, entertainment, and miracles was not very far removed from the ancient world's utilization of steam "engines" and water wheels in temples and other magical places. None of them could satisfy the objectives of a middle class impatient to seize the world. And indeed some of the essential economic ingredients for a true industrial revolution were still lacking in many places on the Continent; the peasantry had not yet been dispossessed, and labor was still costly and "unfree."

The frenetic social and economic explosion of industrialism could occur first only in a new land, in fact, only in a frontier land. And that is precisely what England was in the seventeenth and eighteenth centuries—a frontier of more "civilized" Europe. Furthermore, one must observe that the Industrial Revolution began in England's own frontier, the raw North Country, one of the most backward areas of all Europe. It had been roadless, townless, and poor, and its people had often lived in underground dugouts because they were denied access to woodlands. Yet enough dragon's teeth were sown in this region to provide an army of inventors and innovators, factory organizers, and exploiters of men and machines. The production of silks and other luxuries was most improbable in North England. These were rough men fabricating coarse cotton in a turbulent environment. They were determined to create history, but subject to the laws of nature, which they never did realize had been of their own making. Many were crude, bordering on the illiterate, but they possessed immense pride in what they did. They had little culture and in fact were apt to manifest a massive indifference to it. They were free entrepreneurs fashioning a mass market away from the ruling classes in London. Starting as poor yeomen, they were as determined to succeed as was Richard Arkwright, whose dubious claim to the mechanical spinner gave him a knighthood, a fortune, and twenty factories within a thirteen-year period.[11]

True, the North Country possessed unusual physical advantages: Coal, iron, swift streams, closeness to harbors,

7

and a hospitable climate for spinning were enough to make any nascent industrialist smile with anticipation. Furthermore, there was no hard crust of medieval tradition to pose serious resistance. Merchant-manufacturers could use the little ports without the more common types of red tape, and weavers might set their looms out in the country away from the supervision of the guilds. The Continent was perhaps too civilized to accept such a ruthless economy; beyond the Channel there were too many regulations that inhibited mavericks and adventurers. But on England's frontier up North it was "catch-as-catch-can". In the absence of rigid controls the conditions of life were ready to be made.[12] The juncture of events was extraordinary. Transportation was vastly improved as canals and locomotive and steamboats carried bolts of goods over land and water; steam lent its force for a more powerful driving energy; cotton from the American states assured a steady supply of raw materials; and the earlier era of the merchant-capitalist guaranteed funds for investment. Previous modes of production became inadequate to the task of clothing a world.

Of course, there had been preparation — several thousand years of it — but the time was ripe in the eighteenth century for a leap onto a new plateau. A fair amount of such "social overhead" as ports and roads was already in existence. Nonetheless, it was a fresh ambition for profit and self-satisfaction that motivated the demonic urge to make and market the new commodities. Henry Maudsley, whose improvements in machine tools were of momentous importance, derived sheer physical pleasure from handling a file; Josiah Wedgwood, a proud man, stomped about his plant giving tongue lashings to workers who failed to meet his high standards; James Watt was forever tinkering with and improving the steam engine he had constructed. These men made invention and innovation a way of life on England's frontier. In Glasgow, Manchester, and Birmingham, they did as they pleased: *laissez-faire* was a practice before it was spun into a theory.

AS NEIL SMELSER has said, the new entrepreneur sensed his opportunity,[13] for the spinning problem, evident in the shortage of yarn, could bring a fortune to the lucky man who could solve it. The expectation of change was itself strong enough to fulfill all prophecies. That there was little hope of matching the high quality of Continental industry was not at all troublesome, nor did the burgeoning English textile manufacturer want to do so. His interest was the mass market: His sole dream was to make money. He had given hostages to Mammon, and there were enough free hands around to help him redeem his pledge. The sheep enclosures had converted the English peasant into a beggar. With cheap labor thus harnessed to the machine, it was easy for Manchester to undersell both Europe and the ancient craftsmen of India. The sapping of other civilizations did not disturb the new Englishman. He shipped textiles overseas and traveled up and down his own land selling cheap goods while the old merchant of the South could only curse and rage. He developed a cottage industry, supplying raw materials and capital to workmen who labored in their own homes. He hunted for machines that would work rapidly, and, when he discovered them, he fought the inventors for the rights to use the new equipment or simply committed piracy. He placed men and machines into a single building to create the factory system. One cotton-spinner was advised by his agents to look to invention to speed production, for "... as the Sun shines let us make the Hay." The Industrial Revolution flourished in England's North Country because it was a turbulent society; it was unlikely that such dramatic changes could have occurred in the stable peasant economies of a Denmark or a Holland.[14]

Steam was the propellant that carried the manufacturer to the top of the middle-class pile. Once there, he suddenly discovered an urgent need to justify his grasp for power. He demanded freedom for Nature, but, as he was part of Nature, the obvious corollary followed. Slogans were provided by the French Physiocrats, who had pleaded with their own king to let Nature have its way, to no avail. Adam Smith, the shrewd Scotsman, completed the ideological structure. By the first quarter of the nineteenth century, the middle class had gained its major objective, political power; economic control had been long since achieved. At last, the English bourgeoisie was able to break away from the tutelage of the aristocracy. The latter's mentality always had been framed by the natural turn and rhythm of the seasons and a sometime concern for the welfare of its villeins.[15] The era of the middle class, however, was one of utter callousness. Poverty was too intense to be recognized, and, as in present-day America, the prosperous members of society quickly learned to keep it out of sight and out of mind. The poor were subhuman, appendages to the machine, and poverty simply guaranteed their proper behavior. The middle-class merchant-manufacturer could in no way afford the luxury of an aristocratic purview. His vision was long-run, employing abstinence as a way of completing economic ventures that might not mature for a number of years. Capital had to be carefully husbanded, for failure meant humiliation and debasement before one's peers. As Morse Peckham suggests, the aristocrat did not mind failure: What he regretted was uncertainty—a quality of mind and behavior that the bourgeois accepted.

Technology thus entered into the economic faith of the middle class, for it assured its members that the scientist and engineer would be harnessed to achievement. The philosophy of natural law, with its stress on order, suited the bourgeois very well; the destiny of man, that is, middle class man, was guided by a Provident Unseen Hand. Thus, while the capacities of technology were pushed to the utmost, a new morality was created. Such was the beneficence under which "... only the middle classes had the gall to use every propaganda instrument in their power to persuade the miserable working classes that their standard of living would automatically rise, and to attempt to train them to postpone that gratification to the lives of their great-grandchildren, long after their own lives had ended."[16] Middle-class men were practical and successful. Considering the values of the age, they were deemed to be right.

In the meantime, the machine ground on inexorably: Technology began to augment itself. The flying shuttle required more yarn, and to meet the need Hargreaves developed his spinning jenny. Cartwright came along with his loom when the supply of yarn exceeded what the hand weavers could use. As the market expanded, both at home and abroad, production had to flow from more than a single machine: Many were brought together in one place for mass production. A single prime mover powered by steam was attached to a belt to achieve maximum output. Steam, which was first employed in mines to raise and drain water, moved into the factory and then to the railroad, sustaining and heightening middle-class power. The demands of technology required that iron replace wood as the basic material in machine construction, and soon blackness enveloped the English landscape as the tall towers of the steel mills reached into the skies. The destruction of the environment had begun. The factory became an efficient point of concentration for dealing with anonymous workers. Skills began to atrophy, as alternative employments were closed off through "diseducation." Men were displaced by children; trained artisans by ordinary workers; ordinary workers by machines. Andrew Ure, the manufacturer's chief apostle, advocated withdrawing any process that required dexterity from "the cunning workman" and placing it in charge of a "mechanism, so self-regulating that a child may superintend it." There indeed were the antecedents for an age of automation: It had all happened before. And one must note too that at the start not all workers entered the new factories. During the wars of the eighteenth century, even domestic craftsmen in cottages were able to improve their conditions because of a shortage of labor. Carnage, whether by war or by disease, seemed to increase the worker's wage. Nevertheless, by the early decades of the nineteenth century, the machine had exacted its toll. The hand-loom weavers, the furniture workers, the knitters — all skilled workers — had been completely pauperized, never really comprehending the impersonal forces that had destroyed their craft.[17]

Consequently, it is not too difficult to understand the motives of those craftsmen who occasionally burned a factory or hammered a machine into junk. Such outbursts, however, were easy to control; the militia and the gallows were always nearby. Much more serious were inertia, vested interest, and pressure to conform to time-wonted habit. On the Continent, for example, Bavarian physicians believed that steam-powered vehicles should be banned because high speeds would cause brain disease. Tunnels were utterly out of the question, for a sudden change in air pressure might lead to a stroke. In the latter instance, the Austrian Emperor insisted on a tunnel, for what was a railway without a tunnel? Even on the frontier, in England's North Country, stresses and strains were engendered by the collapse of older, more stable relationships. There were still some who believed that the values the machine was destroying merited survival. For example, Crompton merely wanted to simplify the spinners' tasks and deplored the harnessing of his "mule" to steam to drive hundreds of spindles, for he knew this development would bring changes in the lives of the people, changes that he abhorred. Robert Owen spent his profits on ameliorative projects to relieve industrial oppressiveness. Others tried to make the factory a school from which to send skilled workers back into the cottages.

But technology and the uses to which it was put continued to alter both environment and thought. Industrialism conquered the countryside in short, sharp bursts of energy, and, although it led to prosperity (and depression), it also made human relationships more tense than ever. One needs but call to mind the impact of the railroad. Although Stephenson had built his locomotive in 1814, it acquired practical significance only in the 1820s, when a sturdy rail strong enough to bear heavy loads was developed. In 1830 a steam train began its run between Liverpool and Manchester. There too the British had pioneered, for on the Continent the train was a toy. No longer was the transport of heavy goods limited to water. Major cities had once been located at strategic ports or at the confluence of navigable rivers. Between the cities were farmers and virgin land. But the railroad made it possible for cities to grow at any inland point. Ultimately, the balance between rural and urban existence was reversed. Yet even as the cities gathered the rural dispossessed, the railroad tore at their insides, and life in the centers was disrupted.[18] Not only did giant chimneys excrete their filth upon the landscape, but endless iron parallel bands provided a dubious obbligato to the shrill call of the factory whistle as well. As Mumford remarks, technology made the city a place of stench and disease. Carboniferous capitalism, the offspring of coal and iron, announced the decay of the hinter-lands. "Only the hypnotism of a new invention, in an age uncritically enamored of new inventions, could have prompted this wanton immolation under the wheels of the puffing juggernaut."[19] The machine seemed to acquire an independent existence, with humans converted to mere tenders of its needs. Although it was possible to speak of the inter-dependence of technology and environment, it was the former that came to dominate, virtually emancipated from the restraints of moderation and social control.

THERE WAS, of course, no smoothness, no linearity in these developments. Much of what occurred seemed to possess the quality of happenstance, yet it all moved with a force to be explained primarily by social and economic considerations. For example, the automobile arrived when it did because a *nouveau riche, fin de siècle* society was prepared for a vehicle of marked prestige.[20] The internal-combustion engine was not the necessary condition for the innovation of the automobile, for electric and steam motors, it must be recalled, were quite common in the early days of the auto. Indeed, the first locomotives might have become auto-mobiles, if the rich of the early nineteenth century had been as fascinated by horseless carriages as were their descen-dants. Evidently, more than profitable opportunity is involved in innovation. (A contemporary case in point is the laggard development of nuclear power-generating stations. In addition to local political issues, the investment in a nuclear pile is considerable and the construction difficult. Furthermore, coal-burning plants are still satisfactory from the point of view of the balance sheet.)

In other instances, there is a curious social pressure to innovate because it is fashionable. Industrialists in this country have always been ready to scrap a machine, no matter how good, as long as there is a new one to replace it. Henry Ford, for example, threw out equipment as soon as he discovered more advanced replacements. Maintenance and repair seemed less profitable than acquiring other labor-saving gadgets. In part this phenomenon stemmed from relatively flimsy construction and in part from the

13

breakneck pace at which American factories operated, compared to British plants: But the major motivation appears to have been an impulse to display something new to visitors and rivals. And this impulse was strengthened by the expectation that a better machine or a better mousetrap would always be available to further the game of one-upsmanship in industrial competition. This process happens frequently with automation, in which control of production often is shifted to the computer, whether economically feasible or not, simply because rival companies have installed the new hardware.[21]

Such practices can lead to venerating the machine as if it were a religious icon. The phenomenon is not new: In the eighteenth century various mechanics and scientific societies manifested their abiding faith in the machine with offers of reward for novel devices. The Society for the Encouragement of Arts, Manufactures and Commerce promised "premiums" in 1761 for a machine that would spin six threads simultaneously. But as the Society could think only of improving the old spinning wheel, its objective could hardly meet the need for more and more yarn. Alternative devices were required, and they were not long in arriving. Even the government pressed for more invention; in 1712 the British offered £20,000 to anyone who would build an exact measuring device for longitude, an achievement attained in 1764 by John Harrison with a chronometer that kept correct time within fifteen seconds for five months.

OF COURSE, the state has always expressed a close interest in technology, dating back to the hydraulic societies of Asia, in which large water works were maintained for irrigation and communication.[22] One may add too the temples and pyramids of Egypt, the hanging gardens of Babylon, the bridges and aqueducts of the Romans, and the Manhattan Project of wartime America. In fact, it has been in the waging of war that the state has had the greatest need of the technologist. The public career of da Vinci was matched by that of the Flemish fortification expert Stevinus, whose service to the Dutch Republic in the sixteenth century was invaluable. Lavoisier's work on gunpowder helped to make the armies of the French Revolution almost invincible. States helped also with the patent system, which seems to have started in the North Italian cities in the latter half of the fifteenth century. Undeniably, grants of monoply, which were what patents implied, were important incentives. The United States Patent Office was started in 1790; the Bureau of Standards, established in 1901, which maintains scientific standards in chemistry, physics, radiometry, electronics, and the like, is also an expression of government concern with technology.

The closeness of the state, war, and technology has been emphasized in our own time by that most terrible of all weapons, the thermonuclear bomb, the cost of which could have been borne only by government resources. Sonic detecting instruments, radar, anti-aircraft control, proximity fuses, linear programming, a mathematical technique for inventory housekeeping, and the computer itself were developed under the pressures of war. Only the state can shoot satellites into the atmosphere and pay for the exploration of space. It is not surprising that well over $10 billion of the Federal budget are now regularly allocated to "research and development." The scientific community is virtually dependent on government largesse: In 1961, more than three-fourths of electronic scientists and engineers were engaged on projects paid for by the Federal government.

It is improbable that the state can or will relax its interest in technology, for the latter unquestionably supports its power. Often it is a matter of the highest "security," as in the present-day United States. When the Byzantine Empire discovered "Greek fire," a compound of sulphur, pitch, and naphtha first used successfully to repel an Arab attack in the eighth century, it kept the invention to itself for 400 years. During those centuries, the Byzantines developed all sorts of devices to apply the fire more efficiently.

Throughout the ages — from the Greek fire to huge stone throwers, gunpowder, metals for cannon, bridges, the semaphore telegraph, and mass production in arsenals — technology and the machine have served the gods of war. As Mumford has said, "At every stage in its modern development it was war rather than industry and trade that showed in complete outline the main features that characterize the machine."[23] Interchangeable parts, a basic principle for the modern assembly line, was devised by the Frenchman Le Blanc in 1785 and the American Whitney in 1800, primarily for weaponry. Not until the 1860s was interchangeability applied to nonmilitary machines like the reaper. Bessemer steel provided a cheaper material to contain the explosive force of gunpowder. And the disciplined mass army became the model for the discipline of the factory; the faceless uniformity of the military matched to perfection the men on the production line.

THE ROLE OF the scientist in these developments came late. Man worked for centuries with wheels, levers, pulleys, and planes before he began to ask why these devices functioned as they did. That is to say, technology antedated science. Chemistry had to have weights and balances, just as biology required the microscope. The theory of thermodynamics depended on a vast body of experience arising from the Newcomen and Watt steam engines. Certainly, in the early days of modern technology, it was the working mechanic who conceived, designed, and built the machine. The reaper and the rapid-fire revolver—the six-shooter that conquered the Western plains—were products of nineteenth-century mechanical skill.[24]

Even when science began to flower, the major objectives at first were utility and practicality. Willard Gibbs, pure scientist par excellence, began his career in the 1860s as an engineer, inventing a hydraulic turbine before giving his attention to physics and mathematics. Admittedly, a close relationship between scientist and technologist was inevitable, for the machine was something the former could easily understand. It expressed reality rather than metaphysics and made the scientist intellectually comfortable. Faraday and Oersted could thus demonstrate a connection between magnetism and electricity. This led to the idea of generators and was fundamental to the growth of electrical engineering.[25] Werner Siemens then conceived his electric dynamo (a term coined by him), in which current strengthened magnet and magnet strengthened current to provide, by such alternation, even more energy and to facilitate the transmission of electricity. By 1870 alternating-current machines were available. In 1879 Siemens successfully applied the electric motor to the railroad. Then there was Clerk Maxwell's famous contribution to the theory of electromagnetism, which underpinned the modern radio as a form of technology. A great flowering in American science took place when the Nazi scourge forced Albert Einstein, Leo Szilard, Enrico Fermi, and numerous others to flee. By that time it was difficult to distinguish technology from science, for the mushroom cloud at Los Alamos was as much one as the other.

As the scientist became more and more involved in the machine, technological change itself accelerated. Minor differences aside, Europe in A.D. 1000 was not unlike mainland Greece in Alexander's day from a material point of view. Muscle power, supplemented by animals, was the primary source of energy for over a millennium and a half. Water and the power of the winds were not harnessed until the fifteenth and sixteenth centuries. Then came an overwhelming surge, reaching its climax in the eighteenth century, and within less than 200 years industry and urbanization displaced agriculture as society's chief preoccupation, while the machine came to dominate the life of man. If the speed at which we can cross the earth's surface is a reflection of the rate of invention and innovation, then clearly the pace has been intensified. Between 1829 and the present, the automobile, the railroad, and the jet airplane have added more to man's ability to move than was achieved in all the aeons that went before. It took the crowned heads of Europe about three days to get to London for the funeral of Edward VII in 1910; the death of President Kennedy brought dignitaries to Washington from the six continents in less than twenty-four hours. If the ability to kill large masses of people in war is a rough index of rapid technological change, then surely there has been exponential growth between the fifteenth-century cannon and the hydrogen bomb. Or, as Kenneth Boulding has noted, it took less than a decade to rebuild Europe and Japan, as contrasted to decades in the past or centuries after the fall of Rome. Indeed, acceleration in technology feeds upon itself, devouring earlier techniques and machines in great gulps. Quick obsolescence has become a datum of industrial endeavor. UNIVAC I, the world's first data-processing computer, was retired to a museum by the United States Census Bureau in 1963, after operating continuously for but twelve years, because it was much too slow and too small compared to up-to-date equipment. Enshrined in Washington's spanking new Museum of Science and Technology, it is as archaic as the wood-burning locomotives stored in other Smithsonian buildings.[26]

The acceleration thesis, developed most forcibly by Hornell Hart, has been challenged on occasion. But the counterarguments, which merely tally patents on file, are not persuasive. Granted that innovation depends on the use and disuse of older equipment, mistakes, luck, available capital and labor, and the like, the fact is that invention and innovation today spread more quickly than ever. Symposia and professional associations eagerly pass the gospel along, and no less an authority than George Sarton declared in 1936 that scientific progress was being accomplished in shorter and shorter periods. If the interval between an invention and its adoption is a measure of acceleration, then surely Hart is right.[27] In the eighteenth century, adoption followed invention within a decade or less for almost all the important machines. Somewhat longer intervals appear to have characterized the first half of the nineteenth century. Perhaps more time was needed for digestion. But in the second half about 50 per cent of the strategic inventions were adopted within a decade or less; in the first quarter of the twentieth century about 60 per cent became viable innovations within a decade; and in the second quarter the ratio rose to 70 per cent.[28] As C. E. Ayres so well states the case: "If we suppose that tool-combinations occur in the same fashion as that in which digits are combined in the mathematical theory of permutations, then the resulting series is a progressive one in the mathematical sense of series each member of which is derived from each preceding member by the same operation. In such a case it would be sharply progressive in the sense that the *number of combinations would increase very rapidly.*"[29] Such swift change is not merely a matter of degree, as some writers contend, for, as Norbert Wiener once remarked, the difference between a fatal dose of strychnine and a medicinal one is also a question of degree.

BUT TO SUGGEST that technology manifests an internal drive to accelerate by no means implies a smooth and balanced growth pattern. Development and change are not linear. For many years, even decades, after the Industrial Revolution's take-off, handicrafts subsisted side by side with the mechanized factory. In fact, belief in the values of handicrafts, forlorn as it was, expressed resistance to the machine. At any given time, there were marked differences in the pace at which segments of an economy or an industry were subjected to alteration. In British woolens, for example, the factory system paralleled a still vigorous cottage industry.

This dualism could only come about because the manufacturers did not stem from the same social groups that constituted the merchants who had controlled the domestic mode of production. In Yorkshire there was no transition from the cottage to the factory: One simply expired in agony and helplessness as the other flowered into successful enterprise. Furthermore, Paul Mantoux's genealogies clearly demonstrate that the new manufacturers were descendants of Northern yeomen rescued by the Industrial Revolution from dispossession and destruction.[30] They were not of the same breed that had spawned the earlier merchant. Their pecuniary values, nurtured in an independent farming that was now moribund, propelled them into the infant industries, and they fought bitterly against "inventors" like Arkwright who had sought absolute monopolies for their machines. If the new industrialist needed more labor, as was frequently the case, he took in less fortunate fellow yeomen, as well as paupers and foot-loose ex-soldiers. The youthful textile industry was notorious for its use of ". . . the scum of every class and every occupation."[31] Many were caught in its vortex as it pursued the objective of making profit. And it was untroubled by sneers from London that the whole business was merely marginal.

A like phenomenon was visible in other places and other times: Carriage builders (except for Studebaker) did not become automobile manufacturers, nor was the aircraft industry beholden to automobiles. Telephone companies grew alongside the telegraph, and the filming of movies had little to do with the making of still cameras. As Joseph A. Schumpeter has shown, there were Old Firms and New Firms, Innovators and Sticks-in-the-Mud, and the greatest likelihood was that one was ready to bash in the head of the other.[32] Meanwhile, those unfortunate enough to be working in industries made moribund by rivalry were cast aside to live out their lives in utter desperation. The hand-loom weavers did not go to work in the new factories: They were simply left to rot in misery. As Marx observed, "History discloses no tragedy more horrible than the gradual extinction of the English hand-loom weavers, an extinction that was spread over several decades, and finally sealed in 1838." Poor relief prolonged the agony: The old weaver and his family were allowed to subsist on 2½ pence a day. Mechanization also altered the curious kinship system that abounded in the spinning mills, in which family units had constituted the core of the work force. The masters' control eventually disintegrated, as more and more cheap labor was required: One's own children were hardly enough to satisfy the voracious maw of the factory. Quite early in its career capitalism thus revealed its tensions and strains.[33]

That such developments can create structural distortion seems undeniable: The case histories of the defense and space industries in America offer some contemporary evidence. Here is an important and relatively new sector of the economy, dependent mainly on the largesse of the government and whose technology has virtually no relationship to what the rest of the country does. Drawing on exotic materials, these industries employ high-cost, high-specification methods that require parts to be assembled in dust-free, vibrationless plants with devices and components constantly tested, temperature and humidity carefully controlled, and precision machinery of the kind achieved only by computer calculations. The scientists and engineers who work in these companies manifest habits that are sharply different from those in the usual mass-production plants. Involved in building prototypes, they are utterly uninterested in costs: In an ordinary firm they would drive a controller out of his mind. Yet this is one into which the bulk of the scientists and engineers have been enticed and that includes some four million members of the labor force. With a decreasing proportion of the outlay allocated to capital expenditures—the share of the latter in military spending dropped from about 75 per cent in 1951 to about 47 per cent in 1962—the multiplier effect has fallen to less than two.[34] Meanwhile, the rest of the economy stumbled along with high unemployment, reduced only when the products of these exotic industries are put to use.

ALTHOUGH CERTAIN inventions or innovations represent "breakthroughs" with broad implications, the historian of technology must search for those that have had important social and economic consequences. These latter may be characterized as strategic. It may not be possible to measure their total impact—Kuznets, for example, speaks of the discounted value of the additional product derived from an invention[35]—for the tidal effects of major innovative changes must be judged in terms of altered institutions, social relationships, and forms of behavior. Even in ancient times there must have been strategic inventions: The plow, no doubt, had far-reaching results, for with it Neolithic man converted himself from a nomad and hunter into a farmer. The strategic changes for our time began in the eighteenth century. The sometimes exhilarating, often painful experiences man suffered then revealed that the social process was markedly influenced by "...a sequence of *strategic* inventions..."[36] In the case of steam power, a force destined to alter the face of the globe, change stemmed from several strategic machines, including Newcomen's atmospheric engine, Watt's low-pressure engine, and Trevithick's high-pressure engine.

Strategic *combinations* also are possible, as with Robert Fulton's steamboat. He was not the first to build such a ship; he invented neither engine nor paddle. He did, however, calculate more accurately than did others water resistance, the angle of the paddle wheel, and the size of the engine that would be most useful. His *Claremont* was a crude and poorly designed affair as it chugged up the Hudson River, but it did better than most of its rivals. Having successfully combined the work of others, Fulton was able to exploit it commercially and to become a culture hero forever enshrined in fifth-grade history books.[37]

Consider the clock, perhaps the greatest strategic invention of all time. Doubtless its roots can be traced to the clepsydra or water clock of the third century B.C. For centuries, however, it remained primitive. Not until the seventeenth and eighteenth centuries did it begin to be a refined instrument of regulation. Yet even in its crude and inaccurate medieval form it governed the lives of monks and the routines of the monasteries and, in this very dictation, tore society from the rhythms of nature. The clock's usefulness in telling men what to do when was much enhanced by the escapement, a device that prevented the falling weight in the mechanism from moving at an accelerated pace. Regularity was thus ensured: No longer was it necessary to tell time by the seasons or the birth of a calf. Lewis Mumford argues, and perhaps rightly so, that the clock was a more strategic invention than was the steam engine, for, he asserts, the even flow of energy through a fabricating plant or regularized production or standardization would have been impossible without it.[38]

More important, with the clock, *time* became an abstraction and a commodity. Time was money. By 1500 most towns in Europe displayed elegant tower clocks, even though home pieces were available only to the rich. And in the seventeenth century, with the important work of Galileo and Huygens on the pendulum, the clock became one of the first occasions for joint ventures of science and technology. There is no doubt that the clockmakers contributed much to the shaping of the Industrial Revolution. Precision and accuracy, essential ingredients of modern production, were provided by them. The habits of thought that stemmed from the clock also underpinned the demand for accuracy in weights and measures. Standardization became a categorical imperative: Even the requirements of surface and air travel were to be standardized and embodied twice each year in the ritual of the timetable.

22   Mining, of course, was an important field for the

emerging technology. One of the most ancient of industries, it had not advanced very much over the centuries: It was unattractive, work for slaves and prisoners. In the very earliest days in Germany, mines were operated in a kind of cooperative fashion, but beginning in the thirteenth century these "mining communities" were displaced by more capitalistic forms of organization. (Today, in the United States the process appears to have reversed itself, with unemployed miners joining forces to dig in mines abandoned by capitalists. The latter, however, often protect their remaining investments by flooding allegedly uneconomic shafts, thus denying to discarded workers even the right to scratch bare livings from ground no one wants. The mine owners are evidently highly moral, as digging in abandoned mines is considered bootlegging and illegal. The law does not condemn poverty, however.)

By the sixteenth century most of the mines were privately operated, but they did face a serious technological handicap—they flooded easily, and water had to be removed if the shafts were to thrust deeper and deeper. A steam pump would have been ideal: The first practical device of this kind was built by Thomas Savery in England in 1698, but it was more than likely to blow up in the miners' faces.[39] When Newcomen developed his plug rod, valve gear, and balance beam in 1712, a better, more powerful prime mover was made available, although it was still wasteful of energy. Like Savery's, Newcomen's engine raised water through the condensation of steam, so that the work was actually done by atmospheric pressure; hence the name "atmospheric engine." Watt's use of a separate condenser in 1769 proved revolutionary, for then the heat in the working cylinder could be contained with a jacket. But most important for the Industrial Revolution were his mechanical arrangements, consisting of planetary gears that converted the piston's reciprocating motion into rotary motion. That was the beginning of forward movement for the railroad and the factory belt. Watt added a flyball governor, adapted from windmills, in 1788 to adjust the flow of steam for uniform speed. In this device, the shaft of the governor was geared to the steam output at one end and linked to an input valve at the other. As the engine started, the gear arrangement turned the shaft to which the flyballs were attached. Excessive engine speed impelled the flyballs outward, thus closing the input valve and slowing down the engine. If the engine was itself too slow, the flyballs dropped, opening the input valve. Clearly this process was an early example of feedback. Mercury gauges and glass water gauges to measure water levels and boiler pressure started industrial man on his long career of machine-tending and watching.

The steam engine may not have created the factory system, as Mantoux asserts,[40] but without steam the system would have lacked the impetus and expansive force that it so quickly manifested. The addition of steam power to Crompton's "mule" in textile spinning was a major innovation: Production mounted sharply, as the skilled spinner was replaced by machine tenders, harbinger of the dilution in the work force. As a consequence, technology and the social changes attendant upon its growth moved in leapfrog fashion. While one part of a fabricating process was altered, other parts, not yet improved, fettered production and induced searches for innovation. There are numerous examples of this problem in the modern age: The speed of the calculator was useful only when a print-out component had been provided; the automatic machine gun could not be adopted until smokeless powder was available; the jet engine, patented in 1929, was stalled for more than a decade until metals able to withstand high temperatures were developed; and certain alloys had to await hard cutting-machine tools. Such technological leapfrogging was quite significant, for work was both created and destroyed, while some people were advanced in the system and others were discarded. The drive to accomplish tasks in new ways went on without abatement.

WHEN THE Danzig town council ordered the inventor of a weaving machine to be strangled in 1570, it only revealed that such acts could not suppress the search for mechanization. In England, Kay's flying shuttle, developed around 1730, increased weaving speed by freeing one hand for other tasks. The spinners then had to produce more yarn to satisfy the weavers' demands. They did catch up, thanks to such devices as Hargreaves's jenny, which allowed one spinner to control several spindles without changing their motion, but the spinners soon found themselves with a surplus of yarn, which had to be exported. The weavers then reacted angrily, calling them "devils" seeking to destroy an honorable British craft. The weavers, however, were liquidated by other, more impersonal means, for weaving simply had to match the performance of spinning. Cartwright's power loom met the need, and the factories that then grew in Manchester undermined the hand-weaving trade.

Occasionally, ingenious solutions were worked out for specific mechanical problems. One was the changing of patterns in weaving, a technique that French inventors solved with no little ingenuity. Cards with holes, much like those on some present-day IBM machines, were set up in chain fashion to select the proper set of needles for a particular pattern. The punched cards rotated past the needles of the loom, so that only those needles that matched the holes could pass through. Their threads set the pattern desired. In another machine, the needles were selected by a cylinder pierced with holes. It was quite like the player piano of a later century, in which the holes in the roll actuated the keys to bang out a Beethoven sonata. Remarkably intricate patterns could be woven in this fashion.

Interestingly enough, Charles Babbage, the English mathematician who designed a mechanical computing machine in 1833, thought of using similar cards in his device, with the holes representing symbols, a striking forerunner of modern computing techniques. In French textiles, however, all this cleverness did not match the impact of the English rivals across the Channel, for production was still directed toward the luxury trades. It was left to the British to demonstrate how to exploit the full potential of a mass market stemming from the population explosion that began in the eighteenth century. Within a hundred years England's population had quadrupled; America's had grown sixteen times. People had to be clothed, and the conquest of Europe's perennial textile shortage revealed enough truth in the aphorism that necessity is the mother of invention to enshrine the latter forever in the great body of man's conventional wisdom.

Essential to the spread of technology was information, and information meant printing. Again the historian digs back into the past of ancient China to discover its roots. It is not clear from the experts what this tracing proves, for the strategic combinations in printing were not achieved until movable type, oil-base inks derived from the work of painters, type founding, continuous paper-making, and the mechanical press, the idea for which came from the winery, were brought together to form a single complex. Gutenberg's movable type clearly was not enough. Furthermore, books remained an unattainable luxury as long as parchment was the only substance on which to print. Paper, initially derived from linen, was essential for wide dissemination of reading matter. True, paper had been known in China in the first century; it then moved to Samarkand in the eighth century, to Egypt in the tenth, to Spain in the twelfth, to Italy in the thirteenth, and to Germany in the fourteenth. But the spread of print was still handicapped; individual sheet manufacture was for a long time the major technique, and it was not until the Fourdrinier machine was perfected in the early nineteenth century that it became possible to make paper in continuous rolls. Without such rolls the mass-distribution newspaper, for example, would have been impossible. Rags for the papermaker's vats were another bottleneck; they were always in short supply. As a result, straw and vegetables were tossed into the pot, in fact, anything that contained cellulose. At last, in the 1860s, the chemists learned how to cook wood pulp. This discovery, together with the solution of the critical type-founding problem, that is, holding the type body and end together, at long last made universal literacy a feasible prospect.[41]

History no longer left anonymous gaps: Yet at the same time it was easier to homogenize culture and make the Philistine supreme. The word became omnipresent: It deposited itself behind breakfast eggs; it received vacant stares in the subway; it sustained the coffee break; it became the truth. And with advertising the major source of income for the newspapers, the beliefs of the dominant class could be decked in objectivity for the easier control of the mass of men who now possessed the last word fit to print.

THE COMPONENTS OF modern industrialism were gradually finding their proper places. Strategic inventions, no matter when they arrived on the scene, were fitted into the factory, which itself had only to convert discrete production into a continuous process to meet the requirements of the twentieth century. Such a process was found in flour-milling, bread-making, and the slaughter of pigs. Industrialization would not have attained the intensity it did without the assembly line and its unbroken flow. Continuous production was implicit in the early factory's organization: Its genuine possibilities were first revealed by Oliver Evans with his mechanized grain mill built near Philadelphia in the 1780s.

Almost a century later, the Cincinnati meat-packers demonstrated how even refractory material might be processed in a hitchless flow. A continuous, uninterrupted movement from the receiving platform, with quick transfer through all the stages of fabrication to the finished product, became an industrial reality. Such was the principle that Evans had established and the packing houses perfected. In Evans's system, the product was even untouched by human hands. Belts and screw and bucket conveyors carried the grain into the mill, where it was lifted to the top floor and then dropped through the various processing stages to the millstones. It was a superb model for later generations to follow.[42] The bakers were not far behind: In the 1830s bread trays were carried through hot-air ovens on rails; endless chains moved biscuits for the British Admiralty; and by 1913 bread factories were functioning with baking plates fifty feet long. Only the slicing and packing remained to be mechanized. And as Siegfried Giedion remarks, the modern manufacturer of bread altered tastes enough to make a soft white blob of denatured flour palatable to industrial man for all time.

The main impetus to produce by the assembly line stemmed, however, from the slaughterhouse. The flesh of animals, an organic substance, unstandardized and varying in weight and size, had to be molded and shaped for mass

27

production. The Cincinnati plants solved this seemingly intractable problem in the 1860s with overhead rails and a conveyor system. Hogs were automatically lifted by their hind legs as they entered the abattoir for conversion into food. The process of death included twenty-four operations even before the animal was severed in two. Rotary hoisters prepared the hog for bleeding. Scalding softened the hair and bristles prior to shaving. The carcass was then cooled (by this time the hog had expired) and opened for an inspection of its entrails. Scraping, skinning, and spine-cleaving were all done by mechanical methods. Nor did the industry suffer any shortage of raw material, for the cattle business on the Western prairies provided herds with an impassiveness unknown to the family farmer. With mechanization, all parts of the animal were processed, including the spare ribs that once had been dumped into the Ohio River as waste. With refrigeration and the railroad storage car, developed in the 1870s, slaughtering could be undertaken in the summer, as well as in the winter. Meat-packing reached out to a mass market, and with the rise of the business barons — Armour and Swift — the potentials of the new technology were revealed for all to see and eat.

Henry Ford got the idea for his assembly line from the butchers.[43] The production of automobiles demanded unimpeded speed: Ford's Highland Park plant, opened in 1910, illustrated how such speed could be attained, for it was indeed an achievement of American mechanical art. Scientists may have been sparse in those days, but the technicians more than made up the lack. So skilled had American mechanics become that machine tools were exported to Europe, a case of the pupil surpassing the teacher. Drill presses, lathes, planers, and grinders were beginning to operate automatically, whereas gauges and other instruments made work more precise. Based on a careful design of sequence, the Highland Park installation utilized all the up-to-date equipment provided by the skilled machinist. Tools were not grouped by departments, as in other companies, but were rather placed at particular points according to job requirements. This arrangement allowed the work to flow from one machine to the next in a continuous line without doubling back or interruption. Gravity slides were used to pass parts in process along the line. Moving lines were introduced in 1913, rooting the men to one spot as the work flowed past them without end. By 1914, the whole process had been lifted off the floor, so hastening assembly that an auto could be completed in ninety-three minutes. Production became a river, fed by tributaries that carried in fenders and doors and wheels while men stood by, pushing it along at greater and greater speed. The apogee of industrialization had been achieved — standardization, interchangeability, continuous flow, and unbearable speed.[44]

Inescapably, the assembly line became a way station on the road to production without men. Humans still had to be employed for tasks the engineers had not yet mechanized. But the time was not far off: The question already was being posed in 1916. In that year, a Milwaukee manufacturer wondered if automobile frames might not be built automatically.[45] The search was on for the automatic factory which could function as if it were a set of synchronized watches with split-second timing. Technology was to dispose forever of the need for workers to tend the product-in-process as it gathered shape, from the raw material at the receiving platform to the painting and storing of a finished vehicle. The protest of the worker that the assembly line was a brutal master, driving at inhuman speed would be heard no longer. Eventually the machine would do the work itself.

From the economic standpoint, technology was bound to alter the production function, the relationship of input mix to output. Obviously, the whole business would be pointless unless there were capital or labor savings. That such effects have occurred appears unquestionable. For example, it has been demonstrated that, in petroleum refining, technical progress has achieved, not only an absolute reduction in all input factors, but also the greatest relative cutback in labor. From 1913 to 1955, the utilization of labor in this industry dropped in the ratio of 140 to 1; fuel declined in the ratio of 14 to 1; raw materials, 4 to 1; and capital $2\frac{1}{2}$ to 1.[46] New equipment, improved capacity, high-speed tools, and better layout all contributed to lower capital requirements per unit of output; most authorities suggest that the capital-output ratio has dropped from about three in the 1920s to a little more than one today.

The new technology was quickly assimilated to the forms of business organization that accompanied its development. Ultimately, as Thorstein Veblen was quick to note, business dominated technology. As new sources of energy were discovered and costs of exploitation mounted, much more capital was required than could be supplied by a single entrepreneur or condominium of entrepreneurs. The factory and its costly equipment brought overhead costs to the forefront of economic calculation. Centralization became essential for efficiency. Machine production meant collective effort, for profit could be guaranteed in no other way. Fundamentally, it was all a gigantic transformation in the condition of man, comparable in magnitude to the Neolithic conversion from nomadism to farming. The thrust toward technological change was internalized, creating an irresistible imperative. A tidal wave of mechanization overwhelmed society, flowing from the factory into the home with toasters, tinned food, and washing machines. Cities grew and then gagged as a surfeit of cars and trucks clogged the streets and polluted the air. Technology became, not merely a congeries of instruments to produce goods, but also a rigid system that determined in advance the nature of the output and the actions of those who were caught in its complex of wheels. It established, ". . . not only the socially needed occupations, skills and attitudes, but also individual needs and aspirations."[47] Technology lost its neutrality: The uses to which it was put became as much part of its drive as were the dynamos, moving belts, and servomechanisms that it comprised.

Man was at the mercy of technology: He was helpless when it failed, even momentarily, as in a great snowfall. The character of work underwent profound and irreversible change: New rhythms were established, severing man from a genuinely close relationship to his environment. Production no longer displayed a communal base: In fact, as man was being exiled from that sphere, he was somehow expected to consume its output, even if he had to mortgage his precarious future to do so. Skill disappeared as an end and virtue in itself: It had been merged into the machine, leaving man bootless in a world he could barely comprehend. Desiccated values and parochial attitudes created faceless personalities ready to leap into the first insane mass movement to come along. The artificial and the ephemeral were enhanced by rationalization and mechanization. Society had been prepared for a new mutation. Sometimes man sought to recapture a sense of self with a weekend camping trip. But technology had become his master, and, as he escaped into the woods, he took the machine with him.

A babel of calculators

The drudgery of doing numbers by hand is a task people have always sought to escape. From the ancient abacus to the present-day electronic computer, the mental addition of sums has been supplemented by mechanical devices of one sort or another. The abacus itself, the origins of which are lost in antiquity, was used in Europe well into the seventeenth century. A device of utmost simplicity, it consisted of a number of parallel, equally spaced rods fixed into a frame with movable beads to represent numbers of any denomination. With each rod indicating a numerical position, the value of the digit could be set by the location of the beads. It can still be employed as an aid in adding and subtracting: Skillful clerks in China and Japan, where it continues to be used, can divide and even extract square roots by rapidly moving the beads. A famous arithmetic contest staged in November 1946 between a Japanese clerk using an abacus and an American army private operating a desk calculator resulted in a hands-down victory for the former.

In an age of mechanization it was to be anticipated that arithmetic also would be mechanized. In the seventeenth century, John Napier, the inventor of logarithms, constructed a set of numbering rods as a means of quick multiplication. Called "Napier's Bones," they consisted of several rectangular pieces of wood with four flat faces, on each of which there were nine squares. A digit at the top of each face was followed in each square in descending order by its successive multiples from two to nine. The tens and the units of each multiple were divided by a diagonal. Thus, to multiply 315 by 4, the "three," "one," and "five" rods, identified by the digits at the top, were placed side by side. By reading the multiples in the fourth row from right to left, taking care to add the tens digits to the adjacent unit digits at the left, one could simply call off the product.

The slide rule, whose basic principle is not unlike the one incorporated in modern analogue computers, was invented by William Oughtred in the early seventeenth century.[1] As is well known, logarithms are represented on it by proportional distances. As the log of the product of two numbers is equal to the sum of the logs of those numbers, the sum of the addition of two successive segments of a straight line, with their lengths representing say $\log x$ and $\log y$ on a given scale, will measure $\log (x + y)$ on the same scale. Oughtred was ingenious enough to place one log scale against another and thus could multiply and divide directly. His instrument could be described as a "continuous function" device. A larger slide rule implies greater precision: Unfortunately, the human eye can at best read off a number to two decimal places, so that accuracy is limited. For the ordinary run of engineering problems, however, this device was adequate.

Purely mechanical calculating devices can be traced back to Blaise Pascal's invention in 1642. Pascal, a mathematician and philosopher, did not disdain practical affairs: His gadget was utilized by his merchant father to add accounts. But it was not widely used, for most other businessmen in Auvergne still preferred to figure with pencil and paper. Pascal's machine employed "toothed wheels" or gears, on each of which numbers from zero to nine were marked. With the wheels mounted in a box along an axis, each could be advanced one-tenth to nine-tenths of a turn. The first wheel at the right represented units, the second tens, the third hundreds, and so forth. It was, however, converted into an adding machine by the addition of a carrying device: As the first wheel advanced from its ninth tooth or gear to zero, the "carrier" moved the "ten" wheel at the left one-tenth of a turn. Subtraction could be done by reversing the action.

It took but a few decades to add multiplication to the system, an accomplishment achieved by another philosopher, G. W. von Leibniz, in 1671. He introduced a stepped "reckoner," or wheel, which repeated a number successively to arrive at the product via the addition route. Leibniz's machine, however, was rather crude, as the mechanics of his time were unable to provide the close tolerances that were required. Further attempts to improve the mechanical calculator were made by Lord Stanhope in 1775 and Matthew Hahn in 1779.[2]

By all accounts, the most radical conception of the calculator was advanced in 1812 by Charles Babbage, an irascible mathematical prodigy.[3] All the earlier machines had been mechanical devices, to be operated by cranking and hand manipulation. Babbage proposed no less than to build an automatic computer, an idea he had conceived at the age of twenty. He wanted a machine that would solve difference equations and would print-out the solutions. Babbage was a rather extraordinary man, who invented speedometers and cowcatchers for railroad locomotives, attacked London's street organ-grinders, and did not hesitate to polemicize against The Royal Society. His ability to analyze an industry would put to shame many an economist today, as witness his remarkable study of the publishing business.[4]

The "Difference Engine" was designed by Babbage to compute the values for certain polynomial functions through successive addition. For any function, the machine would work back from the constant differences to the squares, thus making it possible to compute large tables of polynomials and then print out the results — a striking harbinger of the future. Babbage began to build his Difference Engine in 1822 with the financial help of the British government. By 1833, however, £17,000 had been spent, and only a model of a portion of the machine was ready. Parts had to be made by hand, the engineers did not know what Babbage was talking about, and they could not abide his temper tantrums. The whole project was abandoned in 1842.

34

But Babbage was not yet done. Dropping the Difference Engine, he began to plan his Analytical Engine, based on a sharply different conception. There the gear mechanism, utilizing Pascal's idea of toothed wheels, was to be operated by steam. It was to be the first genuine computer, completely automatic and able to do one addition per second. As the main bottleneck would be the input of data by human beings working laboriously from paper, all this labor was to be replaced by a "store," or "memory" device, to hold the information needed for calculation. The store was to comprise sets of numbered wheels holding 1,000 fifty-digit numbers. The data were to be placed into the store by punched cards, an idea taken from the Jacquard loom.

The arithmetic in Babbage's machine was to be accomplished by toothed, numbered gears. This system was called the "mill." Various gears and levers were to transfer numbers from mill to store and store to mill. And there was to be another device to get the data in and out of the whole contraption. Evidently, several contemporary notions had been anticipated: automatic functioning, control units, and the selection of alternative bodies of data. The machine, however, was never completed, despite forty years of work, thousands of carefully drawn diagrams, and the development of new tooling techniques by Babbage himself. And ironically, the Analytical Engine even failed to influence future work, for the modern computer began in the 1940s, and its developers had no knowledge of what Babbage had done.[5]

ALL THESE EARLY machines were digital: Unlike the slide rule, with which one measured a continuous quantity, they sought to operate on discrete numbers. The mathematical operations were performed by counting or adding. A digital computer today can subtract by adding complements, a principle that Babbage had planned to use in his own Analytical Engine. Multiplication can be done by repeated addition; division by repeated subtraction. Powers and root extraction, as well as differentiation and integration, can be done on a digital machine by converting the operations into arithmetic, that is, by employing numerical methods in which certain planned prescribed sequences are required.

Hardware and Software

The advantages of programming all these operations on a digital computer stem from the latter's extraordinary speed and its high degree of accuracy.

The analogue principle was also mechanized. Its usefulness for dealing with certain problems was undeniable. For example, computing the area under a curve — known in calculus as "integration" — may be quite laborious, as generations of students can testify. To deal with this sort of situation, J. A. Hermann, a German engineer, invented (in 1814) the planimeter, an instrument that measured the area under a curve by moving a tracer along the boundary. In essence, the planimeter was an analogue device: Although it measured the area of a plane figure, in effect it solved for the value of the integral of the function represented by the curve. A mechanical motion had been employed that was analogous to the mathematical problem at hand.

In 1876 Lord Kelvin connected a number of mechanical devices to help predict the movement of the tides. His gadget generated trigonometric functions by pulleys and cranking mechanisms.[6] A sundial is a primitive example of an analogue device. It accepts sunlight as its input and produces a shadow that is analogous to the movement of the sun. A more sophisticated case is the common automobile speedometer, which is connected to the drive shaft by a flexible cable and gears. The speed of the car is then measured by the rotation of the drive shaft. That is to say, computation is achieved by continuous measurement of a physical quantity analogous to the problem being studied. The analogue machine, in effect, simulates a particular condition.

The analogue computer still has certain limitations: The basic operations are usually performed by single-purpose devices; its accuracy is more restricted than is that of a digital machine; and it is not nearly as fast for certain situations as is the latter. Today the analogue computer appears to be best suited for problems involving linear or nonlinear differential equations for which solutions to three or four significant figures are satisfactory. The size of the problem that can be handled is directly related to the size of the device, as analogue operations are done simultaneously rather than in sequence, as in the digital computer.

In the modern analogue, the various parts of the equation to be solved are simulated by electronic components, with voltages and other electrical characteristics utilized to represent variables.

Perhaps the first true analogue computer was made by Hannibal Ford in 1915 to calculate the ranges for naval guns. It was still a mechanical device, however. Improvements in such instruments continued through the years, culminating in Vannevar Bush's differential analyzer built at the Massachusetts Institute of Technology in 1931. This device combined wheel and disc integrators and mechanical analogues of angles and lengths with sets of gears for multiplying and dividing and differential gears for adding and subtracting. Multiplication by a constant factor, for example, could be done by meshing two gears in a given ratio. For different constants, however, the gears had to be changed; in effect, for each new problem, new mechanical components had to be installed. The Bush analyzer was fairly quick: It took about half an hour to solve a problem that a mathematician might take a week to do. But it was able to handle only differential equations with one variable each: Equations with many variables were beyond it.

During the war an electrical analyzer was developed to help solve military problems. But it was an electrically driven mechanical machine, not an electronic one. Today, of course, virtually all analogue computers are electronic. About 80 per cent of these machines are now involved in space and nuclear research.[7] The second largest area of application is in the chemical and petroleum industries, where their use is widespread in controlling temperature, pressures, and densities. Dr. T. J. Williams, a Monsanto Chemical Company engineer reported to a Washington meeting in 1963 that computer controls were now standard in the industry. In 1956 no major chemical company had any sort of analogue installations, said Williams; in 1963 all were dependent on both analogue and digital machines. In 1956 electronic instrumentation had been quite primitive; in 1963 the equipment was in its "third generation." In addition to chemicals, the chief industries that have used analogue computers are steel and automobiles. In the aerospace industries, the analogue machine is used to establish preliminary "systems" requirements and air-frame shapes. Control and aerodynamic features are fed into the machine, so that design characteristics can be altered until the "best" configuration is established. In a nuclear-reactor plant the analogue is used to simulate the reactor's functioning for better control. The Polaris missile has a built-in analogue device which monitors its flight performance: If the missile does not behave properly, the analogue cuts its flight short.

Nevertheless, the market for analogue computers and devices, at $50 million a year in sales, is far behind that for digital machines. At the beginning of 1963, sales of the latter approximated $2 billion a year. Their development has been indeed phenomenal—from one machine in 1945 to 20,000 in 1963, with another 5,000 added in 1965.

THE MAIN ROOTS of the electronic digital computer go back to the work of Howard Aiken, who, as a graduate student at Harvard in 1937, tried to devise a machine that would solve polynomials. Recognizing that the underlying logic of all digital machines was essentially the same, he reasoned that a general-purpose computer to handle all sorts of problems was possible. The International Business Machines Corporation was happy to lend its support with a team of four high-powered engineers, and the Automatic Sequence Controlled Calculator—Mark I—was unveiled in 1944. It was only after he had started to build his digital computer that Aiken discovered Babbage: The fundamental principles of the computer had to be reworked a century after they had been set down by the dyspeptic English mathematician,[8] a case of a kink in the development of technology. Mark I was an electromechanical machine with more than 760,000 parts consisting of a bewildering array of switches, wheels, relays, cams, and 500 miles of wire. It was completely automatic in that it could follow instructions fed into it by a programmer. It had an input unit that utilized punched paper tape, a memory unit, an arithmetic unit, controls, and an output device—components now found in all digital computers. But it was rather slow: Addition or subtraction took one-third of a second, multiplication five seconds, division sixteen seconds—and computing a logarithm to twenty decimal places took the unconscionable time of one and one-half minutes.

About a year before Mark I had been completed, scientists at the University of Pennsylvania started to construct an electronic computer that was to make the older machine as archaic as a water wheel. Dispensing with telephone relays and other electromechanical components, J. P. Eckert and John Mauchly put together 18,000 vacuum tubes and related equipment that could do the same switching and circuit operations as Mark I but in about a millionth of a second. Their machine, known as ENIAC (Electronic Numerical Integrator and Calculator), was able to perform 5,000 additions per second. Completed in 1945, it was used to compile firing tables for ballistic trajectories, a prime war need. There were some inherent difficulties in it, however: The memory capacity was small; there were bottlenecks at both input and output stages arising from the higher speed of the arithmetic unit; and the circuitry was such that each problem required rewiring and replugging, causing frustrating delays. It was evident that something new and different would have to be built.

One day in 1944 a member of the Pennsylvania group, Herman Goldstine, met John von Neumann, who had been working on computation techniques for solving certain partial differential equations related to the atom bomb, and told him what Eckert, Mauchly, and he were doing. Neumann immediately associated himself with the project, a fruitful collaboration that led to EDVAC (Electronic Discrete Variable Automatic Calculator). Neumann became a confirmed believer in the computor's usefulness, especially for numerical methods to solve problems once thought beyond the scientist's ken. The major innovations in EDVAC, which was not completed until 1952, were the use of the binary number system, with conversion from decimals to binary accomplished internally, a much larger memory or storage capacity, and instructions placed into the machine itself. The basic operations were now part of the circuitry: The tedious business of plugging and unplugging each time a new problem arose could be avoided.

Using the binary-number system represented a great

advance. Ordinary arithmetic is based on the decimal system, derived from the natural happenstance of man's ten fingers. But many laymen do not realize that number systems are based on conventional usage and that a two-fingered animal would no doubt count in twos. The early computers, of course, made use of the decimal system, with a complex of gears to represent the ten digits and particular placement for units, tens, and hundreds. An electronic computer can also employ decimal numbers with tubes and switches to depict digits, but the circuitry is enormously complex, requiring as it does counters of ten elements each. How much simpler is the binary system, for a light bulb or any electronic component has but two states — on or off, current or no current! Consequently, these conditions can represent 1 or 0, the only digits in binary numbers. The relationship of binary numbers to decimal numbers is fairly straightforward: decimal $0 =$ binary 0; decimal $1 =$ binary 1; decimal $2 =$ binary 10; decimal $3 =$ binary 11; decimal $4 =$ binary 100; decimal $5 =$ binary 101; decimal $6 =$ binary 110; decimal $7 =$ binary 111; decimal $8 =$ binary 1,000; decimal $9 =$ binary 1,001, and so forth. Binary numbers can be added and subtracted as easily as decimals. Numbers in an electronic computer can thus be represented by the open and closed states of the circuit components. Binary numbers can be stored in the machine directly, requiring less equipment than decimals, as it takes only four on–off or 0–1 registers to hold a decimal digit in its binary equivalent.

Underlying this now obvious idea was the extraordinary contribution of Claude Shannon, who in 1937 wrote a master's thesis demonstrating the parallel between switching circuits and the algebra of logic; true or false values were shown by Shannon to correspond with open and closed states of electrical circuits. For example, connections in series could indicate "or," whereas "if and only if" might be suggested by two circuits opening and closing together. This demonstration clearly provided the basis for the logic of computer design.[9] The fundamental notions for this development could be traced to George Boole, an English mathematician, who in 1854 had proposed a two-valued algebra in the theory of logic. Boolean logic said, simply enough, that for every class there was a "not-class."

A hundred years later the scientists and engineers realized that bistate circuitry could be employed to unravel the implications of such a system.[10] With binary numbers not only could the circuit design be vastly simplified, but also the calculations themselves could course through the computer with great speed and precision. Now, whereas in an analogue computer accuracy is at the very best in the order of 1 to 10^4 or one error in 10,000, in a digital machine the precision is much higher, as much as 1 to 10^9. This difference is caused by the sheer length of the arithmetic necessary to solve problems that are fed into a digital computer. With a great number of operations, errors would simply be amplified. Binary digital computers minimize such possibilities.[11]

The "memory," or more accurately the storage unit, is a critical part of a computer setup. It may consist of magnetic cores, drums or discs, or acoustical delay lines. Into the memory are stored instructions, tables, or even the results of various calculations. The magnetic core fixes the location of the information placed into the machine. In other devices, the location shifts, so that reading heads may have to be supplied to pick up the data as the storage unit moves, as in the case of the magnetic drum. The core itself is a ring of ferrous material about one-tenth of an inch in diameter, with a wire running through its hollow center. A few millionths of a watt shot into the wire magnetize the core in one direction; reversing the current shifts the polarity. The directions of polarity in the core thus represent a binary system and can be read as 0, 1; yes, no; or true, false. The cores are strung on wires set in a frame, making it possible to build a memory unit with more than a million of these tiny magnetic doughnuts. Despite the complex circuitry, it takes but one- or two-millionths of a second to obtain data from the machine's memory.

THE GROWTH of computers has been indeed one of the marvels of modern technology. Mark I begat ENIAC, which begat EDVAC, which begat EDSAC, a machine that placed both instructions and data into the memory unit; then came RAYDAC, a second cousin to UNIVAC I.

SEAC, BIZMAC, FLAC, MIDAC, and DYSEAC quickly followed, all utilizing the basic EDVAC storage idea. Mark III was born in 1950, and OARAC, a close relation, arrived three years later. The descendants increased in Biblical fashion—some had no names, only numbers, but ORDVAC begat AVIDAC, and after ILLIAC came MANIAC I. A third generation of computers was created, surpassing the older vacuum-tube and solid-state systems with magnetic thin-film memories and microminiaturization, but some observers began to wonder if the last named computer was not appropriate for them all, as they had stemmed mainly from the demands of war.[12] (In fact, while ENIAC and EDVAC were being built, rumors that they were gigantic white elephants were deliberately circulated so that enemy curiosity would be deflected.) One of the end products of these developments has been SAGE, a monstrous network of computers, perhaps the largest in the world, designed for continental air defense, which processes radar data and provides visual displays of air-space use for the armed services. And the Atomic Energy Commission now has STRETCH, a machine with a storage capacity in excess of 100,000 words, one microsecond access time, two microseconds addition time, an ability to read more than 60,000 characters a second, and an ability to read, write, and compute simultaneously.

STRETCH is a rather large device, compared to which most modern installations appear small. The early machines were also large but only because they were bulky and filled a lot of space. ENIAC, for example, was a huge contraption, occupying a forty-by-twenty-foot room, weighing thirty tons, and dissipating 150 kilowatts of energy. The "ordinary" computer today takes up less room mainly because vacuum tubes have been replaced by transistors. These tiny globules of germanium or silicon require only a few volts to activate them and do not need heat to make the electrons flow. They are therefore as efficient as tubes, if not more so, do not need cooling equipment, are capable of performing several million operations per second, and, most important, allow computers to be much smaller than in the past.

Transistor development started in the 1940s when three

Bell Laboratory physicists produced a "point contact" transistor, for which they were to receive the 1956 Nobel award. (The word "transistor" is a composite of two other words — "transfer" and "varistor." The transistor is a device for transferring signals through a varistor.) Since then, the business of selling transistors and other so-called "semiconductors," solid-state devices that have an electrical conductivity somewhere between that of metals and insulators, has reached a total of almost $600 million a year. The manufacturing process is by no means simple: Crystals of germanium and silicon must be prepared with a certain amount of impurities; items the size of a paper clip must be assembled in dust-free, humidity-controlled shops; and quality control much more stringent than in ordinary plants must be applied. Although transistors are now used in television receivers, radios, model railroads, and automobile-ignition systems, the greatest application has been in the electronic computer, where it has made possible miniaturization. And with the latter, soldered connections that may break and be troublesome can be eliminated.[13]

Efforts have been made also to harness analogue and digital machines, but this process has required such complex electronic tie-in equipment that the efforts often have been more trouble than they have been worth. Some fifteen such rigs have been built to solve problems that cannot be handled in any other way. The analogue has been used primarily in the aircraft and aerospace industries to simulate new engineering designs and flight conditions. Data from a simulated model can then be calculated on a digital machine. But the range of problems for a manned space flight was beyond any single machine and required a hybrid device for their solution. Much of the difficulty arose from the fact that analogue machines do not add, whereas digital machines are unable to solve directly problems in higher mathematics. To analyze pressures or loads in a flow system, for example, the digital computer might take hours to do the enormous quantity of computations required for a problem that an analogue machine can handle in a much shorter period. Devices known as converters, however, have been developed, which transform the physical quantities of an analogue into the input and output of a digital computer.

43

This transformation is based on conversion of the analogue's flow quantities into digits, a process that may employ sampling techniques that evaluate the particular mathematical function at various times, thus deriving a numerical series, by counting the units in the quantity, or by comparing the unknown analogue quantity with a series of possible values to obtain a digital output equal to the analogue input. Hybrid computers are also available in which the digital halves may analyze the logic of a given system whereas the analogue portions simulate the operational problems.

A more recent development is integrated circuitry, in which a fantastic number of computer operations can be crammed into the size of a shoebox. These circuits are tiny chips of silicon, which in effect pack numerous transistors, diodes, and other electronic components on their surfaces.[14] One such box, UNIVAC's microtonic computer, weighs less than nineteen pounds and has a 4,600-word memory, expandable to 16,000 words. Its 800 integrated circuits are equivalent to 18,000 separate components. The speed of these units is greater than ever: The switching capacity is now measured in billionths of a second. To make them requires such devices as micropositioners with magnifying powers of forty to one. High speed is closely related to miniaturization, for the circuitry must be small because of the finite speed of electricity. Speed of billionths of a second is made possible by small distances. More important, the electronics industry and the economics of computer assembly may very well be altered by this new development. In standard operations thus far, circuit designers, component manufacturers, and assemblers have functioned independently: With integrated circuitry, the components are the circuits, and they must be designed from the start as part of a system. The organization of manufacturing may therefore have to follow technology. The future may see fewer and bigger companies in the field.

Integrated circuitry is important for spacecraft computers. Recently, one was built with a double memory system, "majority rule voting circuits," and 99.7 per cent reliability. With such computer systems thirty-story-high Saturn V rockets and forty-seven-ton, three-man Apollo spaceship will be steered during the first leg of the lunar

A babel of calculators

journey to be attempted by the end of the decade. The separate memory systems are to operate simultaneously during the voyage. If an error in computation is detected, operation will be transferred immediately to the other memory. Furthermore, if an electronic part in one of three identical sets of circuits issues an incorrect signal, the computer will disregard it and accept only the correct signals from the other parts of the circuit. This system, in effect,is "majority rule."

A great triumph for microminiaturization was the series of close-up photographs of Mars taken by Mariner IV. The pictures were taken 135 million miles in space, with just enough power to transmit them back to earth in digital language. The pictures were scanned and broken into sixty-four different shades of gray, with each shade numbered and sent back to earth in sequence. The signals were faint—one quintillionth of a watt in strength. Amplified and fed into computers, each sequence of digital numbers was reconverted into one of sixty-four shades of gray, quite like the small dots that make up a picture on a television screen.

With a base in government work, the companies making integrated circuits are able to provide strong competition to transistor manufacturers. Average circuit costs dropped from $30 in 1963 to $9 in 1965. And, with the fabrication of more than one circuit on a tiny sliver of material, the high cost of packaging is sharply cut; with six separate logic devices on one chip of silicon, the cost per circuit function falls to less than $1.50. Metal-oxide devices make the cost even cheaper. If a given calculator could be built now with 5,000 components, it would require only 1,100 conventional integrated circuits to do the job; with metal-oxide devices, the number would drop to forty or fifty.[15]

An even more interesting prospect arising from such "miniaturization" is the impact on the labor force. As *Fortune* remarked, large rooms full of technicians and girls with nimble fingers who now assemble components into circuits and circuits into systems would be replaced by engineers monitoring automatic production. "As the level of skill rises, total employment is likely to decline sharply; with laboratory equipment a handful of people will be able to turn out circuits at a prodigious rate. If production can be fully automated, the need for even skilled technicians may also vanish."[16] Technology thus continues to devour its own tail. Numerous companies have already embarked on the manufacture of miniature, integrated circuits, including IBM, whose own factories making transistors and diodes are fully automated. It is expected that by 1967 sales will be $200 million a year compared with the standard transistor market of $600 million a year.[17]

THE TINY SIZES of these instruments even promise to computerize the housewife's shopping list. John Mauchly, one of the pioneers in the field, told a meeting of industrial engineers in 1962 that he was working on a pocket-sized machine.[18] In a decade or so, said Mauchly, everyone would own a computer with all the data pertinent to himself and his problems stored in it, rather than in his own brain. A shopping sortie was described as follows: "Taking her computer from her handbag [the housewife] enters a vacant delivery alcove and connects the computer into a receptacle provided. Within less than a minute, her packages of groceries, and other supplies such as use-once-and-throw-away clothes come down a chute. They are assembled in advance because she had a home-data booth through which her computer, which kept her domestic inventory for her, had been able to relay in her order." The report did not say how far Mauchly had placed his tongue into his cheek, but, if it wasn't there, he should have been saying something about the weird imagination of the computer builders. (The same meeting discussed the "often controversial question" of what is a fair day's work. The assumption evidently was that work would continue to have meaning in an era of thoroughgoing automation.)

More seriously, the utilization of microminiature high-speed devices can break bottlenecks in computer operations. Some logic functions that require numerous components are now easier to handle. Furthermore, it seems possible to build association techniques into the memory unit, so that information may be organized into related fields much as the human mind organizes it. Reliability in the computer can be enhanced, as in the case of spaceships, by building in duplicate circuits at particular points to take over when one breaks down. In this way, the probability of failure decreases exponentially as the duplicate circuits are increased. With such a system, known as "redundancy," the additional components—and the cost—rise but arithmetically, whereas the probability of failure drops geometrically.[19] Even more striking is the tin-magnesium-aluminum alloy developed by Minneapolis-Honeywell, which repairs its own breaks. When wires containing cores of alloy snap, fine filaments develop that can bridge a gap of one millimeter and carry one watt. Used in electronic components, this substitute is enough to keep the circuitry functioning. The filaments exude from the break surfaces at temperatures of 70 degrees to 125 degrees Fahrenheit.

These advances made possible the construction of huge computer systems like IBM's 360, hailed in early 1964 as a new generation of computer equipment. The 360 spans the range of virtually all IBM computers, with a performance that exceeds the widely used 1401, nearly twice that of the most powerful computer previously built by the company. The central processing unit provides nineteen combinations of *graduated* speed and memory capacity, allowing the user to expand within the same system or to choose any configuration of operation required for his needs. It can use programs within fifteen different IBM computers without rewriting the programs. It also can be assembled in all manner of setups, ranging from a $1,280-per-month card-handler to an elaborate construction renting for more than $100,000 a month. The circuitry is microelectronic, with many of the transistors and diodes only $\frac{28}{1,000}$ of an inch thick. As many as eight million characters, sixty times more than previous capacity, can be stored in the 360, each available in eight-millionths of a second. The 360 is estimated to provide from three to five times as much computing work for a given dollar. The system's forty-four various kinds of peripheral accessories speed the process of getting data to and from the computer, keeping it busy all the time. To introduce the machine, IBM chartered a special train to take several hundred reporters to Poughkeepsie and at the same time displayed the 360 in 165 cities and twenty foreign countries. Yet so rapid are developments in the field that, within a year, IBM announced several significant modifications in its 360 complex, among which was the increase of peripheral equipment from forty-four to sixty-five.[20]

Small computers can be built for specific data-processing tasks. The Monroe Calculating Machine Company has available a desk-sized machine that can be used for billing, posting, and other accounting operations. One buyer who took fifty of these units for his field staff remarked that it was like getting back to the clerk with the green eye shade. (One wondered where the midget computer's eyebrows, from which to hang the shade, were placed.) In any case, the small machine with its fixed programs can make up invoices, calculate taxes, figure commissions, and strike off customer balances. It makes the district manager feel genuinely part of the corporate team, and, besides, he can get his reports in to the main office much more rapidly. To use such devices requires less training than does operating a comptometer, but they do the work of at least four clerks each. Desk-sized and suitcase-sized computers can be dispersed around engineering and production areas to reduce the work load for a large, centrally located machine and can in fact prepare summarized data for the latter to digest. And if the small business concern is told that it can now "face the pinch of competition" from computer-equipped rivals, who would be so foolhardy as to refuse even a midget electronic demon?

NEVERTHELESS, despite their remarkable versatility, machines as yet must be told what to do. Telling them what to do is the art of programming. Of course, the computer can carry on prodigious feats of arithmetic without human intervention, but the prime mover is the programmer, whose function it is to prepare operating instructions and to feed them into the machine. But he has to prepare them in the latter's "language," that is, English must be translated into a form and in a manner that will enable the circuitry to work effectively. Only if this translation is done properly, can the control unit order the arithmetic or operating unit to perform the task required of it. Such orders may consist of instructions to add, subtract, or divide; to transfer data from one part of the system to another; or to select one of two alternatives, depending on certain conditions. Normally, the preparation of a program begins with a flow chart, describing in logical and detailed form all the steps necessary to solve the problem. The sequence must be spelled out carefully. Then comes the coding, which translates the instructions into machine language, so that they may be stored together with the data in the machine's memory section. The basic unit of information is called a "word," which is really a group of characters or binary digits, known as "bits," stored in a register, that is, at a single "address" or location in the memory. The "word" is treated and manipulated by the computer as an entity: It becomes an instruction when put into the control unit and a quantity in the arithmetic unit. There are, of course, other systems as well, like those in IBM's 7080.

It was at this point that programming language reared its Hydra-like head, with no Hercules around to slay it. Each tentacle spoke for itself, and for a while all was confusion. ALGOL, AUTOCODER, CALINT, FORTRAN, COBOL, GECOM, FLOWMATIC, JOVIAL and FORTRAN-ALGOL — computer program systems — all competed with one another to run costs in the industry up to as much as $2 billion since 1950. The problem of programming for the great variety of computers was like trying to converse with inhabitants in the Tower of Babel. The computers were organized differently: Some multiplied in one operation, others in three; that is, the combinations of numbers and letters in the machines varied from one to the next. The absence of a standardized language made a computer buyer a slave to a particular manufacturer or necessitated the purchase of his freedom with the rather costly routine of reprogramming for a new machine. With the rapid rate of improvement in equipment, the expense of writing programs could be a serious bottleneck in marketing advanced machines. Of course, programs for special purposes could be retained on the cards, tapes, or drums for future use, given usable equipment. This storing was like holding on to player-piano rolls, but the cost of working up a new program could be compared to a figure of about $2 a hole on a piano roll.[21] The cost magnitude of a new program was illustrated by the experience of an insurance company, which spent more than $1 million to switch from punch cards to a high-speed computer.[22] Although the market for new equipment is still considerable, American industry has always looked to repeat business: It would be difficult to sell a late-model mechanical piano to a customer if he had to repunch all his rolls.

So important is the computer program, and so great the investment in its development, that companies increasingly view it as a trade secret. For example, in one instance, the recording on tape of all ships in *Lloyds' Register* in order to locate quickly vessels of more than 10,000-ton capacity cost $40,000. In another case, a complicated linear program that enables a quick print-out of analytical tables for market research took two years to develop at a cost of almost $100,000. It is not surprising that companies have sought legal protection for their programs. In most cases, however, the best they have been able to do has been to take refuge in the common law protecting trade secrets, a rather ambiguous area in the absence of specific statutory protection. Sometimes employees working on a program are required to sign restrictive agreements intended to protect the company against disclosures. The Patent Office has thus far rejected applications for patents on computer programs, and it was not until 1964 that the Copyright Office would accept registrations under its regulations. On the other hand, industry action to establish codes of behavior demand caution, as the codes might be construed to be in violation of the antitrust laws. In any case, it appears that a new property is being fostered by the computer.[23]

One of the more popular computer languages is FORTRAN, essentially an algebraic system that includes exponential operations and subscripted data. Used mainly on IBM equipment (although it has been employed on other equipment also), it enables one virtually to write his own program without knowing anything about the details of machine language.[24] The program can be written in terms of FORTRAN words, which in effect are converted immediately into machine instructions. The need for a skilled technician to translate the wishes of the computer user into shape understandable by the machine has thus been obviated. With "automatic" translation, the consumer can code his own problem. By 1962 FORTRAN had gone through several revisions, but each time IBM scientists made certain that the new language retained enough components of the previous one to allow for easier handling on new equipment. FORTRAN II thus added markedly to the power of the original by building in various subroutines or subsidiary instructions. Later improvements added the ability to handle Boolean symbols. The latest generation is FORTRAN IV (although some experts consider FORTRAN IV to be little more than an expanded FORTRAN II).

In 1958, the Federal government, disturbed by the growing confusion, convened a meeting of manufacturers and computer users to work out a standard language for business data-processing. From it there came COBOL— Common Business Oriented Language—in which data were precisely described in standard form through a stylized English. Once the Department of Defense, which by 1962 had spent some $15 million on computer installations, had decided that it would purchase only computers able to handle COBOL, all the manufacturers rushed to perfect appropriate routines. One marked advantage of COBOL is the lower cost of reworking a program: An ordinary rewrite job might run as high as $500,000; with COBOL, this figure can be cut as much as 90 per cent. Manufacturers now supply instructions to users on translating COBOL into specific machine language. For example, COBOL might "tell" an RCA 501 machine to MULTIPLY HOURLY-RATE BY TOTALHOURS GIVING GROSSPAY. To the machine this message would read IT ZEROS OO GROSSPAYCHECK. On an IBM 7070 the same instruction would be interpreted as ZA 3 CB 70003 (0.2). At the beginning of 1963, the Conference on Data Systems Languages (CODASYL), which is responsible for developing standardized computer systems, announced a new version of COBOL, called COBOL-61 Extended. It was to be put to work, after the fashion of FORTRAN II, as soon as manufacturers could incorporate the changes in the master computer programs.

Obviously, a universal computer language would simplify matters considerably by making it possible to shift to new equipment with ease. The armed services particularly have sought flexibility in computer systems, so that military commanders might be permitted to make complicated requests for information through ordinary language rather than through esoteric computer symbols. For example, quick answers would be desirable to such questions as: How many cargo planes of a certain type can ferry how many soldiers and how much cargo from a Texas or Georgia Air Force base to Frankfurt, Germany, against the prevailing winds and still have enough fuel to go on to Spain? Unless the computer has been programmed in advance to deal with such queries, it might take days or weeks simply to prepare the machine. Clearly this lag would not satisfy the normal military compulsion to have answers the day before yesterday. Consequently, the air force now sponsors a special research facility to devise a computer technique dealing with unforeseen situations.[25] In addition to programming specific data for directing, for example a convoy of merchant ships through submarine-infested waters, the computer would be stuffed with a variety of general-purpose instructions numerous and detailed enough to provide the desired flexibility. Computer capacity, would have to be enlarged enormously, however, and the speed increased as well.

Nevertheless, considering developments in miniaturization and high-speed components, such a computer system does not seem impossible. Machines can be designed that do calculations while data are still being fed into them. Some experimental units, notably at the RCA laboratories, have processed as many as ten million items of information a second, about three times as fast as the best of existing machines. Furthermore, microelectronic circuitry can provide more storage in the same space by eliminating 90 per cent of present bulk, most of the wiring, and 90 per cent of the solder connections.[26] In 1963, General Electric patented a microconductor, which promises to further the development of miniaturization. Two tiny metal films, separated by a thin insulating layer, thus forming an electronic sandwich, are chilled to provide superconductivity. The electrons move between the sandwich halves by a process known as "funneling," which, together with the absence of resistance to current, makes the microconductor as different from the transistor as the latter was from the vacuum tube. Its applications evidently are manifold, including that of an efficient computer memory component.

One high-speed machine, built by the Control Data Corporation, was reported to process three million instructions a second, requiring a switching speed in some of its circuits of more than thirty million times a second. The system, called the "6600" can synchronize eleven sets of instructions simultaneously, so that complex problems can be handled without pausing at each step for an answer before continuing. It was suggested that it could set up a mathematical model of the atmosphere and solve the three-dimensional relationships of air flow, temperature, air pressure, and humidity fast enough to provide continuous and accurate weather forecasts. The 6600 is rather small and simple looking. Its eleven computer units are packed into four cabinets crammed so tightly with miniaturized circuitry that there is no room for air to circulate. Copper cooling tubes carry off the small amount of heat generated by the more than 600,000 components. The central memory unit has a capacity of 131,072 words stored in 7,864,320 magnetic cores. All these components are supplemented by ten other memory units, with more than 40,000 cores. Although the machine is rather expensive, available at about $7 million for outright purchase or at $175,000 a month for rent, it can perform a million each of additions, subtractions, multiplications, and divisions at a cost of $1 in machine time. As if that were not enough, CDC announced just a year later an even more powerful machine, the 6800 model, with speeds four times those of the "older" machine. It had been developed in response to IBM's 360.[27]

PRIOR TO 1965 such computers were unique. As major bottlenecks are found at the input and output stages, manufacturers have concentrated on rapid scanners and high-speed printers. For a long time information could be fed into the computer only by the manual preparation of punched cards or tapes. But when work loads reach a volume of more than 10,000 documents a day, key-punch operators can become a drag on data-processing systems. On the other hand, scanners, or optical character-recognition devices (OCR), can pick up, decode, and convert data for computer use with efficiency and dispatch. With a light focused on the characters — on checks, invoices, subscription lists, or credit-card charges — a photosensitive viewer receives the reflected light and changes it into electrical impulses. Logic circuits may be used to identify the characters by various distinguishing features; or the reading device compares the characters with previously stored masters; or imprinted bar codes above the characters may be read by the scanner.

There are now about a hundred OCR devices in operation, mainly in oil, public-utility, and insurance companies.[28] In electric companies, paid bill stubs move by the scanner's eye, which actuates impulses that punch out customers' account numbers and the amounts paid. Dividend checks can be verified and then used after bank clearance to bring stockholders' records up to date. A retail sales tag can be converted into a punch card ready to be inserted into a computer for inventory control. Typewritten pages can be read at a rate of 1,800 words a minute, with the material converted into punched tape that can then activate a teleprinter machine for long-distance message transmission. The possibilities seem limitless.

An IBM optical scanning machine, the 1282, accepts both printed characters and pencil marks, thus reading both constant and variable data, that is, customers' names and account numbers, as well as dollar amounts. A Sylvania scanner uses a cathode tube to pass a beam of light across printed or typed matter. Each character is recorded as a pattern of 320 black or white areas and then is checked against the shapes of twenty type faces stored in the computer. If there is agreement between input and storage, the computer will punch out the character; if there is some doubt, the machine asks for a repeat. RCA recently reported a reading device built like a frog's eye: consisting of six forty-inch-square layers of light-sensitive photo cells, it functions in a manner akin to the six layers of retina in Rana's visual apparatus. The shape, speed, and direction of observed data can be established as the light input passes from layer to layer to establish the detected pattern. If the latter agrees with certain configurations in the machine, a light flashes on a panel to show the outline and direction of movement; if there is no agreement between stored and observed data, then the display is shut out, just as a frog's eye ignores all but the food it seeks. It is said that such a machine will be useful in air-traffic control and missile detection.

By the beginning of 1963, the race was on among manufacturers to give the computer sophisticated vision. A major objective was to carve out slices of the so-called "turn-around" document business, like insurance-premium notices and utility bills. One of IBM's optical readers, though rather slow at fifty characters a second, has been designed to adjust automatically to different type fonts and sizes. Essentially, it is intended as a "universal" machine able to recognize numbers and capital and small letters in a wide range of styles and sizes just as they appear in newspapers, books, and typescripts. With a scanner able to receive Cyrillic as well as Roman letters, one bottleneck in translation programs could be overcome. The newest print reader, using a cathode-ray tube to scan typed or printed pages, can convert 2,000 characters per second into magnetic tape, paper tape, or cards. The machine is able to read mixed type faces, correct mistakes, insert corrections, rescan any character it may have failed to identify, and skip blank areas. The Post Office Department, always on the search for automatic equipment, promptly ordered three of these devices as soon as it had been released by the maker, the Philco Corporation.

Even more striking was the patenting in November 1963 of a proposed machine that would read handwriting with a reported accuracy of 95 per cent. The instrument, a Bell Telephone Laboratory experimental device, would observe the distinctive features in handwriting, group them, and then check back in the memory unit to select the most likely letters. It could also decide where one letter ended and another started. Dots, crosses, slashes, points, closures, strokes, and the heights of letters in cursive script could also be distinguished. A stylus, the movements of which were to be sensed and transmitted through electronic impulses onto a tape, would initiate the process. Interestingly enough, the reader was not actually built at the time of patenting but rather has been "tested" and "proved" by simulation methods, an example of a computer designing a new computer.[29]

Some day the engineer or the business oligarch will simply talk to the computer and get an answer. In early 1964 IBM was reported to be developing a device able to put recorded words together to form brief, but meaningful, replies to questions dialed on a telephone. An outgrowth of an automatic quotation system built for stock exchanges, the instrument, called an "audio response system," contains a vocabulary and numbers recorded by voice on a magnetic drum. When a code is dialed on a telephone connected to the computer, the latter's output signals indicate how the stored words are to be arranged to answer the query. Situations in which unwritten information would be sufficient, like department-store credit ratings or check-cashing in a bank, could readily be handled by such a device.

At the present time, OCR equipment requires less than one full-time operator per machine. More significantly, scanners and readers eliminate key-punch operations, one of the occupations hailed by automation experts as a ripple in the wave of the future. It was estimated in one survey that a certain scanner could do the work of ten key-punch girls. Although two jobs were saved in order to handle rejects, nevertheless the machine was certain to replace at least eight jobs. In about 100 installations since 1956, approximately 1,000 positions have disappeared. An optimistic estimate suggested that only 3,000 jobs would be eliminated by OCR machines from 1963 to 1968.[30] The possibility of the figure's being higher was not denied. The contention that automation would create more jobs thus appears to be dissipated by virtue of the involuted development of technology. As in politics, the revolution devours its own children.

At the other end of the system, a high-speed computer needs an equally rapid print-out component. With machines becoming ever faster internally, even a printer that extracts the completed computer story at a pace of 1,000 lines a minute poses a problem. What is required seems to be more on the order of 15,000 to 30,000 lines a minute, and manufacturers are beginning to supply such devices. In one such instrument, selling for about $500,000, the letters are virtually "sprayed" on as the paper flies by: Tiny metal styluses, activated electronically, dot the paper in number or letter characters at a speed close to that of the computer itself.[31] One leading high-speed print-out maker can string together rollers, each containing twenty full sets of numerical or alphabetic characters on a shaft and so obtain copy 20 to 160 characters wide. The equipment, operating normally at a range of 300 to 1,200 lines a minute, can be pushed up to 3,000 lines a minute – about 150 times as fast as a college graduate can read.

SINCE 1950, when it was thought that about a dozen large-scale machines would satisfy the requirements of science and business for years to come, the commercial electronic-computer has grown to a healthy $3.5 billion-a-year level. In 1963, 4,789 commercial computers costing more than $2 billion were installed; the remaining outlays were for programming or software. By February 1965 the total number of computers in the United States had reached 25,000. There were another 5,000 in other countries. It is anticipated that by 1970 sales will reach $7 billion or $8 billion a year.[32]

The giant in the industry, with sales in 1962 of $2.5 billion, is IBM, founded in 1910 as a successor to Herman Hollerith's Tabulating Machine Company. Hollerith was a Census Bureau statistician who devised mechanical tabulating equipment for the 1890 population count. The 1880 Census had taken over seven years to complete, and the Bureau was in a panic. Hollerith came to the rescue. In 1900 he produced an automatic electric sorter that handled punched cards at the rate of 300 a minute, as well as a tabulator and key-punch machine. In 1903, Hollerith went into business for himself, and began to squabble with the Census Bureau over rental fees and patent rights. (Progress has been such that, in 1960, fifty statisticians and a battery of computers did the work it had taken 4,000 statisticians to do in 1950.) Today IBM has installed three-fourths of the computers in the world—more than ten times the number its closest competitor, Sperry Rand, has placed. As one business magazine observed: "As a company, IBM is probably more pervasive in its influence on the way business is done than any in history. Its products, preceded by squads of salesmen and flanked by corps of educators, are changing the whole fabric of management structure in business and altering the basic methods used in science and engineering."[33] Between 1955 and 1962 IBM sales jumped more than $3\frac{1}{2}$ times, while capital stock and surplus hit a high in the latter year of almost $1.4 billion.

For some time during the late 1940s and early 1950s, IBM made only electromechanical machines. The momentary lapse in judgment was underscored in 1948, when IBM saw the Census Bureau install Sperry Rand's UNIVAC, the first commercial electronic computer. There was little doubt that the future was an electronic one. IBM quickly developed its numbered machines—650, 701, 702, 704, and 705. By 1956, it was far ahead of its competitors. The transition from ordinary sorters and tabulators, used in relatively simple statistical and accounting tasks, to computers for scientific laboratories was not difficult. During the same period, the huge monolith that the elder Thomas Watson had built was decentralized by his son, who took control in 1956. Nevertheless, the corporate structure remained so complex that a distinct management committee was required to settle disputes between divisions. Not counting the World Trade Corporation, which handled overseas business as a wholly owned subsidiary, there were the Service Bureau, Electric Typewriter Division, Supplies Division, Federal Systems Division (selling equipment to Uncle Sam only), a sales division with 190 branch offices, a division for small and medium data-processing systems, another for large systems, a components division, and, understandably, a research and development division. A later reorganization added the Industrial Products and Real Estate Divisions.

The emphasis has shifted from handling past data, like accounting and statistical reports, to current information processing. The latter is the basis for "integrated systems" design, a technique intended to give the corporate officer more effective control of the business heap on which he sits. As one computer man remarked, the aim is to "... bring out trends in a business before the trends are history." In jargon, the objective is to provide "real time processing" of data in so rapid a manner that the results are available in time to influence the process itself. In effect the flow of information is utilized to influence events before they have passed by. This information, the businessman believes, will supply the control that supposedly eludes him, and, if computers will do the job, he does not seem to mind that there may be fewer employees than before.[34] Few businessmen — with the conspicuous exception of Thomas J. Watson, Jr. — have expressed public concern over the irrepressible social tensions generated by the success of the computer.

THE AUTOMATION and "information-processing" business is attractive enough to encourage others to encroach on the giant's domain, but so far they have only nibbled at the borders. None of the seven or so companies trailing IBM can really expect to displace it in the calculable future. But they are all enthusiastic and hopeful. At the start of 1963, Sperry Rand reported a large order backlog for its UNIVAC; General Electric experienced an almost 50 per cent sales increase over the previous year; Minneapolis-Honeywell had the highest sales-rate increase for computers in its history; RCA shipped 280 systems in 1962, an increase of 155 over 1961; Burroughs's deliveries went up from five systems to seventy; and National Cash Register's equipment was so well received that its neophyte salesmen now must be college graduates who receive $15 a week more than beginners did in 1960.

The smaller manufacturers, as well as IBM, have continued to produce new machines with marked regularity. Some are small units allowing everyone to keep up with the Joneses, especially when the rental fee is no more than $1,000 or $1,500 a month. Modular, solid-state systems are offered that are able to perform 500,000 operations a second. One such device claims an expandable memory capacity between 2,000 and 32,700 characters. The control unit transmits two million instructions a second to the system. Or one can make use of RCA's RACE machine (Random Access Computer Equipment), which keeps information on flexible magnetic cards instead of on tape or drums. The advantage of this system derives from the fact that information can be stored and retrieved independently of the location of previously stored data. A tape-reading machine must search for several minutes over 2,000 feet or more of tape before locating the needed fact. Drums and discs, which can also operate on the random-access principle, are faster than cards but are more costly and limited in capacity. The RACE method stores data on flexible magnetic cards, which can then be whipped out at high speed for "reading." Its capacity is 340,787,200 characters, expandible with supplementary equipment to 5,452,595,200 characters. And the basic machine rents for only $3,500 a month. Such high-powered equipment, with speedy printers and card readers, is quite attractive, but the users are unaware how deeply they can be ensnared, for once they start to use a computer more and more work must be fed into it, if only to justify the purchase or rental price. The first computer is outgrown and a larger model invited in. The barrier, of course, is the so-called "software," the programs that ordinarily must be altered with new equipment. But IBM's little 1440, which contains a disk-file memory component that looks like a phonograph record-changer, a high-speed printer with interchangeable type bars, and a 300-to-400-per-minute photoelectric punch-card reader, is compatible with three larger IBM systems.

To ensure that a system will function in hitchless fashion, built-in checks on the operations of peripheral equipment can be provided, so that depletion of the tape supply, for example, can be automatically noted and automatically corrected without stopping work. Furthermore, automatic programming schemes come with the smaller machine and are suitable for banks, insurance companies, hospitals, schools, trucking companies, and retail stores.

IBM's rivals seem determined to catch up—at least they are trying, not only by imitating IBM's sales, service, and customer-"education" methods, but also by introducing faster computers with automatic translation accessories and attempting at the same time to exploit specialized markets.[35]

They have offered a bewildering variety of machines — high-speed data handling equipment that makes possible short-wave transmissions of voice communication in the form of digits; computers that punch cards, transfer data, process, and print simultaneously; and flexible machines designed to accommodate various sorts of peripheral equipment like tape transports and printers.

The biggest customer, of course, is the Federal government, which provides about half the business. The Budget Bureau has estimated that total direct Federal outlays for data processing in fiscal 1964 were more than $800 million and that this figure will triple by 1970. In 1963 Uncle Sam used almost 1,300 computers as against 730 in 1961. It was a nice chunk of business; all the manufacturers yearn for contracts with the Defense Department, Atomic Energy Commission, Space Agency, National Science Foundation, Institutes of Health, Census Bureau, Labor Department, Post Office, and Veterans' Bureau. In fact, the decision to pursue government business, especially in scientific fields, enabled one of the smaller companies, Control Data Corporation, to expand with astounding rapidity — from a few engineers in 1957 to 3,200 employees and $50 million in sales in 1963. CDC's emphasis has been on scientific applications for selected customers, 70 per cent of whom are among the agencies just listed. Because as much as two-thirds of the cost of a computer system may be invested in accessory equipment like readers and devices that move tape past sensing and recording heads, the company decided in 1963 to make its own. And, as is usual in successful firms, CDC has acquired its portion of affiliates: The Bendix Computer Division, Cedar Engineering, Meiscon Corporation, and Electro-Fact (a Dutch instrument maker) have come under Control Data's expanding corporate umbrella.

BUSINESS IN AMERICA is not enough, however, for the companies are also rushing overseas. In late 1963, two Australian government agencies granted an $8.5 million order to CDC, whose salesmen travelled 9,500 miles to underbid six other United States and British competitors.

IBM had to stage a computer-performance contest with a Swedish manufacturer to win a $10 million contract with the Swedish government. American computers are being installed in a Ghanaian university, in a department store in Colombia, in Hong Kong, Japan, and Bombay. Although the overseas market accounts at present for but one-fourth of domestic sales, it is estimated that it will equal them within a decade.[36] IBM's foreign sales are increasing at twice the rate for installations here and by 1970 are expected to match domestic volume. The Netherlands Automatic Information Processing Research Center has estimated that computer installations in the Common Market nations grew from 135 in 1958 to 985 by the end of 1961, with 950 on order but not completed. The Center predicted 9,500 computers at work in the six E.E.C. countries alone by 1971. But, interestingly, the motivation to use computers and to automate in these areas arises from labor shortages. In West Germany, for example, thousands of workers from Italy and Spain must be imported to get critical work done. Process control appears essential to the viability of West European economies.

By 1964, it was evident that American manufacturers were dominating the international computer market. Since 1960 American computer concerns had built or bought more than 20 manufacturing plants around the world, in addition to numerous sales and licensing agreements. IBM's overseas earnings in 1964 were $124 million on sales of $933 million. United States companies accounted for about 70 per cent of all overseas installations, a figure that was bound to be increased by GE's acquisition of the commercial data-processing interests of Olivetti in Italy and the Compagnie des Machines Bull in France. Although American companies have large investments overseas, they do have to contend with nationalist sentiments: De Gaulle was able to prevent GE's original take-over attempt on Machines Bull, and IBM has been having difficulties producing its 360 system in Japan, where the government prefers to have computers built by domestic firms. Nevertheless, IBM is still the leading computer-maker in Japan, holding 41 per cent of the market.[37]

The American companies, of course, are by no means

cultivating virgin soil overseas. Resident computer makers
have their own national prestige to defend, and so IBM,
CDC, and RCA must face the competition of English
Electric, Machines Bull, Olivetti, and Telefunken. Despite
the battle for markets, or perhaps because of it, cartel
arrangements have begun to emerge. Machines Bull, which
had developed financial problems in 1963, was not unwilling
to be in with GE for 20 per cent of its stock. But Charles de
Gaulle's sense of *la gloire* led him to veto the GE proposal:
The Americans had enough fingers in French business
already. But as there was no other solution for Bull's
financial distress, the General had to relent, to the shouts of
Bull stockholders, "Long live the Yanks." And so Bull got a
new lease on life, and another American company had pene-
trated the French market for computers at the relatively low
cost of about $43 million. GE quickly followed up this coup
with a deal for the Olivetti computer interests in Italy,
making it the second largest factor in European data processing. It seemed that IBM's hold on overseas business
was to be loosened somewhat.[38]

The intercompany connections are manifold and complex. Elliott-Automation, a large British firm, makes one-
fourth of its products under license from National Cash
Register and other American computer makers. While
International Computers absorbed Britain's EMI, Ltd., and
Ferranti, Ltd., computer operations, Bull across the Channel
established a joint research and development program
with Compagnie Générale de Télégraphie Sans Fils to
dominate the French sector of the industry. The Banque
de Paris et des Pays-Bas controls Sans Fils and has a
major interest in Bull's financial structure. Compagnie
des Compteurs, which makes the American Packard-Bell
process computer in France under a licensing arrangement,
is also controlled by the Banque de Paris. Sans Fils, in turn,
has under its corporate wing a French firm that markets the
Thompson-Ramo-Wooldridge computer. In Japan, Minneapolis-Honeywell works through Nippon Electric, Sperry
Rand through Oki Electric, and RCA through Hitachi.
RCA also has a licensing tie-in with Siemens & Halske in
West Germany. The hands of the computer makers are
beginning to intertwine in wondrous ways across the seas.[39]

Not that European manufacturers are unwilling to join the battle. Elliott-Automation, a company built by Sir Leon Bagrit, has become Britain's most formidable competition for American firms. Originally a small instrument company, Elliott is now a large $126-million complex producing a wider range of automation hardware than any other company in Europe. The government, as in Japan, is determined to help local manufacturers: In Britain, a 10 per cent tariff is placed on imported equipment. In response, IBM, which is hardest hit by the surcharge, has been absorbing it without raising prices. The result of the fight has been to keep American manufacturers in their place, with about half the British market. Furthermore, the British government has finally begun to lend aid to its beleaguered subject companies by providing development contracts to speed up research in data processing.[40]

THE ART of selling computers does not depart sharply from the techniques employed for marketing other kinds of industrial equipment. The primary consideration is to demonstrate that a computer can reduce costs despite the rather high initial investment. Institutional advertisements will ask: "What are the costs of getting out routine paper work? How many people are tied up in these operations?" It is strongly hinted that the work force, even in offices, can be reduced — and of course the ads are right. The seller may have to make a fairly detailed survey of the prospect's operations before submitting a proposal. These preliminary investigations can be rather expensive for the vendor, but it is all part of the product being sold anyway. Preferably, the equipment should be leased, for such an arrangement extracts more money from the client. The air force, for example, had to be reminded by the government's General Accounting Office in December 1963 that it could save almost $1.8 million by purchasing certain data-processing components outright. The larger companies like IBM train their salesmen to be specialists in data processing in one or more major industries, with the result that the old-fashioned drummer becomes a "sales engineer." Even fashion appeal is not overlooked: UNIVAC III now comes in several color schemes. According to Sperry Rand, this represents the "culmination of coordination between industrial designers, development engineers and marketing personnel."[41] The theory behind the color option is based on the assertion that it can affect the efficiency of people at work and that UNIVAC III should be as advanced in appearance as it is in performance. The company was candid enough to admit that sales were not always made on technical superiority alone (which might or might not be the case) but that "emotional factors" generated by color also played a part. Finally, as computers are prestige items, it was said, they should be displayed as attractively as possible. With ivory, charcoal, and yellow applied to the computer's fixed components as the basic motif, the customer can have his choice of Roman gold and earth brown, surf green and sea green, or steel gray and marine blue. Light and dark "values" are also available. And to make the whole assembly quite chic, a list of decorator ideas, "coordinated" with the color selected, was offered, including wall colors, flourescent lamps, floor covers, tables, telephones, and wastepaper baskets.

The whole computer business is likely, however, to be thrown into an uproar by an impending patent suit not unlike the famous litigation over the radio inventions of De Forest and Armstrong. It seems that John Mauchly, the builder of ENIAC, had refused to assign to the University of Pennsylvania whatever patents he might have obtained. Required to leave, he joined Sperry Rand, to which he preferred to turn over his claims. Issuance of the basic patent rights was delayed for fifteen years by interference from IBM, Bell Laboratories, and others. Finally, in early 1964, Rand extracted a letter of patent on the ENIAC, placing the firm in a commanding position to demand royalties from all its rivals. Similarly, Jay Forrester secured patent rights on the magnetic core, to which IBM responded with a $13 million payment for unrestricted use of the tiny components. What patent fights will do to the new multibillion-dollar industry remains to be seen.

Meanwhile, with the proliferation of new machines and the pressures to be always up to date, the American phenomenon of the second-hand market has arisen to tempt the unautomated entrepreneur. Marginal to the main business as yet, it promises to do for the computer maker what the discarded Lizzie did for Detroit. (One cartoon showed an Honest Einstein telling a hesitant customer, "Now here's a baby that was used only by a little old M.I.T. professor on Sundays.") The bargains can be substantial: Often costing half or less than the original price, the old machine, although psychologically obsolete, frequently continues to perform competent data-processing tasks. In 1962 Sperry Rand took back an ancient UNIVAC I used by a chemical company since 1959, reconditioned it, and resold it to an insurance company at one-tenth its original price of $1 million. It has been estimated that some 4,000 used computers had been delivered by the end of 1963. Of all the computer companies, only IBM was reluctant to enter into the obsolete-machine trade. Technological advances were too rapid to make it worthwhile, IBM argued. In any case, the company now is willing to sell used equipment to its customers, if not to third parties. For the other computer makers, however, the entree into a new-computer sale may very well be via reconditioned equipment. The major problem, of course, is programming, as machine characteristics vary so much. The development of common language systems may very well overcome this seemingly insuperable barrier.

But what of business concerns that simply cannot afford to purchase or lease computers? Are they to be left behind in the race for efficiency and profitability? Of course not! All the small entrepreneur needs do is turn for help to a broker of idle computer time. Some firms with large installations do not mind getting part of their expenses back by allowing smaller organizations to use the equipment during idle hours.[42] An owner of a machine may thus be paying $100 an hour up to 176 hours a month, plus $40 an hour for time in excess of the contract figure. "Free" time, usually in the early morning, can be sold through the broker at $100 an hour, of which $80 may go to the owner. Broker and owner make money, and the secondary user buys a service at a cost otherwise unobtainable.

Or if this arrangement is not satisfactory because one may have to wait around with cards and tapes in hand for a machine to be available, the small company may prefer to purchase machine time from a commercial service bureau.

One such organization keeps the books and records of four Wall Street brokerage firms. The SPAN Data Processing Center does a massive bookkeeping job for several insurance companies in Hartford, Connecticut.[43] Some twenty mutual-savings banks in Brooklyn support a similar operation. Although at first it may be difficult to estimate cost savings, one service bureau has estimated that the paper work is now done with half the number of clerks used by its clients under the older system. A SPAN client eliminated ninety-seven office machines and seventy-three operators in its tabulating section. The saving amounted to more than $300,000 in 1960 alone. The major computer manufacturers provide similar services, a rather long-standing practice. In the old days, any company wanting a tabulating job done could go to a service bureau, which operated very much like laundromats. The largest of them was conducted by IBM, but it had to revamp its setup by virtue of a 1956 antitrust consent decree. It now has some twenty-five "datacenters" renting large computers by the hour. Although the service bureau will do a complete job, including programming and operation, the datacenter simply provides the use of a 7070 computer for about $300 an hour. The customer must do his own programming and operate the computer himself. RCA started a Wall Street service with two of its 501 machines in 1960, as did IBM. The RCA service center handles a variety of paperwork for brokers, including account and security data, trial balances, purchases and sales, commissions, interest, and dividends. The center, in effect, combines the capabilities of eight computer systems and the skills of nearly 100 technicians. Such centers allow smaller companies to participate in the computer revolution. By 1964, there were almost 600 such centers across the nation, with many more planned to do the clerical work of smaller concerns.

An alternative rental approach for actual installations was devised by the Philco Computer Division of the Ford Motor Company, which has based its rental fees only on running time, so that customers would not have to pay for a full eight-hour shift. Underlying the scheme was the hope that once installed the computer would be operated more and more, with the customer eventually moving up to full time use. IBM cannot compete on this basis because of certain conditions embodied in the 1956 consent decree.

On the other hand, IBM has not been restricted in the time-sharing business, which permits many people to use a computer simultaneously. The trick is to juggle the demands of each user back and forth and to work on each problem so rapidly that it all seems a simultaneous operation. First offered by GE in early 1964, the time-sharing technique could also help companies tie together multiple branches and offices in a total management-information system. Within a year IBM was out with a system that embodied an internal relocation method, making it unnecessary for the user to keep track of where information was located in the memory unit, as well as channel controllers that would allow up to four central elements in the computer to share a pool of two million characters in the main memory section. Furthermore, the system can be tied into the 360 complex. Another such system can receive inquiries from more than 3,000 remote locations at a time, keep track of their sources, and transmit the correct answers to the proper places. The outcome is the development of an "information utility," supplying services to many subscribers, as is the case with an electric or telephone company. The information is supplied to the client at his own location and in a form he normally uses. Furthermore, the service charge can be on a per-transaction basis. In effect, the computer is able to solve many problems at once. As many as 1,000 clients can use the equipment in such a time-sharing system.

Such "time-sharing" computers were being installed at M.I.T. and the University of California at Berkeley. The Cambridge computer would be able to provide simultaneous service to more than 200 users at remote terminals at M.I.T. and fifty-one other New England colleges and universities. The Berkeley operation was to handle as many as six simultaneous conversational users at once, with response from the computer in less than one second. A slight increase in response time would permit the addition of about 24 users. The machine might also be used for teaching purposes, initiating dialogues with students on mathematics, physics, and engineering design.[44]

Despite these advances—in technology and in its

helter-skelter application—there are complaints that management has not moved rapidly enough in clasping the computer to its corporate breast.[45] In a survey of more than 300 installations in twenty-seven companies by one consulting firm, it was found that only one-third of the firms were making "effective" use of the new equipment. They were large companies, spending a total of more than $100 million a year on data processing. For each $1 million they spent, they were getting back $1.3 million. In all these cases, it was said, the top executives were "... devoting a substantial amount of time to the computer effort." They, rather than the technicians, were the decision-makers, forcibly "integrating" computers into company operations even if the latter had to be revamped. As one expert remarked, if computers, magnetic tape readers, and similar equipment may permit such a giant as General Motors to program the work of individual sections and if multiple-purpose production devices can be built to provide flexibility, then there is no reason why automation must be limited to mass-production processes. Clearly, control, and ever tighter control, appears to be the objective. With humans automated out of factory and office, only the archon and his machine will be left to contemplate with equanimity the mountain of reports flowing out of the computer.[46]

The programming of Minerva

The numerous parallels between the computer and the brain are extraordinary. Take a machine, add a computer and servomechanisms, and behavior once thought possible only for living organisms can be readily simulated. Machines now pilot aircraft; adjust the flow of materials onto a production line; control the volume of output; do mathematical calculations; and easily spin out logical deductions – all work of the human brain. True, the computer operates as an extension, as it were, of the brain, but it does so with incredible efficiency, achieving results that man can visualize but cannot reach by himself.[1]

Persons making such comparisons necessarily adopt a mechanistic view of behavior. They have had to believe that certain functions of the mind can be located in particular cerebral areas and that consequently to speak of a dualism of brain and mind is otiose. The brain, they insist, is a machine; to support their position they have called on the evidence of recent brain research.[2] Long before, certain philosophers, beginning with Descartes, had asserted that all the attributes of the universe could be reduced to mechanisms and mathematics. Hobbes went further and argued that even thought was mere motion in a corporeal body. In a cosmos of geometry, behavior is completely mechanical and the brain but a complex computer.

True, the brain is not entirely electronic and operates in a digital manner for some actions and not for others. The final results of both the computer and the brain are said to be similar, however. Let us suppose that the latter is more a collection of on/off switches than of drums, cores, and other components. Then a computer built with only on/off switches in which some were used for storage and others for arithmetic and logic operations would be quite like a brain. Here the parallel with neurons connected only by nerve fibers is evident.[3] In any case, all that seems necessary to establish the comparison between computer and brain is the fact that the nervous system functions by the passage of electrical impulses from neuron to neuron.

A counterargument has been made that a computer must be electronic and therefore is not to be compared with a brain because the latter has chemical components. But nonelectronic computers are quite possible, operating hydraulically or on air. A number of manufacturers, including IBM, are working quietly behind closed doors to develop computers using jets of air or liquids. Such devices promise to be cheap, reliable, and versatile. In one such unit, a jet of water flowing rapidly through a Y-mechanism is directed to one of two stable positions by a control valve, thus providing the hydraulic equivalent of a switch. The major drawback is its relatively slow speed: An operation takes a few thousands of a second. Nevertheless, such a device would be fast enough for automatic cash registers and desk calculators. Molded plastic forms can be used to build complex fluid circuits, and, with miniaturization, the switching unit need not be much larger than a match head. Furthermore, such units would require virtually no maintenance, and for some purposes they are more reliable than electronic components. The main point is that electrical energy is not essential to computer technology.[4]

Nevertheless, most authorities agree that the brain and its related nerve structures do have electrical properties, even though they appear to operate in a rather mixed fashion.[5] That is to say, the cerebral system functions stochastically, in a probabilistic fashion, utilizing both analogue and digital modes. The handling and storing of information bits are evidently done by an electrical wave process.[6]

Computers too can be made to work in mixed modes. At Purdue University, J. E. Gibson has mated an analogue and a digital computer to solve new problems by the random recall of past experience. It has been predicted that the next generation of such hybrid computers will achieve greater integration of the parallel computing elements of the analogue machine with the sequential stored-program technique of the digital device.[7] At Stanford University, scientists have developed a machine based on an assembly of special memory cores or "memistors"—essentially electrochemical resistors with memory capacities—which enable a conventional computer to "learn." The memistors are gathered into adaptive linear networks, thus providing the computer expert with an approach that is not quite digital nor quite analogue. It is this sort of mix that may bring the computer closer to the way in which the human brain works.

HOW DOES the computer compare with the brain? The brain's general organization appears to be quite orderly and quite "computer-like"[8] The basic on/off switching mechanism in the nerve structure allows information to be transmitted in an electrical manner. Although many brain functions operate in an analogue fashion, it appears that various parts behave as do arithmetic, storage, and control units in a computer system. John von Neumann estimated that the memory capacity of the brain is equal to thirty billion on/off switches for each nerve cell. According to other authorities, this figure seems rather high, for it assumes that every "input" is recorded in an average lifetime and that information flows incessantly into the human organism via all the senses. But if only vision were considered as the input channel, human memory needs would be much smaller, perhaps only six million storage units per neuron. Of course, this figure still would be rather large for a man-made computer.[9] It is likely, though, that the brain stores but a part of the input it receives, thus reducing the requirement for duplicating its major functions to an equivalent of perhaps four or five switching mechanisms per neuron. Considering the ever increasing storage capacities of the computer and the feasibility of transferring data from one machine generation to the next, "learning" itself could be much faster for a computer than for a brain.

Other comparisons: The computer occupies a space of about 50,000 cubic centimeters, although with miniaturization this space can be reduced sharply. The computer equivalent of the brain would probably be about the size of a large building. The brain has 10,000 times as many components and a fiftieth of the volume of one of the original computers. A neuron is about one-millionth of a cc. in size; a small transistor is one cc. The impulse time in a neuron is about one-thousandth of a second; the computer is a good deal faster. Most of the brain's work is to control unconscious automatic actions, without which the organism would expire. As such actions are in the realm of the reflexes, it is evident that much data processing takes place at this level.[10] Evidently, only a small part of the brain is used for the higher intellect. Furthermore, much of the job of processing information in the human is done by peripheral components — hearing, touch, and smell. Computer systems are beginning to work that way too. They also have such control or feedback mechanisms as gyroscopes, thermostats, and directional devices. Humans could not function without their feedbacks — sweat glands or inner-ear balance. Sometimes human neural connections go awry, creating pathological conditions. Such malfunctioning may also occur in a computer, as when current flows continuously through the closed loops of components causing "machine schizophrenia." It is cured by sending a large pulse of electricity into the system to "chase" the wild units back into the proper track. For a while, human schizophrenia was treated in much the same way.

Why try to build a machine that is like a brain? Because it can do things that brains cannot, for it is speedier and more precise. It enhances brain power, just as other machines enhance muscle power. As one writer put it, the difference between doing a calculation with pencil and paper and doing it on a computer is akin to having $1 as against $1 million. So fast are computers that engineers now speak of the nanosecond, or one-billionth of a second, and the picosecond, expressed in the fraction one over the digit one with eighteen zeroes trailing after it. Considering the advances in peripheral sensing apparatus, it does not seem impossible to construct a brain-like machine. It is evident that some of the work of the brain can be simulated as long as its activity is defined as the acquisition and processing of information. Norbert Wiener used to tell of a machine that was planned to enable the blind to read by converting shapes on a page into audible tones. An apparatus was designed involving selective scanning by the machine. When the schematic was shown to an anatomist unaware of the work, he asked, "Is this a diagram of the fourth layer of the visual cortex of the brain?"[11]

A good deal of the work in this area draws its inspiration from "nerve-net" theory which purports to analyze neuron firing and perception in a purely abstract manner. The objective is to obtain a general theory of automata. To do so, one starts by assuming that all neurons are synchronized, abstracting from the effects of hormones and chemicals on the brain and ignoring interactions among neurons. This theory is based on a simple question: If neurons or nerve nets are constructed in certain ways, what are the consequences?[12] In fact, it seems possible to study such consequences without knowing anything about the neuron itself — the "black-box" problem.

Suppose an engineer were given a sealed box with input terminals into which voltages of any strength could be introduced and output terminals from which data could be obtained. The problem is to say something about the box's contents.[13] The inputs and outputs purportedly give all the information required, and the character of the box can be ascertained by comparing its behavior, or output, with certain criteria. The problem is not an abstract one, for this procedure is the sort employed in studying brain damage. Of course, if the black box happens to be an unexploded land mine, the investigation may cease peremptorily. At any rate, this problem offers a theoretical approach to the formal construction of neural nets to describe behavior. As A. M. Turing was once reported to have remarked, the computer itself might one day reach the black-box stage. "When that happens," said he, "we shan't know how it does it."

BORROWING FROM PHYSIOLOGY and ecology, computer engineers are wont to speak of the internal controls required to assure a balanced system. Living organisms have open systems in which energy is exchanged with the environment in order to overcome increased entropy or degeneration, the inevitable outcome of the Second Law of Thermodynamics. Such an exchange results in what the physiologist calls "homeostasis," the process of getting back to an original condition: In mechanical or electrical systems that are of the closed-loop type, cybernetic controls are required to regulate the oscillations. The mechanism here is feedback, a procedure for regulating the performance of the machine at every moment, depending on the result produced in the immediately preceding moment. That is, part of the output is fed back to the input, and the latter is thus based to some degree on the output itself. The results of the system are continuously used to correct what is going in at the start of the whole business. Agreement is thus assured between performance and goal. Although the self-adjusting reactions look like human behavior, they can be explained by ordinary physical processes.

The simplest feedback device is a room thermostat or the governor on a machine that maintains a steady speed of rotation in the flywheel. Strictly speaking, these devices use negative feedbacks, for an excessive output reduces the input. A positive feedback would merely lead to accelerated motion and ultimately to a breakdown in the equipment. In humans, positive feedback may indicate a disorder of the central nervous system – perhaps a continuous manic state or a psychosomatic ailment that leads to death. A more prosaic illustration of positive feedback would be the amplification of foot pressure by a power brake on an automobile. The notion of feedback, however, does not imply a return to static conditions, for in living organisms there may be movement to new levels of integration, such as occurs in growth from childhood to maturity. Yet, at each level, feedback and homeostasis take place. Mechanical systems will also attempt to return to prior levels of equilibrium, as when certain crystals assume particular patterns or chemical configurations that reveal "regulatory" behavior.[14] There action is taking place, albeit of an inorganic, physical nature.

This analysis implies that the machine or system is "observing" itself and that one can predict its behavior. There are then similar features in the computer and in the nervous system, in that decisions are based both on stored information and on information from feedback operations.[15] Feedback permits the machine to overcome increases in entropy, just as the human organism uses "data" flowing from sweat glands, body temperature, and the chemical content of the blood.[16] An illustration of human homeostasis occurs when a sudden chill causes shivering, the purpose of which is to generate body heat. In essence, these features are the basic elements of the science of cybernetics, a term invented by Norbert Wiener, which he coined from the Greek word for "steersman." Cybernetics then studies controls and communication in both machines and animals. Not only are control and communication closely related, but also, says the science of cybernetics, behavior can be explained and even approximated by mathematical methods installed in a computer.

More than that, the machine can be made to "learn." Such a device was designed a few years ago at Cornell University. Called the Perceptron, it was intended to demonstrate the learning methods of randomly organized systems. The stimuli, or input data, are presented to a grid of some 400 photoelectric cells, which are randomly connected with "associator" units. In turn, the latter activate response units when the input exceeds a certain limit, just as a neuron will fire only when the stimulus exceeds a critical level. Feedback from the response unit to the associators provides for adaptation and adjustment. The level of the stimuli flowing out of the associators can thus be regulated by homeostasis, as it were: In effect, the internal random circuitry allows the machine to "teach" itself. Certain shapes are recognized by the Perceptron after a number of exposures; practice improves its performance. Of course, the binary response is not like actual physiological action. So far, this procedure has been experimental; the major application of its principles has been the development of various peripheral sensing apparatuses. But it does suggest a model of a brain, albeit a quite primitive one.[17] It is as yet unknown, however, whether brain functioning is related to complex structure or to complex connections. The Perceptron approach employs the latter notion; it may be that the whole business will founder on the inability of the engineer to duplicate structure.

The underlying concepts in this phase of the new technology have generated a furious debate over whether the machine thinks or does not think. But this debate, in turn, has required a definition of "mind" that has not always been apparent and that, to some philosophers, simply defies adequate description.[18] The notion of mind appears to involve consciousness, knowing, being, and doing. Yet these elements are processes, if we may employ the word, that function at various levels of complexity; for automation, the central question to be resolved is the degree to which all or some mental processes can be duplicated. The participants in the argument seem to agree that complex responses, intuition, and emotion cannot be simulated by the machine, but it is difficult to deny that the latter does certain things that once were the exclusive province of mind.

We have seen how the computer is able to give meaning to conglomerate masses of data more efficiently than the mind can. At such levels, there is a strong presumption for the statement that the machine "thinks," at least in an operational sense. This statement need not in any way suggest organismic behavior, for all one speaks of is "objectively identifiable events," which can be ordered and described and which occur in a computer. The events are actions: They are "thinkable" actions. As James Newman remarked, machines cannot wonder, but they respond, and they are more like the brain than any device ever made. Or as Anatol Rapoport asked, "If one says that machines are (or are not) capable of performing mental operations, what does this statement imply about the speaker's conception of mental operations?"[19] Consequently, it all depends on the definition of a mental operation and the purely empirical determination of the capacity of a computer to do the job. If thinking then is defined as a continuum of infinite dimensions, there is some range in which men and machines are comparable. What scientists are trying to do is to "push machine behavior further out into this continuum."[20]

The strongest argument against this position has been offered by E. T. D. Calhoun, a Bell Laboratory scientist.[21] Machines, says Calhoun, are artifacts without consciousness. Insisting that the pattern of observable behavior is irrelevant, he finds the significant differences between man and the computer to rest in their respective functions. His rebuttal, however, founders, for if a "... function defines how some agent or agency gives some object or order of objects the capacity to be affected..." then observable behavior must ensue and surely must be relevant in describing the function itself. To suggest that thinking implies caring about results, as does Calhoun, is to confuse different levels of mental activity; nor is it helpful to deny that thinking is an activity. And when Calhoun asserts that the information in a computer is not information because it does not add to knowledge, his entire argument collapses, for, although symbols and signs are manipulated, it is precisely these operations that increase knowledge. Furthermore, whether or not all these operations are cases of "complementation, substitution and augmentation," as another writer insists,[22] rather than replication or simulation, appears to be a semantic quibble, for at some point there is a transformation into simulation. With sensing equipment, machines "see," although they are as yet too primitive to enjoy it, an attribute that Calhoun insists is essential to "seeing." It may be that a computer cannot write love letters, but that depends on the sort of correspondence one wants to undertake. If an artful swain wanted to use a letter-writing manual, he no doubt would be more successful with a machine. Essentially, the requirement of "enjoyment" for "seeing," when the latter involves merely the transmission of information, is to posit a form of anthropomorphism.[23]

Now, Calhoun may have been reaching for implications that have nothing to do with the machine as technology but, rather, with the social context in which the new equipment will be placed. For it is the pursuit of the mechanistic that troubles the observer. To deny that these facets of human behavior can be duplicated in artifacts fails to face up to the crucial issue of the modern age, to wit, the urge to control society. There is great danger in blinding oneself to the extraordinary possibilities unveiled by scientists, for what is taking place is an incessant drive to intensify the automatic character of "systems" and to reduce human participation in them simply because behavior is presumed to be mechanistic. The one saving grace is that parallels can be easily exaggerated. There may be more to human behavior that is nonlinear than the linear methods of the machine can handle. Nevertheless, there is nothing in the logic of the machine that would forestall the arrival of a condition in which it and it alone might decide whether or not to push the last button. Reliance on the rules of impossibility—the Second Law of Thermodynamics, the principle of indeterminacy, and Gödel's theorem that in a consistent system there is something that cannot be proved—is not persuasive. To assert, for example, that there are problems that fall outside the fixed procedures of the computer and that the latter, therefore, can not provide solutions for them, does not prove that no machine can act, at least in part, as does a brain. Possibility rules appear to provide outer bounds, but such limits have not yet been approached in computer technology.[24]

Suppose one considered speech or sensitivity to light an attribute of thought and consciousness. Machines exhibit these characteristics, and for the modern scientist that is sufficient. Questions on whether the machine is dead or alive are irrelevant, and, although the application of the term "intelligent" may or may not be appropriate, the fact is that a computer can behave as does a brain. But the brain is not "intelligent" either: It is the person who is intelligent. The confusion, we are told, stems from the use of nonmechanistic concepts. If a machine were built that used personal terms in "talking" about people and mechanistic terms to describe other machines and could then be made to know truth from falsehood, it might know whether or not it "possessed" human attributes.[25] It could then conceivably pass the test of consciousness. It might even pass an identity test, as in Turing's famous game in which the questioner would be unable to tell, from answers to problems and queries, which of two rooms contained a machine and which a human being. Naturally, there are many questions that the computer would flunk, but the fact that enough useful and important answers would be correct and indistinguishable from human responses suggests, according to Turing, "thinking" properties.[26]

Turing made short shrift of the objections to asserting these properties in a machine. The description of thinking as a function of immortal souls is theology and irrelevant, said he; the fear of unknown or unintended consequences is an evasion of the problem; there are no limits to the kinds of machine that might be built, for "there might be men cleverer than any given machine, but then there might be other machines cleverer again, and so on";[27] the expansion of storage capacity and random circuitry makes the machine more diverse; and, as we shall see, machines may be on their way toward forming concepts. Even emotions and feelings may be simulated, as in an experiment not too long ago at the University of Nebraska, in which a computer was programmed to replicate love, fear, and anger in response to satisfying, frustrating, and painful situations. Emotions were graded, with strong ones dominating weaker ones. And with long-term and short-term "memories" built into the program, artificial behavior based on accumulated experience appeared possible. There is thus a fair amount of evidence to warrant saying that machines "think," in the sense that an automobile "travels" and a pile driver "works." That a machine cannot write music like Beethoven's is no refutation, for what other human can? Those who reject the notion that a machine thinks may console themselves by defining "thinking" as something a machine cannot do.

THE MOVEMENT in the new technology, then, is from tools, clockworks, and heat engines, which use and store energy, to controls based on communication and the transfer of information. These controls essentially are the unique quality of automation. The power of the machine is "mental"; it simulates not effort but thought, and in this manner is able to guide the work process itself. Decisions are made by the computer concerning the direction in which energy is to flow. This decision-making involves information theory, an abstract set of relationships based on the transmission of stimuli and the evocation of desired responses. The word "information" as used here simply means the transfer and acquisition of knowledge in symbolic forms. It assumes that every datum can be expressed as a discrete electrical impulse, making information available to the machine's whirring appetite. It is a restricted technical and even statistical definition, although some scientists want to go further by making meaning itself measurable.[28]

In any case, to carry on communication in a mechanical manner one needs to specify sources, transmitters, channels, and receivers. Much of the research has had to do with getting signals through channels in the face of noise or interference in the circuitry. Problems of meaning have been held in abeyance, while getting the signal itself through has been stressed. Repetition or redundancy is applied to overcome noise; however, when considerable interference exists, transmission becomes a purely statistical accident, and, with a fifty-fifty chance of getting information through, one might as well flip a coin. Interestingly, it has been the psychologist who has made much of information theory, for he seems ever ready to purchase anything that promises a new way of controlling man. Yet as the machine begins to handle the semantic problem more effectively, control becomes a disturbing reality. Even Saturday-night dates may be arranged by the computer. A program at Iowa State University has matched students for physical and personality traits, intelligence, and background to select partners for a student-union dance. Naturally, it was a psychologist who figured this one out.[29]

That the computer may solve various puzzles, even historical ones, is apparent. At M. I. T., a computer went to work on a problem that had troubled historians for a long time — which of certain Federalist papers could be credited to James Madison, and which to Alexander Hamilton? Authorship of all but fifteen of the seventy-seven essays had long been established. The known writings of Madison and Hamilton were then catalogued to determine their idiosyncracies, and the distinctive traits were fed into the computer along with the doubtful documents. The machine analyzed the materials and gave credit to Madison for eleven papers, quoted odds of eighty to one that he had written another, and assigned to him most of the responsibility for two joint papers. The authorship of one remaining paper was uncertain.

Of course, when information has to be collated, sorted, and retrieved, the computer is invaluable. Law cases, for example, may be stored together with related data and then used to provide a lawyer with complete information on prior cases and decisions relevant to his subject within twenty-four hours. Ordinarily, the search for such material might take a week or more. One such program utilizes about a million references on New York State legal cases[30] and is able to check 120,000 references a minute. Another program at the University of Pittsburgh put 6,230,000 words of Pennsylvania law on four reels of tape. Key words referring to a particular type of action are fed into the machine, and, after a minute or so of search, the pertinent case citation is produced. Once the status of the case has been checked, summaries of past cases similar to the first one are obtained to provide precedents. Names, dates, decisions, appeals, and the like are included in the summaries. Information can be developed on the credibility of witnesses or on whether it might be better to go to a jury rather than to try the matter before a judge. The decision can be guided by what the machine has to say.

Presumably, retrieval methods would be helpful in any sort of library research. Anyone who has ever had the courage to brave the call-slip system of the Library of Congress in Washington knows that it is better to build one's own collection or go elsewhere. No doubt computerized methods there might improve the present chaotic condition, as was conceded in a recent report on automation and the library.[31] Large quantities of material could be stored in digital form allowing high-speed processing, and information now in catalogs could be converted for machine digestion. In the Library of Congress alone there are forty-two million items on 270 miles of shelving, containing about 10^{14} computer bits of information. The task would be formidable but quite feasible, for it is reported that only 10^7 bits are changed or altered in the course of one day's work. It was estimated that the cost would run between \$50 and \$70 million, a sum equal to a three-year operating budget for the Library. Would an automated library be worth while?

Yes, says the Council on Library Resources, for automation would permit tailor-made reports, bibliographies, and reading lists to be produced with great speed. The nation's intellectual activities would be enhanced, and we would be able to keep pace with the information explosion. Even browsing can be made meaningful by providing special collections that "can be seeded with analogous or related materials which the librarians believe to be of value..." Is the extraction of materials that one wants also to be controlled?

No doubt the computer is useful in such knotty administrative tasks as the registration and enrollment of students. Its use can eliminate the tedium of standing in long lines and the frustration of getting to the head only to discover that a desired section has just been closed out. Students fill out preregistration forms, which are then put through the computer to work out class schedules and balance various sections. The machine can be primed with data on students' individual programs, the numbers and sizes of rooms, the number of faculty members, and the varying time patterns for classes in a forty-five hour week. Within perhaps a half-hour, thousands of possible combinations may be analyzed and printed. Tentative scheduling plans can be run through the computer as often as needed. Such automated techniques, employed at a number of schools, including M. I. T., Yale, Purdue, and Massachusetts, can enroll 1,800 students in an hour.

Retrieval methods, such as have been suggested for lawyers, can also be helpful to scholars, according to computer experts. The latter have argued that books per se are on the way out and that storing written material on magnetic tapes in vast central libraries will provide knowledge in the future. Computer analyses of Chaucer, Aristotle and Aquinas have been attempted, and, it is argued, concordances can be assembled more accurately and more quickly than by teams of scholars working laboriously over the years. The power of literary criticism can be enhanced by machines, say some computer men, by quantifying such favorite descriptions of style as "muscular" and "nervous." That is, a computer program should be able to detect elements of style to which ill-defined terms have been hitherto applied. The

83

question of whether or not Homer had any help might be answered on a computer. Literature is to become "literary data."

There has been some reaction against such trends. It has been argued that the mechanization of literature might divert attention to secondary works and that the nature of literature would be distorted if computers were to change qualitative expressions into quantitative forms. This distortion, as Jacques Barzun has said, is the fallacy of assessing importance by numbers. Such views, of course, are criticized as a species of anti-intellectualism and as reflections of sentimental attachment to nineteenth-century methods. The debate, however, merely suggests a confusion between indexing and art. The counting of symbols in Chaucer by computer only demonstrates the diligence of the programmer. Nevertheless, the perspective of the computer expert reveals a certain irony: Although it is conceded that computers are unable as yet to write poetry or compose symphonies, such creativity is not impossible, we are told. "In so far as we understand what *processes* are involved in creativity, none of these processes appear to be beyond the reach of computers." Whether or not the machine will be "creative" is immaterial at the moment: It is the belief that it can be that is so startling.[32]

Automation is also being employed in the practice of medicine. There it is more than a question of storing data and retrieving them. For example, feedback is beginning to influence the design of artificial limbs.[33] The old peg leg provided only support; new artificial limbs not only grasp and handle objects but also can be built with kinesthetic sense. One artificial hand works by means of a cathode contact pressed to the skin near a muscle in the surviving part of the limb. A light movement of that muscle generates current, which is transmitted through transistors to a motor that controls a flexible hand. Heart-disease patients might be fitted with tiny sensors to keep them in touch with their doctors. Hospital patients would be under continuous supervision, from admission to discharge. There seems little doubt that physiological monitoring and computer diagnosis will become widespread techniques.[34] Various instruments are linked to measure and observe a patient automatically.

The monitoring instruments could be hooked into a computer which would not only control all the electronic devices but would also analyze the data obtained by the monitors. Such a procedure might reduce the number of nurses and save as much as $140,000 a year in nurses' salaries for each twelve-bed unit. At the Massachusetts General Hospital in Boston, a computerized information system, using the "time-sharing" technique, is taking over most of the paper work and allowing admissions staff, nurses, pharmacists, physicians, and researchers to have simultaneous access to stored data. In Missouri, laboratory results are made available to patient-care areas almost instantaneously.

As might be expected, the computer makers, with visions of a $500 million-a-year market, have been cultivating the field. RCA, GE, Honeywell, and Control Data, as well as a host of smaller companies, have fostered "automatic" methods. But the ballyhoo has not quite paid off; one fancy installation at Roosevelt Hospital in New York was yanked because of "operational" difficulties. It was discovered that a sick patient does not care to be wrapped in wires and that resentment against what he may feel to be further debasement can become especially severe when rectal probes and blood-pressure tubes are applied in a never-ending sequence. As with hospital routine generally, nurses were more interested in the gadgetry than they were in the patient.[35]

The computer may also be useful for diagnostic purposes.[36] It was discovered in one study that the traditional head-down position for shock victims can be harmful. In another experiment, the computer was programmed to analyze congenital heart disease. A matrix comprising thirty-five different disease entities and fifty-seven symptoms associated with congenital defects was fed into the machine. The data, including twenty-two heart murmurs, seven electrocardiographic findings, eleven X-ray reports, and three age categories, were applied to Bayes's theorem (which asserts that the probability of a certain event is altered by the circumstances of prior events), so that the equation in the theorem might be solved in accordance with the symptoms presented by the patient. The matrix, in essence, represents past experience; from these data the computer translates the symptoms into a diagnosis.

It presumably did as good a job in some forty cases as did skilled cardiologists.[37] In another experiment, at Kansas State University, a computer was fed twenty-one symptoms related to thyroid cases, together with various mathematical equations. Diagnostic data on 268 patients under treatment for thyroid problems went into the machine as well. In all but eleven cases, the computer diagnoses agreed with those of the attending physicians. Pyelonephritis, a major kidney disease caused by certain bacterial infections, was said by an IBM computer to be really a combination of four different diseases on the basis of sorting 800 facts about each of 400 patients. And in the Soviet Union it was reported that computers are employed to diagnose ambiguous cases in which symptoms superficially suggested several possible ailments. The machines were said to be able to take into account a large number of minor symptoms whose significance is not easily assessed by a physician.[38] The machine might very well replace the quick diagnoses that mothers so often get over the telephone. Said one practitioner, doctors may become mere data-collectors for the computers.

Some experts, however, remain dubious and skeptical. It has been argued that translating diagnostic data into charts would be just as good as putting them into a machine, for then the doctor could read off his answers as quickly as he could feed the information into a computer. Furthermore, diagnosis is much too empirical an art; many situations are far too complex for conversion into digital form. Diagnosis as a means of identifying and tabulating disease characteristics, which is about all the machine can do, takes the physician away from his major task of understanding the afflicted person and preparing a program of treatment. It would be unfortunate if fascination with machinery were to trap the physician into mistaking the art of labeling for the art of medicine.[39]

THE FOREGOING APPLICATIONS of computer technology are rather straightforward; their impact is much less striking than in the area now known as "artificial intelligence," or the use of the machine in language translation, writing music and television scripts, playing chess and checkers, and generating proofs for mathematical theorems—the mechanization of what the psychologist calls the "cognitive process." In mathematics, for example, algorithmic procedures require an exhaustive investigation for all possible derivations that might provide a proof. That is, the algorithm is a completely specified method guaranteed to lead to a solution. But this method can be long and costly on a computer, and in the case of chess would take centuries, as in this game there are about 10^{125} possible combinations. An alternative approach is the heuristic, in which several arbitrarily chosen techniques with no guarantees attached to them are explored in "hunch" fashion.[40] This technique, based on the conditional transfer, consists of instructions to the machine to seek satisfaction of a specified condition. If this condition is not obtained, the instructions cause the computer to proceed in its normal sequence. The machine can thus select one or more possible paths based on some previously indicated criterion. Without such instructions, the machine would have to proceed in algorithmic fashion, exploring every alternative; with the heuristic technique, assessment and evaluation occur. When the latter is built into a computer, one may very well speak of a form of "artificial intelligence." The computer employs rules of thumb and trial and error, it relates stored data to a careful logic, and it explores new relationships between sets of known facts. All that seems necessary is to devise a "search" method, pattern recognition, and random nets, and then we begin to get fairly close to a learning system. The only answer that man would have to mechanical systems that learn is to pull the plug—although this answer may not be possible considering recent experiments with devices that plug themselves in. Let us see how the heuristic approach works with translation, computer music, chess, and the like.

Machine-translation projects, of course, were motivated by a desire to find out what the Russians were up to. American military intelligence can be satisfied by less than 1 per cent of available Soviet material, but to obtain even so small an amount it would be necessary to translate about five times more than is done at present. Machine-translation techniques date back to the early efforts of Andrew Booth, an English mathematician who in the 1940s devised a word-by-word matching program that turned French into mangled English. Then, eight years later, IBM demonstrated a program for translating Russian into English based on a vocabulary of 250 Russian words. It required storing more than 200,000 bits and 2,400 instructions. With word roots stored in the machine, word endings could then be examined before deciding on the proper translation. The latter program was crude, but, as with the dog that walked on its hind legs, it was amazing that the machine did it at all.[41] More recently, IBM has demonstrated a program for translating Chinese into English. Although still incomplete, the system renders a Chinese text into broken but fairly comprehensible English. An important element in the program stems from Lin Yutang's famous Chinese typewriter. Marks on keys correspond to portions of Chinese characters, which are then scanned by an operator to identify their top and bottom elements. The whole group of up to sixteen characters that possess the characteristic top and bottom is consulted by the operator, who then selects, by number, the proper character in the group. Three typewriter keys are necessary to define each character, making the process rather slow. In any case, the information is then punched on a tape and fed into the computer, where the memory store, consisting of 10,000 ideographs along with linguistic instructions, enables the machine to carry through the translation.[42]

Technical papers have been gathered from various Soviet scientific fields and, with the large storage capacities now available, some translations can be done in about three minutes, compared to a skilled human translator's time of one day. Of course, the machine's English is not especially fluent, for verbs and nouns are often not distinguished, and the rich variety of meanings is frequently lacking. Word order is a troublesome problem. Yet by 1960 there were several machine-translation programs at work able to translate, albeit haltingly, from one language to another; one even claimed an accuracy of 75 per cent. In all these projects, the steps are essentially alike: The document is put into digital form; a dictionary search is made, followed by an analysis of syntax; the new syntax is formulated; and the translation then follows. In some programs, a semantic analysis preceding the new syntax is provided. The dictionary search is simply a matter of looking for stored words in the computer's memory unit.

Machine translation raises the problem of linguistic analysis; the desirable objective would be to develop universal language concepts to analyze word formation and rules of combination. If this universality could be achieved, translation by computer would be vastly simplified. Changes in word forms that indicate case, gender, tense, mood, and the like make it easier to store a word base with a subsequent search for the ending, as in the IBM program described above. Syntactical analysis has been more difficult, but, theoretically, application of the rules of syntax by the search technique could yield a reasonable solution. Where multiple equivalents are possible, the computer would simply print them all out. Translation programmers have been arguing over whether sentences can be meaningfully broken into segments or whether the sense of a phrase depends on the entire composition. Of course, translation would be quite easy if the first were true, but syntax is often rooted in the relation of dependence suggested by the latter. Yet even this relation may be computerized, according to recent research.[43] As translation is extremely complex, it may require the heuristic approach rather than an algorithmic one, for there is no one-to-one correspondence in moving from one language to another, an elementary principle that the experimenters sometimes forget. A now classic illustration of literalness is the report of a translation program that rendered the English "out of sight, out of mind" into technically accurate Russian as "blind idiot."

According to some critics, this phrase would be an apt label for all such programs. The late Mortimer Taube savagely attacked machine-translation efforts.[44] He rejected both the dependent and the segment theories and insisted that meaning is carried by the entire sentence. But if sentences are to be stored, the magnitude of the job would be enormous, for it would require at least 10^{50} English sentences of twenty words or less. Taube asked if it might not be cheaper to train human translators, a good question no doubt, as the $3 million per annum spent on machine-translation research could supply at least 300 human translators a year. But the fact is that everyone wants speed; at best, a skilled translator working steadily eight hours a day the year round could produce about a million and a half words. And so the Japanese now have a transistorized computer to turn English into their own tongue; the Russians have developed an algorithmic procedure to translate English, German, Chinese, and Japanese; and we are furiously at work on computerizing translations from Russian and Chinese. The military mind, which has been behind all this activity, is ever hopeful that it will obtain its intelligence by merely pushing buttons.

COMPUTER SCIENTISTS on occasion try to be really creative: In their spare moments they get the machines to compose music and write television scripts. Of course, in computer music, live composers have to be brought in to work on the problem. An early experiment done on the ILLIAC yielded a rather banal twenty-minute suite for strings. The procedure was to generate random numbers equal to the notes of the musical scale subject to certain "composition" rules. Later instructions were worked out for rhythm and dynamics. One expert, L. A. Hiller, Jr., a composer-scientist, has argued that, as the writing of music is essentially a matter of extracting order out of a multitude of possibilities, it can be studied in quantitive fashion.[45] Because order in music involves pitch, time, meter, rhythm, and the interaction of melodic lines, statistical probabilities presumably can be imposed on these elements. The aesthetic factor, however, has escaped both the computer and the programmer.

Indeed, it is at this point that one discovers striking evidence of the separation of thought and art from their human context. Such products of the spirit are necessarily involved in the human situation. It is this involvement that gives them their characteristic tension, and, in the absence of such involvement, the limits of art are provided by the machine. The quantification and regulation of dynamics, timbre, pitch, tone, and time give the computer its real

90

chance. A kind of interior monologue ensues, in which the complexities of existence are excluded, leaving only mechanistic attributes that can be readily fed to a computer. With thought cut away from the act of creativity in this manner, only a dehumanized product can be offered.[46]

Fundamentally, such efforts are experiments in information theory, and they presumably add to the scientists' knowledge of the random choice of symbols. Hiller is confident that the machine not only will be able to study harmonic practices but will also write counterpoint, correlate rhythm and dynamics to note selection, work out orchestration, and even compose fugues and sonatas. "In time, it is conceivable that the handling of many elements involved in the writing of standard musical textures might be carried out relatively simply and efficiently with a computer."[47] No doubt this development will take music well past the achievements of a John Cage and will perhaps accustom us to microtones even smaller and stranger than those found in some contemporary compositions. The experts are sure that the machine will produce "synthetic average Beethoven."

If the computer might be programmed to churn out singing commercials, it could also be directed to write television scripts. To judge by one experiment in 1960, the results do not deviate much from standard television fare. Two M.I.T. programmers spent several months preparing written instructions for a computer, which then turned out a performing script in two minutes. As usual, the story dealt with cops and robbers—the robber takes a drink; the sheriff is at the window; he shoots; he enters the room. Variations in action were obtained by having random numbers select alternative courses of action.[48] The results were quite like any episode in a "B" western movie. Close-up and long shots were written into the instructions, but sometimes matters became confused, as when one sequence directed the sheriff to slip his gun into the robber's holster. This kind of problem required the program to impose certain logical rules or constraints to make the action genuinely dramatic. Although there was no wish to convert the computer into a Shakespeare, the effort was certainly a striking case of "artificial intelligence."

Those who think this activity a rather frivolous use of expensive equipment may be encouraged by more serious investigations in science and mathematics. The computer has facilitated precise calculations in quantum physics; it makes complex correlations for multivariate analysis; it studies brain waves to discount the influence of random electrical activity; and it solves differential equations not amenable to traditional methods. For example, the computer was employed by two professors, D. H. Lehmer and H. S. Vandiver, to test Fermat's last theorem, a mathematical statement that had defied proof for more than three centuries. Fermat, a seventeenth-century French mathematician, had written in the margin of a book: "If n is a number greater than 2, there are no whole numbers, a, b, c such that $a^n + b^n = c^n$. I have found a truly wonderful proof which this margin is too small to contain." No one uncovered any record of such a proof, however, and generations of mathematicians have failed in the attempt to construct one.[49] But the computer demonstrated that Fermat's theorem is correct for all values of n less than 4,000. The theorem consequently holds, to all intents and purposes, even though a logical proof or disproof is still lacking.

One mathematical computer technique, called ALPAK, makes it possible to perform algebraic calculations on a digital computer at 10,000 times the human speed. As algebraic expressions include numbers as coefficients and exponents, they can be written in digital form. For example, $3x^2y^4z^5$ may be written as "3 245," when 3 is the coefficient and the other digits the exponents. Archimedes's cattle problem—to determine how many cows and bulls there are in four herds of different colors, with a majority of bulls—was solved on a computer at the University of Waterloo in Ontario in 1965. There were actually eight answers, each 206,545 digits long, suggesting why the problem had baffled men for more than 2,000 years.

The computer can thus take us quite far in achieving solutions of certain long-standing problems in mathematics or even in logic. In fact, machines to solve syllogisms were built as far back as the eighteenth century, as with Lord Stanhope's "demonstrator."[50] W. S. Jevons, the versatile

British economist, devised a "logical piano" in 1869 that handled Boolean algebra quite effectively. But really dramatic possibilities came with the age of the computer. In 1959 a mathematician put the whole list of more than 200 theorems in the first five chapters of Russell and White-head's *Principia Mathematica* into an IBM computer and proved them in about three minutes of running time. One proof was even more elegant than the original. A more difficult set of some 150 theorems took somewhat longer. When heuristic methods are employed to work out such proofs, it may be said that the machine has "exhibited" intuition or perhaps luck.

The machine may also be used to derive one area of mathematics from another and to discover mathematical definitions. For example, because theories of natural and real numbers can be evolved from set theory, theorems developed on a computer from set theory that would manifest unique correspondence with the axioms of the number system would in effect establish the expressions to be used as definitions for the basic concepts in the particular number theory itself.[51] "Mechanical mathematics" can thus help to formalize proofs, a basic task of the mathematician. The latter would escape the pain and boredom of laborious paper work and he could use his time to discover the nature of intuition and the heuristic. Even geometry problems can be solved more easily on the machine, given an appropriate heuristic scheme. To explore all possibilities via an algorithm in a ten-step geometry theorem would take the computer centuries to do. But a heuristic program permits the machine to "think" just like a high-school sophomore: It works backward by selecting from its memory the appropriate axioms and theorems necessary for the base of the proof and then generates the connecting steps. In one experiment, a computer, in less than one minute, developed a proof for the theorem that states that the point on a bisector of an angle is equidistant from the sides of the angle. A program devised at M.I.T. in 1961 performs indefinite integration, as well as definite and multiple integration, all difficult procedures in the calculus.[52] The original program's speed compared favorably with that of college freshmen, but had it been revised for a fast computer it could have been 800 times quicker. Although the cost was about $15 to solve one average college final-examination problem, advanced programming could cut this sum to about four cents. At this rate, college students could find machine solutions fairly attractive.

ALTHOUGH Baron von Kempelen's Automaton Chess Player, which entertained the court of Maria Theresa, was a clever hoax, modern chess-playing machines cannot help but be honest. To get a computer to play chess is perhaps the ultimate in artificial intelligence. No computer, at least none of those that we know now, could play a perfect game by working out all the variations in algorithmic fashion. With 10^{125} variations for an average game of forty moves, the computer would take about 10^{95} years to decide on the first move. A more practical approach is to have the machine explore two or three moves ahead and to employ heuristic methods of play. In effect, a collection of rules of thumb are built into the program.

An early device for playing chess was built by Claude Shannon.[53] The device required a code to represent the pieces and squares as numbers, a specified strategy, and a program to translate the latter into machine language. Positions could be indicated by numbers from one to sixty-four, with zeros for empty squares; this system allowed storage in the memory unit. A move necessitated two numbers, one for the square on which the piece was located and one for the square to which it had to move. Strategy was more difficult, but later developments showed how attacking rules, blocking rules, and mobility could be programmed for the machine.[54] Shannon's method was tried out on MANIAC I in 1956, but with a reduced board. Certain pieces and moves were deleted to make the program tractable. Two years later another try was had on an IBM 704; this machine was more sophisticated. Subsequent programs took into account material balance and control of the board's center, critical aspects of chess playing. These experiments suggest that problems can be solved without our quite knowing just how it is done. In effect, a heuristic program for chess suggests that the machine evaluates the positions itself. And if the machine can alter its judgments in accordance with its "experience," it may be said that it "learns," for at each stage it has improved its "thinking" without guidance from the programmer, albeit its behavior is somewhat different from that of a Bobby Fischer.

However, as Norbert Wiener once remarked, a learning machine can go beyond the person who prepared the program. In a game of chess or checkers played with a machine, the human antagonist may indeed catch up with the computer, but there is the possibility that the machine will learn new tricks and surpass the human. Such a possibility implies that there is not complete control over the machine, and, if, for example, the latter is to make the decision when to press the button for a war, then it is the humans who are courting trouble. For a program in such a machine would have to be based on the experience of the last war, and, although it might function well within the older assumptions, there is no assurance that these assumptions would be right for the next world outburst. As Wiener said, this can be dangerous.

A more practical application of artificial intelligence may be in the computation of gambling odds. One scientist wheeled his computer into a Las Vegas casino and walked off with $360 in a game of blackjack. The computer decided how much to bet on each hand and whether to draw a card or not. It was quite simple, for all the machine did was to calculate probabilities quickly. One mathematics professor, E. O. Thorp, of New Mexico State College, worked out a system for beating the gaming tables on an IBM computer and tested it by taking $11,000 out of Reno's casinos in twenty-four hours. For his pains, he was barred from a number of Nevada gambling houses. In Britain the betting laws allow only those games that give all players an equal chance. There was some doubt about baccarat, but it was given a clean bill by a Ferranti Atlas computer. In this game, the "house" plays simultaneously against two different players, with the objective of getting as close to nine as possible with two or three cards, but not over it. As the banker has only one hand, his advantage is reduced and his strategy fairly complex. The computer digested a series of individual computations, one for each ratio of the stakes and the strategy of the players. It took forty-five minutes to handle the calculation, involving over a trillion operations. A desk calculator would have taken about 1,000 years to do the job.[55]

With artificial intelligence, actual problems are solved. But the computer can also be employed for simulation, in which models or theories of behavior are fed into it to spin out implications. As a simulation model is essentially an analogy, it can be manipulated to see what happens when its components are altered or shifted about. The major elements of a real situation are reduced to symbols, which can then be processed in the computer. Companies can thus check pilot plants before they are built by running figures through a computer. Simulated data for the construction of bridges, bombs, boilers, and highway traffic jams can be analyzed to see what happens before anything actually does. For these tasks, scientists have had to come up with mathematical techniques designed to handle simulation at various conceptual and computational levels.[56] The initial specification is a "system" whose current state is described by a set of variables. Additional information on inputs and the effects the latter have on the state of the system makes it possible to decide how to carry through change. As this possibility implies a need for control, the next step is an "optimal" policy, one that will permit change at the lowest cost. With iteration used as the approach to a solution, the computer is ideally suited to do the job.

But let us note that the philosophic preconceptions in computer technology are quite mechanistic. Nowhere is this point demonstrated more sharply than in the simulation models of the psychologist. There is a presumption here that all behavior is thoroughly objective and that reality can be squeezed and compressed into mathematical equations. Once this "squeezing" is done, prediction comes easily and so does control of the human being and his society. Certitude, such as was never known before, can be provided, particularly with a high-speed digital machine. Man has no soul, says the psychologist, and his emotions and irrationality are mere outputs emanating from a "black box" whose electronic characteristics will soon be revealed. Introspection is utterly useless, for behavior can be explained in the relatively simpler terms of stimulus and response. The actions of intelligent human beings can be understood as products of complicated but finite and determinate "laws."[57] It is this philosophic outlook that underpins rote-memory experiments, the generation of visual displays on the computer, studies in mechanical perception, and artificial concept formation. It is confidently argued that all this work will eventually demonstrate how images are transformed into ideas and actions by the brain.

A remarkable intellectual arrogance infuses the thinking of these specialists. One went so far as to assert that there is too much irrational reverence for human intelligence and that, in fact, there is nothing special about either intelligence or creativity. Intelligence as ordinarily conceived, is deemed to be but "an aesthetic question, or one of a sense of dignity," not a technical matter. It is really a complex of performances, he averred, which we may respect but not necessarily comprehend.[58]

Consequently, it would be just as easy for these creators of androids to simulate large-scale organizations as to replicate the behavior of individuals. Artificial social structures and processes are made to develop according to certain rules, as the game of philosopher-king continues unabated. For example, in one investigation, the operations were restricted to a large group producing something—x for goods, y for services. Formal lines of communication were established, utilizing messages, directions, and commands. A set of symbols for these entities was given to the computer; rules were defined and properly stored; "agents" were identified by binary numbers; and skill profiles were added to the whole business. Learning was said to take place when the skill profiles were altered as a result of manipulating the various symbols. Then the computer related skill data, of which there was a huge inventory, to activity data, providing at long last a simulated technological system.[59] Why engage in such complex computations? Presumably because intricate problems become tractable when put into the machine; but the unstated premise is always control. "The presence of the computer not only makes possible the study of large complex models, but also encourages their construction..."[60] The program just described is called "Leviathan."

In 1960 a computer was used to predict voter reactions to various positions that the late President Kennedy would be apt to take. It accurately forecast the outcome of the election some three months before the campaign was to end. The method was a simulated model of the electorate based on more than 100,000 interviews obtained in opinion polls between 1952 and 1960. Voting habits, attitudes, and opinions on some fifty political questions, including data on the religious issue, were classified and fed into the machine.[61] Naturally, the political parties are the best purchasers of such "facts," for they are so anxious to know their chances, but the political scientists who sponsor these simulation studies go much further. They wish to discover the factors that can be manipulated to assure victory for their clients. "Somewhere along the continuum of coercive persuasion, at a point between the poles of buncombe and brainwashing, lies the optimum formula for producing consensus . . ."[62] And it is the computer that can provide the formula. Political surveys become market research, with the machine conducting campaigns in miniature. The party boss does not need to guess, for voter simulation will tell him which issues are appealing and popular, and which questions to avoid. The social scientist, who does this work for him, no longer really cares about politically meaningful matters; he has put debate and confrontation aside while he engages in manufacturing persuasion. He now operates a consent factory, but in doing so he is unaware that he really subverts the democratic process.[63] How much more scientific and objective simulation is than ordinary politics! No commitment is demanded but only the determination of decisions on a computer. Questions of power and issues of choice are thus to be eradicated, lest they challenge the model of the simulator.

OF COURSE, there are more useful political tasks to which the computer may be applied. For example, redistricting in accordance with the Supreme Court's decision could be carried out quickly. According to one system, each district would be cross-listed with a complete map of the state: Using the latest census figures, the computer could scan and count the population units, relating them to geographic coordinates, thus dividing the state into the desired number of regularly shaped districts with equal population counts. The data would then be converted into a visual pattern, which, superimposed on a map of the state, provides a complete district map. Although redistricting a state like New Jersey might take a staff about four months to do, the computer can produce the data in thirty minutes and can convert them into map form in less than a minute. During 1964 the states interested in employing these techniques included Massachusetts, Minnesota, Connecticut, and New Jersey.

Even voting may utilize computer methods. In one county in Georgia, primary voters punched holes in computer cards inserted in a device the size of a brief case. In a California county, traditional paper ballots were converted for tallying by an electronic machine that could do the job five times more quickly than could earlier hand counts. But faith in the magic of electronics blinds people to the great possibilities of manipulation. A case in point was the New York City clerk convicted of altering electronic records to secure better jobs for his friends. Improper appointments or promotions had been "given" to thirteen employees over a three-year period. Said *The New York Times* facetiously: "A clerk is arrested; the machine not only goes free but keeps right on working for the city. Equality before the law should be no less sacred in a cybernated universe than in one ruled by men."

The computer also helps to enforce the law. A device at the side of the road scans the license numbers of oncoming cars. The report is relayed to a UNIVAC or other machine, stocked with thousands of plate numbers of stolen vehicles, cars owned by drivers with suspended licenses, and cars owned by "scofflaws." Comparing incoming numbers with its "wanted" list, the computer responds before the culprit can reach a nearby police patrol. No doubt such methods can inculcate a healthier respect for the law, but somehow the average citizen resents all this activity as unfair. More seriously, the computer can be employed for an invasion of privacy altogether unknown in earlier days. The enormous capacity for a fantastic range of information about people could, in the absence of effective controls, turn society into a replica of Orwell's *1984*. If the prosecution in a criminal trial could use electronic data systems, while barring others, the weight against the defendant might be insuperable. According to some experts, new concepts of ethics and new laws would be needed to protect the individual.[64]

One whimsical report suggested that the standardized responses supplied by the State Department to ambassadorial entreaties might very well be handled by a computer, thus dispensing with policy committees and other ceremonials in the foreign service.[65] But though the computer is still unable to displace the rituals of international relations, it does have simulation models to work on. One might think that history, law, sociology, geography, resources, trade, and a host of other elements impinge on international relations, but the simulation expert believes he possesses enough quantitative factors to warrant building still another model. If a sufficient number of quantity modifiers and correlations is fed into a machine, one can easily come up with a 1,500-page computer book, like one tome called *Cross-Polity Survey*, which listed facts for fifty-seven characteristics in 115 political systems in an elegant 1,399-page volume providing enough numbers for everyone in the family. Or one can think of the "Crisiscom" program to simulate the behavior of political leaders in international crises, drawing on thousands of bits of data from history books. These works are excellent illustrations of the computer scientist's principle of GIGO — garbage in, garbage out.[66]

Or one might even throw L. F. Richardson's famous war-escalation formula into a computer to calculate the precise point at which the final explosion will occur.[67] Such factors as "war potential" and the "propensity to act" would be evaluated, together with military manpower, atomic capability, delivery systems, and other recondite notions of the Cold War. These "facts" could then be stored to help compute war potential indexes. One machine calculation along these lines revealed that there was a marked tendency for strong nations to act in concert. Now, if everyone made such simulation studies, perhaps computers would get to fight one another. Or the machines might decide that war was indeed intolerable, in which case we should have to concede to their superiority.

In any case, the military does not look upon simulation as a piece of science fiction. The army has a War Games Division in its Combat Developments Command, which attempts to project as realistically as possible the nature of the battlefield of the future. Imaginary wars are fed into computers to test the ideas of army officers and to arrive at decisions concerning the weaponry soldiers ought to have. Whether or not to cross a river, the amount of gasoline, or the number of spare parts to take along on a sortie can also be determined in this way. It is reported that chemical warfare and atomic attacks have been simulated as well. The mock battles, which take three months to prepare and three months to "fight," allow time out for lunch for the colonels who run the show. And the officers even become angry when the machine fails to credit them with as much damage as they know their weapons should have inflicted.

The air force's SAGE complex, referred to earlier, has taught scientists more about simulation than has any other computer installation. Attacks are continuously simulated on the huge network of machines into which radar keeps feeding data from the air space all around the United States. Generals, comfortably seated in a command-and-control room, watch the computer play its game of war. SAGE took seven years to construct, and the original programming required 1,800 man years to write. There is also an improved version of this scheme, developed for NATO, called NADGE, designed to protect Continental Europe from enemy aircraft. In this system an international consortium of computer manufacturers has been involved, including Westinghouse, Sperry Rand, Elliott Automation, Marconi, Telefunken, Sans Fils, and several IBM overseas affiliates. The total cost is expected to be about $310 million, with the United States paying about 31 per cent of the total.[68]

Yet some air-force officers have grave reservations about all this game playing. Colonel F. X. Kane, writing in *Fortune* (April 1964), argues that the theory of predicting war by computer is inadequate and even dangerous, for it fails to reckon with acts of will that have always determined how war is conducted. That is, the methodology of hardware has to be checked by the real world, and this checking is precisely what the simulation expert fails to do. One has only to reflect on the unique events that have determined the course of history—Soviet missiles in Cuba or the assassination of Archduke Ferdinand—to realize the shortcomings of simulation, for the latter assumes that human behavior can always be quantified. Nevertheless, the military mind demands instant information. Attempts are being made to develop "adaptive" computers, in essence, machines that can draw on accumulated experience to solve problems; ultimately, the Pentagon would like a fully automated command-and-control system that would display in "real time" all the elements in the decision-making process. This system might require computers that "talk" to other computers, with data flowing from all military sources, C.I.A., and the State Department.[69]

Some experts have thought that perhaps the computer might be employed for peace research.[70] If the computer can diagnose the imminent collapse of institutions, it might invent strategies to salvage them. It could be fed data on values, incomes, aspirations, needs, motivations, beliefs, interests, attitudes, and spiritual resources, which, together with binary translations of economic systems, politics, sociology, technology, ideology, law, and morality, would provide a "causal" model of the world. The machine would tell us whether we can get along with or without the United Nations, with or without capitalism, with or without Communism. After this work, there would not be much left for it to do.

BUT AT THE MOMENT we must deal with more prosaic uses of simulation techniques. One company, the Simulmatics Corporation, is developing a simulation of consumers' exposure to advertising. Another study, designed primarily for election purposes, has been used to evaluate the influence of "messages" on attitudes, so that persuasion through the public media might be enhanced.[71] Department-store pricing methods, site selection for warehouses, sales forecasts, and inventory strategies have all been simulated on computers. How to handle inventories, one of the more volatile elements in the economy, can be quite important to a business. This problem too has been simulated on the machine by playing the inventory game to demonstrate how lead time in ordering and lag time in production can produce either insufficient or excess inventories. Poor inventory strategy for an individual firm can cause losses or worse: Surplus inventory can start the economy on a downward spiral. By simulating an inventory system on a computer, the business manager can study specific failures and correct them. In fact, the entire operation of a business can be replicated on a computer: At M.I.T. such replication was done to cover eight years in the life of an imaginary company.

The technique is not always successful; the complex social systems the simulators have tried to put into the machine have to be reduced to relatively simple segments, or they end in a tortuous chain of equations that no one quite understands. The likelihood that a household will buy certain goods thus depends on the extent to which a product is used (heavy users being more apt to manifest larger replacement demand), timing of previous purchases, consumer attitudes, and, of course, advertising.[72] Differences in purchase probabilities for various goods over a given time period have to be estimated and added to the data. And some picture of household characteristics must be attached to the assumptions employed. The computer then calculates the likelihood of certain purchases, and the businessman can decide how to stock his store and how to order from his suppliers. The advantages of doing these computations on the computer arise, of course, from the latter's great speed. Meat packers, for example, may want to forecast beef prices six months in advance. But this forecast depends on many factors, including the number of cattle on feed, steer- and feed-price ratios, and conditions out on the range. To compute all these relationships by hand for a period covering five to ten years involving thirty to forty elements would be impossible. But in one meat-packing company, it took some 200 man hours to program the analysis, comprising about thirty statistical series to calculate twelve monthly formulas. The computer takes but a few minutes to scan the data, compare the various series, and then print out the best equation.[73] With forecast errors reduced to 5 per cent, the number of cattle to be slaughtered can be readily established. The computations necessary to solve a problem in linear programming also require the computer. Linear programming is a mathematical technique developed during the war to establish optimum levels for stockpiles and inventory. It is thus concerned with the allocation of limited resources, in order to maximize a product or minimize its cost. Production is broken into concrete, detailed steps, and specific methods for doing a certain task are described as "activities." As resources are not limitless, certain constraints have to be introduced into the program. In this manner, linear programming can tell a manufacturer how much of each product he ought to schedule, how to ship newsprint from different mills to various customers, how to transport a standardized product from several warehouses to a number of locations, or how to mix the most nutritious feed for animals at the lowest cost. Although the mathematical ideas behind linear programming were known before the widespread use of the computer, the involved computational work could not be done without it.[74]

AS MAKING MONEY is a prime motivation in our society, it was not unexpected that the computer would be put to work figuring out the most profitable securities for Wall Street investors. Common-stock values are calculated to select the best portfolios. IBM has developed a "portfolio program," and Merrill Lynch, Pierce, Fenner and Smith, a leading investment house, paid for a massive study of rates of return on common stocks. Earnings of utilities and pipeline companies are also studied by computer analysis. Another IBM program, Bond Trade Analysis Program — BTAP — is a series of computer instructions that enables a bank to measure the net dollars-and-cents effects of trading on its bond holdings. BTAP will help a bond buyer to increase his yield by pointing to particular issues that should be acquired or sold, and it will also help decide how to realign maturities and how to convert to capital gains. Another program simulates an investment-trust process. In this one, data on companies, industries, and general economic conditions are put into the computer's memory.

Rules of thumb, like those of a human investor, are stored as instructions, and a search procedure is employed to extract data when needed for manipulation. The data also include current values, ten-year averages, and rates of change in values to formulate "expectation" lists. The latter are then matched with the value lists in order to arrive at investment decisions. This process is roughly similar to IBM's portfolio program, in which potential risks are weighed against possible returns. Once the data are fed into the machine and processed, the programmer can extract an expected net return, the risk factor, and the amount of each chosen security to be included in the portfolio. The securities to be studied, however, have to be selected in advance, and some future price must be estimated, as well as the latter's probability of error. To many bankers, this approach is starting at the wrong end, for they want the computer actually to pick the best securities for them: They want a program that will tell them how really to make money. It seems pointless to construct a portfolio and then have the machine decide whether or not the guesses were any good. Eventually, the machine may accomplish prior decisions too.[75]

Such problems appear rather minor when we visualize the possibility of studying an entire economy on a computer. In one such analysis, the United States household sector was simulated, by means of a stratified sample with twenty-three different economic and demographic variables.[76] Probability values were assigned to various types of consumer behavior. Models have been put through the computer to study price formation in a competitive industry; some have introduced time lags to see what happens when demand is changed; prices and physical flows through the various segments of the hide, leather, and shoe industry have been fed into the machine to detect the relationship between the movement of materials and prices. One elaborate model devised at Cambridge University was based on an input-output matrix,[77] in which the internal elements comprised such technological factors as capital-output and labor-capital ratios, as well as behavioral equations involving consumer expenditures, investment plans, and the like. As the matrix contained 257 cells, the analysis could be carried forward only on a computer. Tapes were prepared for EDSAC II, which could do a million multiplications a minute. The operations included various arithmetic rules, counting the number of times a sequence had been carried out, and instructions for retrieval and transfer of data. Of interest was the fact that the machine was given only general instructions, from which it constructed the necessary detailed sequence itself. As a consequence, the model could explore alternative economic policies without really having to try them out, and it could suggest measures required to keep the economy close to some desired growth pattern.

All this activity seems directed toward developing guides for decision-making. In fact, as Herbert A. Simon has said, the machine will itself generate the "time stream of decision-making processes." The patent difficulty with simulation, however, is the putative certainty and credability that it lends to whatever theory the computer operator happens to have in mind. Now, in the social sciences particularly, there are no theories that are absolute: It is always a case of "perhaps." Worse yet, the simulators seldom take the trouble to check their computations against ordinary observation and expect the common man to accept what they say virtually on faith, simply because complicated equations have been stuffed through a computer. In a sense, mechanical or electronic craftsmanship has been substituted for meaning, and, as Robert Solo remarked, formalism has replaced human thought. It is seldom asked why the choice of the computer is necessarily superior to that of judgment rooted in experience. But the simulators insist that the imitation is better than the real thing, and they seek to create reality out of the illusions engendered by the machine.

THE PROGRAMMING of Minerva has other curious facets, some of which appear as indurate attempts to control human behavior, as in the recent vogue of the teaching machine. In 1960, a large computer manufacturer, Thompson-Ramo-Wooldridge, announced that it was prepared to build an electronic classroom. The school of the future would offer televised lessons emanating from four or five master studios, with color if necessary. The teacher, if there was one, could use the resources of an automatic library by consulting a television directory and dialing a number. A microfilm of the requested book would then appear on a screen, page by page. There was no *technical* reason, according to the company, why all schools could not be brought together in a vast educational network, assuring absolute uniformity in the transmission of culture. The student would have his own headphones through which he might listen, assuming no autistic thinking, to prerecorded lessons. Questions could be asked through an intercom system, so that the rest of the class would not be disturbed. Individual recitations would be staged in private study booths, with the teacher flicking a switch to listen in. And automated teaching of this nature could give pupils the best instruction — Arthur Schlesinger, Jr., on history, Milton Friedman on economics, or Herman Wouk on literature.

Such is the new George Orwell tale that threatens to become real. Simon Ramo once described how it would all work.[78] The student would be registered by a computer, which would give him a small plate, identifying him and his course of study. Insertion of the plate into a data-processing machine would quickly provide his entire record and progress to date. Some time might be spent with other human beings — fellow students and teachers — but most of the day would be occupied in communion with the machine. Teachers would not have to be present to ensure that the proper circuit had been tuned in; they would be raised, rather, "to a higher level," although Mr. Ramo leaves the specification of this level hanging tantalizingly in the air. Buttons would be pressed by the student; he would have no daydreams (a time-honored privilege gone, alas); he would always be in touch with his real teacher, the machine, which, if programmed properly, might graciously allow a few moments for contemplation before demanding an answer. No one would acquire a sense of inadequacy, for bright students could move from one machine to the next, and slow ones would stay put until released by time or a dredged-up right answer.

Of course, although science, mathematics, and "language skills" may be "taught" in this automatic, cookbook fashion, even Mr. Ramo concedes that the teaching of literature might still have to be done by humans because the machine is not yet equipped to handle the creative aspects of education. Teaching machines, however, merely store and regurgitate facts: They do not teach; they can only test one's ability to memorize. They teach about as well as a book might, yet no one who has ever been involved with the classroom will assert that learning can be imparted solely through a book. Mechanical teaching can be so rigid as to create a vast distaste for the acquisition of knowledge.

Philosophically, the teaching-machine movement dates back to John B. Watson's repudiation of human will and consciousness. Watson's behaviorism restricted the psychologist solely to what was observable. As meaning was not a property of the subject, but rather of his overt behavior, one might, by proper manipulation and control, transform the human being. It was little wonder that Watson wound up in a Madison Avenue advertising house. With B. F. Skinner, one of the major protagonists of the teaching machine, behaviorism reached its apogee. Personal decisions and freedom to choose goals were discarded as otiose, for with Skinner people were to be made to behave according to his criteria: To control man, said Skinner, is to control the future. The arrogance was astounding, to say the least.[79] And it was not surprising that, to Skinner, the only difference between humans and pigeons was the former's "verbal behavior." If some writers have ascribed human characteristics to things not human, then surely Skinner has reversed the procedure.

A "teaching machine" had been built by S. L. Pressey as far back as 1926. It was a simple mechanical device employing multiple-choice questions and was intended as a self-scoring tool to escape the burden of grading conventional essay questions. (A good teacher knows, however, that the best examination for a student is to ask him to write for three hours on what he has learned in the course!) Skinner's method, developed in the 1950s, presented information in small bits, or frames, with the student tested immediately after each bit. There were "schedules of reinforcement" or rewards for correct answers after each test before the next question could be presented. This system would ensure "effective control of behavior."[80] In this manner, pigeons were taught to play a midget baseball game and to peck out tunes on a toy piano. Skinner then taught his young daughter arithmetic in the same manner. As far as he could see, the only difference between pigeons and humans was that the birds had to be fed corn to elicit proper answers: Being correct was enough for humans.

The method was easily mechanized by printing the lessons on rolls of paper and enclosing them in a box with a window and a turning device to bring up the next question after checking a previous answer. The "reinforcement" could be anything from a pat on the head to an approving smile. Reinforcement is the feedback or "knowledge of results" in Skinner's system. As the teacher cannot supply reinforcement to all the children in the classroom, why not devise a method that would; is there anything better than a machine that might flash bulbs in carnival display everytime Johnny hit the jackpot? For Skinner, teaching as a personal process is a downright nuisance, for it "confounds" variables in educational research. Without teachers, education would be so much easier to measure. In fact, the argument goes, the machine is like a private tutor; it follows the Socratic method implicitly, leading the student step by step to the right answer. But Skinner and his disciples have forgotten that Socrates was a man, and in the give and take between himself and Crito and Simmias and Charmides and Phaedrus there was generated an intellectual excitement that, by contrast, reveals present-day mechanism as degrading and vulgar. To read Skinner and Pressey and Crowder is to traverse the weird world of mechanomorphic minds that seek nothing less than complete power over others.

Teaching-machine enthusiasts insist that there will be more creative tasks for humans in the schools, though it is difficult to see what else a teacher might do except become a clerk. Clearly, all the automated school system might require is an engineer to travel through the district adjusting equipment and replacing transistors. Some writers have asserted that the teacher would be relieved of "repetitive instructional duties" to engage in the "motivational and

109

inspirational" aspects of his art.[81] Most educators, however, assume that motivation and instruction are rather intimately related. No doubt a certain amount of rote teaching could be done in mechanical ways, and, considering the parlous state of our educational apparatus, it is just conceivable that society will fall for the blandishments of the mechanists.

Experiments with the machine have indicated that binary arithmetic, spelling, and vocabulary can be taught via the computer. There is a program at the University of Illinois, fed into ILLIAC, which employs slides and closed-circuit television. It is called PLATO (Programmed Logic for Automatic Teaching Operations). The computer there does not engage in any computational work but acts rather as a data-storage device, transferring information and making decisions. The teaching technique is not much different from that devised by Skinner or Pressey: The questions are fed out in frames, cues supplied for correct answers, and approval given when success is attained. Another device, the Autotutor, has some forty buttons, which are to be pushed to feed in answers. It is asserted that even golf can be taught by the machine, although it may be difficult as yet to get a robot out on the course to check a duffer's stance and swing. The Autotutor employs the "branching" method, which is the new jargon for multiple-choice questions. If the student makes a mistake, the machine will then supply additional instruction. The materials are put on microfilm, and the whole business rents for a mere $57.38 a month. One company trains its staff and customers in servicing various kinds of electronic gear with an Autotutor. The "student" reads the material and studies the drawings and is then tested by the machine, which also keeps track of all mistakes, presumably calculating a grade. Of course, programmed instruction is nothing more than a careful outline of the relevant materials, with appropriate testing. This work has been done without machines for years. Drug companies have long taught their representatives the nature of their products in this manner. But now it seems easier to put it all into a machine: Besides, it provides the personnel department with a heightened sense of status.

One recent device offers "computerized situation simulation instruction." This phrase means that a chemistry student, for example, sitting at his desk, may type instructions to a machine that would simulate chemical experiments. A viewer shows the student what would happen if he added potassium chromate to hydrochloric acid. If an explosion occured, he would see it on the viewer. The machine would then go back and repeat the basic instruction for mixing, thus correcting any errors. Similarly, a simulation course in foreign language and even musical performance can be developed, at least so say the advocates. Professor C. E. Nelson of the Union Theological Seminary reported on a programmed religious textbook, *Step by Step in Theology*.[82] With this modernized catechetical method, the Sunday-school pupil will receive his religion from the machine, while the teacher will be left free to develop "understanding" of religious truth.

THE IMPETUS to mechanized education was supplied by Sputnik and the Ford Foundation: The first created the hysteria, and the second provided the money. The Foundation helped set up the National Educational Television and Radio Center and to resurrect the National Association of Educational Broadcasters. It was first thought that broadcasting Shakespeare, chemistry, and elementary economics at 6 a.m. twice a week might meet the educational needs of the nation. But it was not enough, and in its wake came the audio-visual experts; equipment manufacturers; assorted peddlers of film libraries, projectors, and recording devices; and then the computer. By 1962 there were over 100 commercial companies producing electronic and mechanical teaching machines. It has become a multimillion dollar business for at least a dozen firms. The largest is the Teaching Materials Corporation, a subsidiary of Grolier, of *The Book of Knowledge* fame. In 1961, sales were $5.5 million and were expected to double in a few years. Encyclopedia Britannica, Prentice-Hall, McGraw-Hill, U.S. Industries, Rheem Manufacturing, and Litton Industries sell equipment or programs or both: The total volume may reach $100 million by 1965. Dupont, ATT, Eastman Kodak, RCA, and IBM "train" engineers and salesmen in this no longer unique fashion.[83]

Hardware and Software

A few researchers have asked some cogent questions about this raging educational fad. Do mechanical methods reinforce uniformity and discourage diversity? Is an atmosphere of surveillance and detection encouraged? What of the personal relationships so essential in the teaching-learning process? Can a piece of hardware really substitute for a good teacher? Might not mechanical teaching be somewhat like the training of rats? Is the human being nothing more than a bundle of reflexes to be conditioned and reconditioned? Does automated teaching create much greater interest or heightened motivation? And is there, in fact, any marked difference in achievement between machine-taught students and those who have had to suffer through lectures by live teachers? On the last question, there is no single study that has yet demonstrated any significant difference in learning, and one report states that students rarely reach 100 per cent mastery of programmed material.[84] Furthermore, who will control the programmers, those preparing the materials the machine will teach? For programming, in the last analysis, is the decisive area, regardless of all the fancy devices that may enchant school boards and supervisors and business concerns. Will it be a foundation? A textbook publisher? Video producers? Or perhaps Madison Avenue?

As Paul Goodman asks, does not programmed teaching tighten the process of conformity to consensus? Does it not pervert the aim of nurturing an inner growth of knowledge, and does it not enforce the dictum that "we" want students to "know" what we want them to know? Is not education thereby converted into "training"? In effect, programmed learning strengthens the purposes of those who seek to control the behavior of men. Yet there is always the gnawing question: Who are the "we," and what are the limits of "want"? In any case, it is clearly evident that the whole movement, and especially its automated phase, has arisen from the discovery by the electronic industry that there is a market to exploit. The roots of automated teaching are not to be found in the educational field itself. The issue of control thus becomes central to the whole endeavor, for the most obvious impact is the conditioning of children at an early age to the apparatus of a technological society.[85]

One observer became so angry at the high-pressure peddling of programmed-instruction machines to private firms that he exploded: "The fastbuck phonies are making another killing and management is making some sadly familiar mistakes."[86] Teaching machines seemed the latest in business glamor, and programmers were telling business men that the machine could handle all *their* training problems, just as they had promised the educator that budgetary ills could be cured by investment in hardware. As another expert advised, ". . . if you don't have a teaching machine, don't get one. If you have such a gadget get rid of it. Don't give it away, for someone else might use it . . . Remember that a good teacher is a more complicated, flexible teaching machine than you could possibly build. If you can't get a good program into him, you will never get one into a mechanical gadget."[87]

But the new planners of the future insist that the child of tomorrow will not be taught; rather, he is to be plugged in. A New York World's Fair pamphlet describes how it will be done: The child will be enclosed in an egg-shaped "studysphere," with a complete retrieval system for information from any part of the world. Temperature controls will provide a purer atmosphere to facilitate learning. The "studysphere" will contain antenna, television and film screen, microphone, tape recorder, and speakers, as well as an adjustable seat. Great teachers will be able to lecture to students plugged in anywhere, without leaving their homes. The "school of tomorrow" will cover an area of fifty city blocks, enrolling 60,000 pupils. The teacher will become a "program coordinator, a highly trained, self-respecting, deeply compassionate person engaging his charges in broad avenues of creative thought, act and deed in an unhurried atmosphere of human diversity and understanding."[88] No doubt quite fanciful, all this talk—but it does reflect the ambitions of some educators enchanted by gadgets.

Efficiency may not be the only criterion for the good life. The learning process has much to gain from human relationships that only a teacher can bring into the classroom. If the standards of the factory were all that was necessary, we should eat all our meals out of a vending machine. Yet the enjoyment of food is heightened by the cloth napkins and personal service of the restaurant. As George Arnstein has remarked, it may be efficient, but there are people who dislike the automated elevator so much that in many places human operators have been employed, even though they are unnecessary.[89]

But what is so disturbing about these efforts to mechanize and automate existence is the creation of conditions that facilitate the manipulation of people. It is assumed that, once an equation has been formulated, virtually all pertinent factors have been encompassed. As Jacques Barzun has said, the individual is to be given a number, stripped of differences, and turned into a manufactured object for analysis and abstraction. The sentient man is replaced by the Compleat Robot, for, to many scientists, man's hope and fate are irrelevant.[90] Complex social and psychological situations are cast into a framework suitable for the computer, and the intricacies and subtleties of human response are ignored. Such activities can be rooted only in a callousness and a sense of expediency that readily sustain a mass society in which individual uniqueness cannot survive.

TWO

Use and Impact

Work without men 4

Although manufacturing methods became increasingly automatic in the course of the twentieth century, humans were often still required to exercise control and to guide the machines and tools and belts of the factory. Even with the transfer machine, the heart of "Detroit automation," there was need for men. The semi-automatic machine tools – grinders, shapers, and planers – provided only energy: The skilled machinist was still around to decide how deeply to cut into the piece or how to reset the tool. It was when the computer and its associated controls were hooked into traditional equipment that man could be made redundant. For with these new devices information on performance could be fed back into the process to make all the necessary adjustments for error – precisely the task that humans had always performed.[1]

During the decade of the Fifties, the spread of computers in industry began in earnest. In 1951 only seven general-purpose digital machines were being used in manufacturing: Ten years later there were almost 7,500 such systems in operation. Some industries were able to move quickly into the new technology, for both the materials input and the product exhibited continuous-process characteristics easily adaptable to the computer – for example, in oil refining, chemicals, power generation, and even steel. In the last, sheets must move through rollers at high rates of speed: Variations in thickness must be detected quickly if a sheet is not to wrap itself around the roller. In chemicals, even more variables must be watched: Raw-materials mixtures must be carefully balanced, containers must not become too full, impurities have to be removed, temperature and pressures must be measured constantly, and distillations must be drawn off. In electric power, heat generation and loads must be controlled to avoid breakdowns.

Yet more and more the production of discrete products is handled as a continuous process. This change was demonstrated by Western Electric in 1961 with its computerized manufacture of carbon resistors, small devices that are used to control the passage of electric current. An air-conditioned, dust-free plant produced 1,200 resistors an hour, and the product was much more reliable, for the sweat of human hands no longer contaminated the delicate carbon covering. The resistor itself consists of a coated ceramic core with a metal cap at each end. The work is now done on a 120-foot long line with eight work stations, four inspection stations, and a computer control system. The parts move from one station to the next by pneumatic tubes and pallets on conveyors. Feedback mechanisms check the performance of the line at each station. The capping, helixing, marking of wattage and resistance values, cap-lead welding, and packaging are all done in a virtually continuous flow. Aside from some watching at the work stations, the only human effort expended is in removing the package at the end of the line. Distinct units of production are processed as though they were droplets in a country stream.

Such methods have been particularly striking in the electronics industry. As many of the manufacturing steps are essentially chemical-metallurgical, conventional assembly of components and units used to require careful hand operations. But in the 1950s the printed circuit board eliminated the mass of wiring behind the television tube or radio speaker. Laminated paper and phenolic plastic bonded to copper foil, on which a wiring pattern could be printed, provided the circuitry. Components for the circuit were then attached to the board at designated places to make contact with the copper. Soldering was done in a single operation, and, because everything was in one plane, the whole unit could be handled by automatic machinery. Transfer equipment moved partly assembled units from one line to the next. Not only was tube manufacture mechanized, but testing too was done by a machine that could handle 1,800 electron tubes an hour. A computer-controlled line making resistors doubled one plant's output to 2,400 units an hour. Even the manufacture of miniaturized components was automated.[2]

THE ADVANTAGES of the new methods are obvious: Greater capacity, higher productivity, less time in production, increased time for machine operation, reduced inventories, reduced variability in the product, less floor space, easier maintenance, lower costs per unit of output, and, in some cases, even smaller capital outlay.[3] These changes are decided material gains, and no doubt they enhance the balance sheet. Nevertheless, there are countervailing costs that do not enter into financial statements: The pursuit of technological advantage tends to brush them aside. One thinks of the humans who were once involved in industry. But no matter; if a bolt or a valve can be made without hands, that is feat enough. An innovation in construction materials makes the carpenter unnecessary; with synthetic fibers, no master craftsman need evaluate the properties of cloth; and, with computer controls of tooling equipment, there is no need for a machinist to "set up" the operation.

And indeed such is increasingly the case, particularly in metal working and machine tools, the material bases for modern industry. Machine tools are power-operated devices that cut, forge, and press metals into shape to create the actual instruments of production. One of the more common ones is the lathe, in which the work, or workpiece, is held and rotated about a horizontal axis while it is cut to size and shape by a cutting device guided by a skilled craftsman. Some lathes cut screws; others drill, bore, grind, and polish. In a turret lathe, the cutting tool is brought into action from either the front or the rear of the workpiece, and as many as eight operations can be done with one setting.[4] Multiple spindles make the lathe even more versatile. But, with large

119

pieces, hoists have to be employed to place the work properly into the tool. In the past, accuracy was a major problem, for after each cut the operator had to stop the machine, check his blueprint, measure the workpiece with his caliper or micrometer, and adjust the machine. It was painstaking work and demanded a high order of care and skill. To ease the handling problem, transfer machines were developed which conveyed the work from one machine tool to the next. This development was the essential idea for "Detroit automation," in which a transfer device placed a rough block of iron into position for drilling. When this was done, the clamps holding the work retracted automatically, as the block went on to subsequent stations for reaming, tapping, and other operations.

Such a line, however, common in automobile manufacture, was not at all characteristic of the machine-tool industry itself, in which innovation had lagged for many years. The industry comprised numerous small shops, dominated by a few giants — Cincinnati Milling, Warner and Swasey, Sunstrand, American Steel Foundries — who sold their output to automobile makers, airplane builders, and, of course, to themselves. The greater productivity achieved in 1960 — about one-fourth more than that of a decade earlier — stemmed mainly from increased work speeds.[5] By 1963 there were more over-age machine tools (more than ten years old) than at any time since the Great Depression. The machine-tool industry seemed ready for a fresh burst of activity. And indeed it was, for new technological developments were beginning to alter the nature of its work methods and its products.[6] By the early 1960s new metal-forming techniques, precision casting, high-speed cutting tools, electrical and chemical machining, and the computer had made their entry.

New abrasive cutting methods were introduced, reducing the need for batteries of milling, broaching, planing, cutting, and transfer machines. Although abrasive cutting is an ancient technique, the newer applications brought spectacular results, in one case increasing the output of auto camshafts from a low of twenty-three units an hour with the older two-step method to a high of thirty-five shafts with a single high-speed grinder. In addition, the change eliminated the need for thirty-six cutting tools. Although abrasive cutting might be traced to primitive man's use of sandstone to sharpen spears, the newer devices represented more than an evolutionary development. In the late 1800s a pottery maker tossed a mixture of emery, water, and clay into a kiln and emerged with the first grinding wheel. Later E. G. Acheson discovered that fused silica, sand, and coke could form the extra hard crystals of silicon carbide. His work laid the basis for the Carborundum Company, one of the giants of the abrasive business. The grinding wheels now are larger and self-sharpening and have been applied to actual machining operations.

Such techniques as cold forming are currently employed to make small exotic shapes. A metal—aluminum alloy, carbon steel, or stainless steel—is placed into a stationary die and is then pressed into shape by a moving punch. Cold working increases the strength of the part, so that small components for other machines can be produced with high reliability. At 600 a minute, the speed is rather high. Cold extrusion had been developed in Germany during World War II; not too long after, it was adopted by American metal-working shops. With a phosphate coating to separate the tool and the workpiece and to act as a lubricant, the method was quite practicable. Molten glass could be used as a lubricant also; the insulation this material provided was especially useful in forming high-temperature alloys. Copper tubes can be produced by an underwater extrusion method capable of providing heavy tubes with small diameters 230 feet long. The process, involving a hydraulic extrusion press and a variety of conveyors and transfer equipment, is, of course, automated and requires but one press operator and few helpers.[7]

The laser or the maser—acronyms for "Light [or Microwave] Amplification by Stimulated Emission of Radiation"—can be concentrated to a fine point with an electric force of up to ten million volts per centimeter to cut or weld metals in a flash of about ten-billionths of a second. High frequencies are used to make longitudinal seam welds and end-butt welds on tubing ranging in size from fractions of an inch to several feet in diameter. The materials welded include steel, cast iron, brass, aluminum, copper, and even some exotic alloys. Some of these materials had never been successfully welded before the use of high frequencies. The latter are introduced into the edges of the workpiece by inductors, which transmit energy from motor generators and vacuum-tube oscillators. High explosives blow metals together instead of apart, so that the bonds are as strong and as permanent as conventional welding will make them. Self-drilling screws that eliminate both drilling and tapping of holes are now available.[8]

Chipless methods like forging and extrusion, which avoid waste, are now common. Die casting allows the forming of light metal parts without machining, as in aluminum cylinder blocks. These techniques are all ways of preventing the accumulation of chips, the metal scrap that used to pile up on the floor of the old machine shop, in which perhaps one of every three pounds of steel might have to be swept away. But more important, these techniques reduce machining work, yield better quality because the metal grain can follow the contour of the workpiece, need less labor, and can be automated. Man-hour requirements are drastically reduced. In one case study reported by the Stanford Research Institute, the cutback in total production time was 53 per cent. This period covered planning or down time, design, and actual fabrication and machining.[9] Inspection, measuring, counting, sorting, and testing are done automatically by machine. Lubricants and coolants are, of course, injected automatically. Feedbacks adjust the working tool when prescribed tolerance limits are exceeded, and, should the tool fail altogether, the whole operation ceases. The machine can run for days with a minimum of attention. And the calculations for the nineteen-odd variables and the 342-odd relationships between them can be readily worked out on the computer.

PERHAPS THE MOST striking development in the machine-tool industry is numerical control, in which the computer itself guides the drill press or milling machine. Here machine operation is taken completely out of the hands of the human operator, as complicated parts are carved quickly, accurately, and automatically. Rectangular blocks of metal can be machined into a complex missile valve or pump housing with only a punched tape as a guide. The numerically controlled machine tool operates in all three dimensions, automatically employs up to sixty separate tools to do its job, and replaces as many as six conventional machines and their operators. The origins of this startling technique go back to the early 1950s, when a small Michigan manufacturer employed a computer to determine the points for the initial boring of holes in making helicopter blades. When Lockheed Aircraft decided to carve out the wings for a jet plane from a single slab of metal instead of building them up from components, the air force asked M.I.T.'s Servo Laboratory to perfect the Michigan method for the job. By 1952, the lab had a conventional milling machine working on numerical controls. By 1955 the technique was good enough to be displayed at trade shows. By 1957 airplane wings were being machined from single chunks of metal. By 1960 universal numerically controlled machine tools had been developed with five axes of motion able to perform a wide range of operations. By 1963 there were almost 4,000 numerical control machines in use, and annual output of these devices had reached 25 per cent of the total output of all machine tools, or about $200 million, six times what they had been in 1959, although numerically controlled machines were a small fraction of the total machine tools installed. In fact, this part of the industry had become mature enough by 1964 to have developed a second-hand market.[10]

With mathematical calculations provided by the computer, numerical control brings a new automaticity to the machine tool. The information that the skilled machinist used to get from the blueprint is now stored in the computer's memory, and the computer can determine the direction, distance, speed of motion, depth of cut, injection of coolant and lubricant, and when to change the cutting tool. The part to be machined is described mathematically, with the computer given all the variables in appropriate symbols. In essence, the geometry of the part is transposed from the engineer's drawing to the computer in numerical form. These symbols are then processed by the circuitry and translated into command signals for the machining operations. Gauges measure the machining motions to check on accuracy, and feedbacks and servos monitor the whole system.

In conventional manual control, the human machinist had to obtain his instructions from the blueprint, and, as he worked, he would often stop the machine to measure the workpiece. As he neared the end of the job, he would frequently slow down to ensure accuracy. Such seemingly tedious work was eliminated with numerical control. Data from blueprints and drawings are entered on program sheets, which contain the instructions, machining plan, machine commands, and perhaps some of the geometric solutions. Then come the card punching and verification and a check of the listed data against the program sheets. The data on the punched cards are then transferred to computer tape to calculate the cutting path, time, and distance for each axis of the machine's motion. As the positioning of the tool is done automatically, there is no need to adjust mechanical stops; furthermore templates and jigs are eliminated. The turret punch press, stepturning lathe, drilling machine, spot welder, shears, grinder, and borer all work steadily. The operator is no longer a skilled machinist, for all he needs to know now is the initial position: then he can load the workpiece, insert a reel of tape into the computer, and press a button. The work moves at top speed toward the required position. Machining begins and continues as long as the operation remains within preset tolerances. Coolants and lubricants are injected automatically, as the feedback mechanism "supervises" the work.[11]

Although numerical control was first applied in the aerospace industry and in airframe fabrication, it is now employed for making jet engines, pumps, television gear, kitchenware, turbines, farm equipment, and office machines. A large run is not essential for its use, as it is particularly adaptable to batch production, that is, to runs of ten or twenty units. At 4,500 square feet, the required floor space is markedly less than in an ordinary machine shop. Scrap averages 4 per cent of the metal handled, as against 10 per cent in the older methods, and tooling costs are reduced by an extraordinary 60 to 90 per cent.[12] At General Electric, lead time on certain operations was reduced from sixteen weeks to one week. A gearbox cover was made in forty hours instead of in the 150 hours it had once taken. Furthermore, running time is vastly greater: An ordinary turret lathe functions about 20 per cent of the time; with numerical control, it reaches 85 per cent of the possible time.[13]

There are two principal types of numerically controlled machine. First, there are point-to-point, or positioning, machines, which simply move the workpiece around so that it is properly located for drilling or milling; the computer controls the horizontal and vertical motions. This system is particularly useful when the path traveled to reach a point is immaterial, as in a drill press or in spot welding. Second, there are continuous-path, or contour, machines that can cut curves and make complex three-dimensional shapes. The tool is guided over the surface of the workpiece, with the coordinates of movement carefully plotted and directed by the computer. Whatever the type used, a numerically controlled machine will select from its own magazine of tools the appropriate implement, whether for milling, drilling, reaming, tapping, boring, turning, grinding, chipping, shaving, or contouring. It will then position the work and proceed with the operation.

It is even possible to combine the two systems in one machine, as in the Cincinnati Milling Machine Company's Acramatic, which calculates all machine measurements from a single reference point. The contouring control is absolute, in contrast to earlier methods, in which movements were derived from increments of motion based on antecedent tool positions.[14] In a more advanced system, developed by Sperry Gyroscope of Canada, the control of different machine tools is exercised by changes in the computer memory rather than by shifting the actual hardware. It is simply a matter of feeding in two paper tapes, one of which tells the characteristics of the machine to which the computer is attached while the other tells the dimensions of the part to be produced and the instructions for producing it. This system, in effect, avoids changing the second tape whenever the computer is moved to another machine. Furthermore, moving a tool point around the surface of a part results in measurements that are automatically stored in the computer memory.[15] The International Harvester Company has fourteen numerically controlled machines to position diesel-engine blocks in a transfer-machine line such as is used in automobile plants, thus achieving a more flexible system that can produce a variety of engine sizes and designs. The result is that a total of forty machines does the work that ordinarily would have required sixty-five.

With this sort of automation, a turret punch press can bang out up to sixty holes a minute in large sheets of metal or laminates, with the positioning table moving at a rate of up to 750 inches a minute by hydraulic actuation. Directed by tape control, a contouring machine makes precision templates up to twenty-six inches long, grinding rough pieces to an accuracy of ten-millionths of an inch. A grinder produces a number of successive diameters on a long cylinder with only one setup on the tape-controlled machine in as few as twenty-two minutes. An automatic tool-change drum allows the Milwaukeematic — an ancient device dating back to 1959 — to do five major machining operations. And a contour miller produces complex forging dies in half the normal machining time and almost, but not quite, does away with hand finishing.

Not only is the skilled craftsman automated out of his job, but the engineers who dream up the new machines are not immune either. The most sophisticated examples of automation are turning on their masters and taking over traditional engineering work, much as they have taken over the grinding and milling and boring. Computers design motors and decide on the best shapes for drying kilns. Original design problems involving variations of standard product lines can be solved by a computer in thirty minutes, compared with six days for a man with a slide rule. In one technique, the design method itself, rather than past solutions, is stored in the computer. That is to say, the logic of the engineering design is stored, so that, when information from a new order for equipment is fed into the computer, it uses its stored knowledge to generate design plans and also produces all the paper work required to start the manufacturing process. Automatic drafting machines draw aircraft wings and layout circuits in electronics. The design cycle for automobiles is accelerated with the computer, drastically cutting the time from sketch to tooling. In this system, the apparatus includes a computer, a graphic console with a television-like screen, and an image processor. The design problem is put into the computer, which can then produce a drawing on the graphic console in a variety of views. Tapes can then be produced to control automatic drafting machines or numerically controlled machine tools. The functions of an engineer's brains and the work of his hands can thus be given over to an electronic contraption. The automatic drafter utilizes engineering data worked up by a computer to control the movement of a mechanized pen as it sketches the desired part. It is said that this machine eliminates a major engineering bottleneck by quickly producing the hundreds and even thousands of drawings necessary for a complex component. And no doubt it does, considering its speed — 200 inches a minute — as it calculates the course of the pen. The motor drive can move as little as .002 of an inch from one point to another. The machine will draw in any two axes and with a flick of a switch can reverse these axes to make a mirror image.[16]

CLEARLY, discrete production can be converted by today's technology into a continuous process. And, when the latter is inherent in the production of a good or service, as in the electric-power industry, there is no question that automation is a *sine qua non*, an indispensable condition. There the computer is employed for data logging, scanning, warning systems, and measuring performance. Power loads for a wide area are calculated on computers, which then decide on the basis of optimum operating rates what the generating requirements and power-routing instructions ought to be. Automatic data logging makes it possible to operate the most complicated substation without anyone in attendance and with no less in reliability or safety. Digital and analogue computers are hooked together, and information fed to the first machine is transmitted to the second, which automatically controls generator schedules in a power system. It is estimated that automatic dispatch systems control 80 per cent of the electric-power capacity of the country. Even the customer's meter may be read by electronic equipment located at a central office. Such a machine, tested in 1964 by the Transitel International Corporation, can read meters when the housewife is not at home, and, more important, it eliminates the translation of a human meter reader's figures into machine language for the billing computer.

In cement manufacture, the computer solves raw-material blending problems. At the Ideal Cement Company's Castle Hayne plant in North Carolina, all operations—from limestone crushing to cement storing—are controlled from a single console, in which closed-circuit television gives the operator a clear view of kilns and storage area. A similar operation is in existence at the Alpha Portland Cement Company in Catskill, New York. At U.S. Steel's captive Atlas Cement Division, fourteen old kilns were replaced with a single giant, 620 feet long, which was fully computer controlled, the most automated of all cement operations. The rest of the industry, a notoriously backward one, is beginning to move toward automatic equipment and materials-handling devices also.

Technological shyness has not by any means been an affliction of the petrochemical and related industries. By 1963 there were several hundred process-control computers in use to help produce plastics, synthetic materials, rubber, petroleum derivatives, and a great variety of chemicals, with sixty systems installed in 1963 alone. The continuous process was evident in the early thermal-cracking technique by which gasoline was extracted from fuel oil. In catalytic cracking, continuous processing is necessary over long periods of time, as the catalyst, silica aluminum, for example, must flow between the reactor in which the cracking occurs and the regenerator in which carbon is removed. Polymerization and hydrogenation, chemical procedures for blending gasoline stocks, require continuous measurement of the temperatures, pressures, and flows of the fluids and gases. The automatic computer controls of these variables are a far cry from the rule-of-thumb methods of seventy-five years ago, when steam temperature was judged by color or the steam's effects on a piece of paper.[17]

A Phillips Petroleum plant in Texas uses a digital computer to operate a cracking furnace. Standard Oil of California has an IBM setup in San Francisco, which controls a catalytic cracking plant in El Segundo, 450 miles away. In Santa Fé Springs, California, an electronic computer system blends gasoline, delivering the prescribed quantities at the right time. If an error crops up, the machine sets off an alarm, and, if the human overseer is out for a coffee break, it shuts itself off. In Houston, Texas, a synthetic-rubber plant operates via computer controls. Monsanto Chemical's huge complex in Chocolate Bayou, Texas, has computer systems to monitor the manufacturing processes and to do the data-logging work, that is, the recording of what takes place, essential in any chemical-plant operation. It requires but 450 persons to run this installation. In gas manufacture the ratio of hydrogen to carbon in the liquified petroleum gas may have to be increased and the carbon dioxide and sulphur removed. This process too is monitored by computers and gauges. Oil companies have a system called "lease automatic custody transfer" (LACT), in which wells, storage tanks, and pipelines are automatically monitored and controlled by computers. This system reduces the labor required to measure and switch tanks, and crude inventories can be smaller. Lockheed Electronics enthusiastically advertises a computer-controlled oil field to operate 180 oil wells in the Poso Creek field from a central office located seven miles away. Equipment and flow variations are reported instantaneously, well-production data computed, and the transfer of oil from field to pipelines controlled — all by electronic devices. The photograph accompanying the advertisement shows computers and wells but no people. A final touch of unwitting irony is provided by the slogan, "An equal opportunity employer."[18]

CONSIDER THE ANCIENT art of paper making. Paper making is now an industry that requires a large investment of capital: A modern, integrated newsprint mill, with a daily capacity of 600 tons, costs more than $70 million to build. The investment per employee is perhaps three times what it is in other manufacturing industries. Paper making is a continuous process and early lent itself to mechanization, and now to automation. The materials move from one step to the next in a semifluid condition, or as continuous sheets, by conveyors, pumps, or pipes without human intervention. The pulp is deposited in a stream on the wire-mesh screen of the paper-making machine to form a wet sheet, which dries as it moves over huge drums at high speed. This process is a long way from the old craft of hand washing and pressing. Continuous-sheet production came in with the Fourdrinier machine in the nineteenth century, but it has been vastly improved since then. By the 1950s automatic pulping was well advanced. Central control units direct conveyor belts to move materials about without hand labor. Continuous pulping equipment is much more rapid than conventional batch pulping and, furthermore, reduces labor requirements. In 1945 there were only three such systems in operation; by 1958 there were fifty, and they were increasing in number with each passing year.[19] Magnetic flow meters measure and control the flow of pulp through the refining vats. Such instruments, utilizing a magnetic field and electric current, measure continuously and accurately the velocity of pulp flowing through a pipe, regardless of variations in consistency, temperature, and pressure. The central control station, with its one operator and sometimes an assistant, contains light and sound signals and flow diagrams to show what is happening. Computers provide data on stock flow and composition. Electronic detection devices determine the weight of the paper and measure its thickness. Then automatic systems transport paper rolls through banding machines and onto the loading platform for shipment to the printing plant.

The way in which the computer can function in this industry is illustrated by an installation at the Fitchburg Paper Company, a specialty paper manufacturer. Because of the large variety of papers the company makes, its Fourdrinier machines seldom run very long on any one item. In fact, there may be as many as six different runs on a single paper-making machine. Furthermore, there are extra chemical problems involved, for the company produces photographic-base papers. Speeds, feeds, temperatures, composition, tensions, and many other variables must be monitored. And customers insist on uniformity in the products they order. Therefore the computer—to ensure uniformity and consistency—reads ninety instruments on the paper machine every three minutes and warns when the process goes awry. The computer is just starting in paper making: As of 1963 there were only twenty-two computers used in paper making in the six major producing nations. But its potentials are evident: In the not too distant future it will control the Fourdrinier itself.[20]

In food-processing too the product is being automated. The handling of ingredients in food preparation was mechanized as early as Oliver Evan's automatic flour mill in the late eighteenth century, but most of the other steps— blending, sifting, and mixing flour and the baking itself— were at best semiautomatic. That is no longer the case, for programming a loaf of bread is now practicable. In one bakery, the automated system starts with pneumatic tubes to handle the bulk dry raw materials; the system is itself operated from a master control panel with a full panoply of lights, batteries, and switches. Oils and fats are pumped into the plant through steam-heated pipelines to keep them liquid. These methods eliminated seventeen of twenty-four workers employed prior to the installation. An automatic bread line takes care of the baking, as ingredients flow from bins on upper floors to the mixing machines below. Photoelectric cells attached to scales set up the proper proportions of ingredients. The right consistency is ensured by rigid control of the atmosphere. The number of employees in this part of the baking operation was cut in half while output shot up almost two and a half times. Pans are greased automatically, depanning after baking is done automatically, and slicing and wrapping require no human hands. Labor requirements in this phase were reduced by 70 per cent.[21] But even more, bakeries are using the computer to monitor bulk storage and to control batch blending and mixing. At a Consolidated Food Corporation plant, an automated line capable of making 600 cakes a minute is supervised by a process computer. The relevant variables are monitored every fifteen seconds, so that control can be exercised through feedback mechanisms over speeds of equipment, humidities, and temperatures of ingredients or of ovens whenever there is any departure from programmed instructions. The computer also oversees the movement of loads of cake into a 7.8-million-unit holding freezer, and it also controls inventory by shipping those products that have been in storage the longest.[22]

Ice cream is mixed by push button at the H. P. Hood Plant in Boston. Pipe valves activated by a computer connect raw-ingredient storage tanks with blending tanks, portion out the ingredients, and are then closed by the computer. The amounts of butterfat or sugar to inject are determined by a single-purpose analogue computer especially designed for the job. It is given six or seven basic ingredients and then instructed to calculate the proportions needed to produce a certain amount of ice cream of a given grade. It would take a recipe man about twenty minutes to run through each formula, but the computer can supply the answer 20,000 times faster. Adjustments in the recipes have to be made daily, for the cows do not supply a steady level of butterfat and solid serum. After the chemist has analyzed the daily batch, the computer is fed the information, and it then comes up with the number of pounds of sugar or water that have to be added. In California's canneries, automatic can fillers let two women do the work of twenty. Mechanical arms unload empty cans and sweep away the jobs of eight men as well. An automatic pitter eliminates dozens of hand workers. The hot dog too has been automated, with a stuffing and tying machine that takes a meat mixture and transforms it into a finished frankfurter without any hand operations and much faster than ever before. It also cooks, smokes, and packages the delicacy. Another automatic hot-dog maker processes frankfurters at a continuous rate of 960 pounds per hour, with two men in attendance: This operation contrasts with conventional methods, which require ten workers per 1,000-pound batch. The meat packer can also use an automatic scanner that judges the fat content of bacon and guides the slicing knife, so that the resulting packages will have the same numbers of slices and the same weights. The apparatus contains a camera lens, which transmits images of the bacon through thousands of strands of optical-glass fibers. Light from the fiber ends, picked up through a slit in a revolving disk, is thrown on to a photocell and translated into electrical signals to perform the required task.[23]

THERE IS THUS no serious problem in automating manufacturing processes that are continuous and easily adapted to steady and unceasing flows. Furthermore, the process-control computer can operate in "real time." The memory system is armed with information indicating how the process should behave; it receives feedback on everything occurring and then issues instructions to correct errors instantaneously. In 1960 there were only thirty-five process-control computers in use; in 1965 there were 600 such installations, and it was expected that sales of process computers would reach 700 a year by 1970.

The real key is in applying automatic controls to discrete production. Yet we have seen that such application is not impossible, as in the machine-tool industry. And in fact similar developments may be observed in other forms of fabrication — steel, autos, coal, materials handling, and printing. Even services like retailing are not immune from the ubiquitous line and the computer. The foundry, for example, in which metals are prepared for machining, was a place where workers simply poured metals into molds, then checked the results to see if they met specifications. If not, they threw the metal away and tried again. The method involved shaping patterns made of sand, which were shoveled and stirred into the right shapes. It was more an art than a "science," for, as the molten metal hit the mold, water would be steamed off, changing a mold's shape. Now, a remote-controlled sand slinger drives mulled sand — a mixture of water, clay, and sand — at high pressure into big patterns, which are then automatically carried on a turntable to a lifting device that flips them over and drops the completed mold. Sand mixed with phenolic resins — a technique developed by the Germans in World War II — makes a very hard mold when baked. Furthermore, the resulting metal surface is so smooth that some parts do not have to be machined. Automatic pouring and precision gauges complete the process.[24]

All this activity is a prelude to what happens in steel. There technological changes have been building up over recent years to a dramatic climax. The American Iron and Steel Institute once listed some sixty innovations that had come to fruition over a twenty-five-year period, including oxygen injection, vacuum melting, continuous casting and pipe welding, electronic measurement of sheet thickness, and, of course, computer controls. One of the more striking advances is the basic-oxygen method, a technique known in Europe for more than a decade but only recently adapted in the United States. Still, by 1963 eight major steel producers had built oxygen furnaces, and nine others had announced that they would also. This acceptance was a far cry from the hesitation and massive indifference toward this technique that had been manifested by steel producers in the 1950s. It was not until 1954 that the first basic-oxygen furnace was built in Michigan by the McLouth Steel Corporation; three years later Jones and Laughlin followed suit. Of course, open-hearth steel making, the dominant method of production since the early days of the auto industry (steel's major customer), is still supreme, but basic oxygen is increasing in capacity. The appeal of this newer method is its lower capital costs, lower production costs, and faster operating rate. In July 1962 Jones and Laughlin produced a batch of almost 240 tons of steel in an oxygen furnace in twenty-seven minutes, compared with the six to eight hours it would take in an open hearth.

In the latter method, a charge of limestone, steel scrap, and molten iron is exposed on a hearth to a sweep of flames over the surface. After the boiling metal is brought to the desired chemical state, the furnace is tapped and the molten steel poured into ingot molds. In some open-hearth furnaces, oxygen is introduced through lances to increase the temperature and speed up the process. In one steel mill oxygen is forced through the roof of the hearth at a rate of 693 cubic feet per ton of steel, increasing the rate of production to about 105 tons an hour, compared to a fifty- or sixty-ton hourly rate in a good open hearth. In basic-oxygen steel making, considerably larger quantities of almost 100 per cent pure oxygen are blown into a vessel that looks like the old Bessemer converter. The blowing removes impurities from the molten iron quickly and reduces the amount of scrap that has to be added to the mixture. As many as 2,000 cubic feet of oxygen can be used in making a ton of steel: Companies supplying oxygen, of course, have discovered a new market, quite aside from medical emergencies.

Hard on the heels of the new furnaces comes continuous casting, a process in which steel can be cast directly into semifinished form, thus bypassing several costly and time-consuming steps. Shortly after U.S. Steel introduced its oxygen furnaces, it announced its intention to install continuous-casting machines. The technique, like so many others, originated in Europe. American firms at first merely watched: Most likely they were inhibited by a heavy investment in conventional methods. In the latter, molten steel is taken from the furnace in huge ladles to a casting pit, where it is tapped into a series of ingot molds. The molds are then stripped after cooling and the ingots heated in a soaking pit prior to being rolled into the type of product required, either slabs for conversion into plate and sheet steel or "blooms," squat bar-like shapes used for rolling rails and other structural forms. Continuous casting cuts short this whole cycle. Molten steel is poured directly from the ladle into a reservoir or "tundish" that sits at the top of a bottomless vertical mold, which cools and partially shapes the steel as it passes through a cooling chamber. The steel continues on, pulled by adjustable rollers, to a flame cutter, to come out at the bottom in small blooms ready for further rolling into finished products. Continuous casting thus eliminates pouring, molding, transporting, and reheating. Furthermore, it is faster than traditional methods, saves space and fuel, reduces chemical segregation to provide a stronger steel, cuts scrap loss, and, as might be expected, reduces labor requirements per unit of output.

The method has no single origin: Sir Henry Bessemer thought of something like it in 1865, and in the 1930s Siegfried Junghaus, a German engineer, and Irving Rossi, a New York businessman, developed a similar system that was tried out at Allegheny Steel in the late 1940s. Later a variant of continuous casting was introduced in Swedish steel mills, and with the Russians it is fairly common. In this country, it remained for the smaller firms like McLouth Steel to push for its development; now there are several continuous-casting mills that can produce just the sort of steel that had been the mainstay of older methods — thin sheets and thin plates.[25] There is also pressure casting for stainless and high-alloy steel, an innovation again advanced by smaller companies. This method is somewhat like sipping iced tea through a straw. Just as the sipper gets the tea and leaves the ice, so pressure casting gets the steel and leaves the slag. The ladle of molten steel sits inside an enclosed chamber, which rests under a graphite mold, with a tube extending from the ladle to the slab-shaped mold, through which air pressure forces molten steel up into the mold. In addition to skipping the cooling, soaking-pit, and ingot-rolling steps, the graphite mold gives the slab an extremely smooth surface, thus obviating the necessity for any grinding. Furthermore, the virtually slag-free steel does not have to be chopped off before being rolled into sheets and plates: Yield is increased from about 72 per cent to 95 per cent.[26]

Here then is the continuous process in what was once production by discrete units. Today one can see an automatic blooming mill, in which the entire operation of passing a twenty-two-ton ingot rapidly back and forth between rollers is controlled by a computer. The McLouth Steel Corporation claims to have had the first fully automated hot-strip rolling mill, with computer control, completed in 1962. And not far from McLouth's plant near Detroit is a Great Lakes Steel computer-controlled eighty-inch hot-strip mill installed by Thompson-Ramo-Wooldridge and Daystrom. With the computer, the speed and degree of control over mill operations are raised far beyond the ability of humans to react. If the computer detects an error on a finishing-roll stand, it can correct it by making compensating adjustments on the next roll stand only a few feet and a fraction of a second away. Over 1,000 variables have to be controlled, with 200 analogue signals and 100 digital-computer-generated signals involved in the process. A slab of steel is not simply a hunk of metal identical with every other slab. It has its own chemical and physical characteristics that require variations in rolling schedules, with the result that adjustments are always necessary. Although human operators were able to reset mill operations in about two minutes, the computer does it in eight seconds at the most. The computer, of course, is essential, for, with steel sheets coming through the rollers at a speed of forty-five miles an hour, no human could cope with all the data on thickness, temperature, quality, and the like. Here is how it works: While the slab is in the reheating furnace, a card containing data on its chemistry, thickness, width, length, and weight is placed into the card-reading unit to set the adjustments necessary for rolling. Sensors report the positions of side guides through which the slab must pass. If the guides are too close or too far apart, the computer activates an electrical control to move them to the proper setting. The operations are repeated for the various roughing stands, and the computer calculates the amount of elongation required as the slab passes from one stand to the next. And as the speed of passage increases, up to 3,000 feet a minute, the computer will adjust the stands to the successively faster speeds. Temperature and chemical variations are monitored, and new settings are made to compensate for errors. As the slab passes through the last rolling stand, overhead water sprays controlled by the computer reduce its temperature. The whole process takes about four minutes. Even the extraction of iron from the ore can be controlled by the computer: There is no barrier to "computerizing" the furnace as well, as is demonstrated by a U.S. Steel installation at Duquesne. There the computer determines what raw-materials are to go into the furnace, calculating the quantities of iron, scrap, flux, and other additives that must be loaded to meet the specifications of a particular order. It controls oxygen injection and the positioning of the lances that blow in the oxygen. A better balance of inputs can thus be achieved. And with that step the fully automatic factory in steel will have been completed: As one commentator remarked, the computer does everything but vote at union meetings.[27]

Such methods have had a marked impact on costs. In 1958 a ton of molten steel ran up a bill of $35 or more per ton; by the middle of 1963 it was down to $31 or $32 per ton. A new hot-strip mill, running at 3,500 feet a minute, compared to a typical rate of about 1,800 feet a minute, inevitably shaves the cost of producing steel: At Great Lakes's plant in Detroit the cost is estimated to be 10 per cent below the standard for the industry. At Crucible Steel such an operation was reported to be saving the company $7 million a year, on an investment of $28 million.[28] Continuous casting cuts from $4 to $20 a ton off steel-making costs by integrating all the steps necessary to preparing a slab for the rolling mill. As a consequence of these developments, the labor cost per ton of steel shipped dropped some 7 per cent in 1964, compared to 1961, and the decline is likely to continue, with man-hour output rising perhaps three times by 1965. The American Iron and Steel Institute estimated at the end of 1963 that steel mills paid an average of $61 in wages, salaries, and fringe benefits for each ton of steel shipped during the first ten months of the year, a drop from $65.50 in 1961.[29]

The number of production man-hours needed to turn out a ton of finished steel was cut to 10.4 during the same ten-month period, compared to 10.9 in 1962 and 12.3 in 1957. During 1961–1963, output per man-hour worked rose 4.7 per cent a year, compared with an average of 2.4 per cent a year for the two previous decades. Furthermore, industry spokesmen do not deny that these cost-cutting operations have helped build profits. (One might think that the consumer would be the beneficiary, but in this age of administered prices it was unlikely.) In fact, steel profits jumped 29 per cent from the 1962 level during the first nine months of 1963 – all with an assist from higher output and prices. Profits in the latter part of 1963 were more than 5 per cent of the sales dollar. Some of the companies had no difficulty in raising dividends for their stockholders.

AND WHAT IS one to say of automobiles, the industry that gave us the word "automation"? Earlier, we described the origins of the assembly line in auto manufacturing. By the middle of the 1950s transfer machines had made "Detroit automation" a byword, and Del Harder, a Ford executive, could insist on "more of this – what d'you call it – automation." In 1955 Ford's Cleveland engine-block lines were considered the last word in automation. Three years later they were outmoded. At first, automation took the form of monster multiple-spindle machines that did a dozen or more drilling and machining operations all at once, working the top and sides of an engine block simultaneously. But when something went wrong, it became a painful chore to discover exactly what the trouble was. The problem was solved by dividing operations among several machines, linked by automatic transfer equipment. This division made it easier to position the work and to watch the cutting ends of the machine tools. Furthermore, inspection could be continuous, with gauges installed along the line to check each part automatically on its way from one machine to the next. With such checks on cylinder bores, crankshafts, and camshafts, the line could move smoothly, for a defective part could be removed automatically as soon as it was detected by the gauge. A further development was to install whole banks of special-purpose machines, all linked by transfer equipment and electronic controls. Even the production of the crankshaft, a difficult part to make because of its eccentric shape, was automated.

The auto industry was quick to adopt many of the newer methods — plastic molds for casting metals, numerical controls, and powder metallurgy. An outgrowth of missile and space research, powder metallurgy, the technique of squeezing an intricate part out of fine metal powder, is so far the only practical way to make parts out of materials otherwise difficult to machine. Transmission parts, some of which must withstand stress of more than 40,000 pounds per square inch, can be made in this manner. Furthermore, powder metallurgy reduces costs by as much as 80 per cent, with a sharp cutback in the number of machining operations needed to produce each part. Cold forming, in which a slug of cold metal is pushed through a die by a powerful ram, makes it possible to turn out in one step precision parts like gears, which in conventional methods require many machining operations.

But the problem today in Detroit automation is "flexibility." After four decades of trying to turn out an eight-cylinder engine block as automatically as possible, the auto makers became "model happy," demanding that a line be versatile enough to switch from model to model within a few hours and, in some cases, even to turn out different models at the same time. During 1964 Chrysler Corporation planned some ninety different automobile models, and, as a consequence, its new $80-million Sterling, Michigan, stamping plant had to be adaptable enough to make "even the least expensive automobile customized." Each of the 167 major presses in the new plant can force sheets of steel into

Use and Impact

autobody shapes with a force of more than 250 tons. But the massive dies needed to form these parts are easily shifted in and out of the presses, although each weighs several tons. The shifting is done with overhead cranes that simply lift the dies from the machines and lower them through openings next to the units to a basement storage area: On their return the cranes raise new dies into place. A whole line can be changed in this fashion in less than six hours.

More automation for such flexibility no doubt will be added by a new machine, the Chargematic, developed by U.S. Industries, which needs only one operator to feed sheet-metal blanks at one end, while out the other come doors and dashboard panels. A blank goes through six presses, is turned and transferred about thirty times, and emerges as a finished part. The various moving fingers, rails, and holding units in the system can accommodate a wide range of sizes, and the press dies can be changed in ten minutes each. Such methods make it possible to turn out a variety of products on the same line, enabling a manufacturer to change his product mix almost overnight. At the Ford Dearborn plant each of three engine lines can produce any one of three power units. It takes only two hours to change a line from a 352-cubic inch displacement engine to one with a displacement of 406 cubic inches. At the Cleveland plant, the line can run 3,000 Galaxy hoods, 1,500 different ones for the Falcon, and 750 others for the Mercury Comet and can shift from one to the other in a matter of hours. In 1958 the switch would have required months, because the presses could handle only one set of dies, whereas the transfer equipment had been designed to handle only one kind of part.

Again, the basic idea for such flexibility came from Europe, where most auto companies build their own machine tools, standardizing only a few of the basic dimensions for structural parts. American auto firms, finally convinced that their counterparts from overseas knew what they were doing, persuaded machine-tool builders to follow suit, so that there are now only five sizes of tool-making machines, depending on how much load the tool must take, instead of the immense variety that existed previously. With standard structural members—bases and vertical columns that support the tools—representing more than half the cost of the equipment, an auto maker can now produce eight-cylinder as well as six-cylinder blocks merely by installing motors and tool heads on structural parts already in place. An additional boring head may have to be added also. A new line at Ford's Livonia, Michigan, transmission plant produces housings for three different-sized manual trans-missions. About thirty of the system's 117 work stations, however, do not have tool heads: They are in reserve to produce housings for the larger four-speed manual trans-missions. Or the production of a going unit can be speeded up by simply tooling in an idle station.

The computer comes into its own in the automobile plant, not only in processing manufacturing data, but also in solving such problems as "line balancing," without which flexibility would be difficult to achieve. Balancing simply means coordinating the various products scheduled to flow along the assembly belt. It involves the assignment of tasks and the juggling of materials so that each worker is busy for the maximum amount of time. For years such coordination was done by intuition and slide rule, but now a computer can calculate 1,000 manpower and material combinations and then select the ten best. An instrument-panel line, for example, may have thirty-six work stations and more than 140 assembly operations, representing more than a billion job combinations. Although it would require perhaps sixty hours for an industrial engineer to discover the optimum combination, the computer supplies its proposed selections in an hour and a quarter. In preparing the data for the computer, the engineer breaks down the assembly line work into distinct jobs and determines the standard time required for each, the tools needed, the number of workers, and other required facilities. A chart is then prepared showing the sequence of steps. Three decks of cards are punched, one giving the operation, sequence number, and standard time; another sets forth the "constraints"—location and re-quired tools—for each job, and the third determines the line speed and product mix. A computer converts all these data into tape, which is fed into a larger digital machine utilizing random techniques; the latter then comes up with the thousand or so assignments that fit the criteria previously established. One of the criteria is the least-cost combination, the standard established by the economics textbooks. In effect, the computer advises how much production can be squeezed out of a particular line combination.

In addition, the computer provides quality controls. The heart of one such control system at Chrysler is an IBM 1710 computer with a memory core that can call upon two million bits of information and make 5,000 decisions a second and relay instructions to every part of an assembly line quicker than the snap of a foreman's finger. In one assembly plant, there are seven electronic reporting centers in a five-mile line. As each car moves into a quality-reporting station, it is checked by inspectors — human ones — who circle code numbers on cards. This information is relayed electronically to a central control computer, which in turn reports defects to a correction system before the car moves on to the next manufacturing station. At the same time, the computer alerts the area where the error occurred, so that the cause can be eliminated at the source. An imperfect weld can thus be spotted and reported to the welding department before an imperfect welding gun can do much damage. The control system can correct as many as 30,000 items a day with 2,000 cars moving along at one time, each with 6,400 parts and 4,500 welds. The computer can also inquire at the final inspection point whether or not the changes and corrections were made.[31]

IT MIGHT have been thought that shipping would be a less fertile area for automation than would other industries, as human judgment appears so essential in guiding a vessel through water. But in January 1964 President Johnson pressed a button in the White House to start a welding machine at the Avondale shipyards in New Orleans. The machine joined two plates for a keel of a Lykes Line freighter that was to be the first of eight semiautomated 14,000-ton ships, each to be operated by a crew of thirty-two men, instead of the forty-six needed on conventional vessels of the same size. Computers were to be placed on board to calculate bearings and to provide data on speed, course, and time of arrival. Such devices, each about the size of a shoebox, take over the work of the men of the bridge and permit the operators to cut the sizes of ships' crews.

The desire to put automation on ships comes not only from the owners but from the Government as well. The operators argue that the $227 million subsidy could be cut in half with single consoles controlling both boiler room and bridge. A data logger could record critical operating data on the propulsion system and perhaps reduce fuel costs. This possibility is no dream, for by 1964 there were twenty-three such ships on order in American, German, and Japanese yards. Among the prospective purchasers were eight of the fifteen major United States lines. One freighter, completed in March 1964 at a Pascagoula, Mississippi, shipyard requires a crew of thirty-five, compared with the standard of fifty men. Its main feature is an electronically operated engine room in which two men at a central control place need but turn valves, regulate pressures, and start generators and burners by merely pushing buttons. On deck there is remote control of winches, anchors, and hatch openings, reducing the necessary number of deckhands by at least four. On other ships, the cargo hatches will be opened and closed by hydraulic systems.

For its part, the Federal government, through the Maritime Subsidy Board, told shipowners in August 1963 that it was revising its standards to encourage automation. The operators were advised that, to qualify for subsidies, new ships would have to install centralized engine-room control, simplified power plants, and direct bridge control — in effect, automation. And in October 1965 an interagency Maritime Task Force proposed "the fullest application of automation." In response to such prodding, some of the lines asked the Maritime Administration and the General Accounting Office for permission to send vessels already in service back to the shipyards for automated "retrofits" — a new word in the marine lexicon — thereby cutting crews from forty-five men to thirty-five. In all likelihood, the Maritime Administration will not disapprove, for it has several research and development projects under way that stress automation in navigation and marine engineering. The ultimate objective in all these efforts, stated rather bluntly in the various reports, is the same—the reduction of manpower.

What could be done to automate a ship was quickly demonstrated by the Japanese. In December 1963, a newly built 12,000-ton freighter, *The Mississippi Maru*, left Kobe on a maiden voyage to southwest Africa. It was then the world's most automated cargo vessel, carrying a crew of only twenty-eight men. The innovations incorporated in its design included automated mooring, cargo handling, and other deck operations, with an automatic warm-up and stand-by control system for the main engine. There are two closed-circuit television systems that enable an officer on the bridge not only to scan the waters directly ahead or astern but also to observe the mooring operations at bow and stern. Automatic hawser winches enable the synthetic resin-fiber hawsers to be paid out or reeled in easily from a pedal on deck. The crew required for mooring can thus be eliminated entirely and operations can be conducted by remote control from the bridge. Anchoring at the moment is semiautomatic: A crewman on the forecastle deck observes the anchor on a television screen while controlling brake, clutch, and speed. But this job too will eventually be done by remote control from the bridge. The control room for the ship's machinery is filled with dials, gauges, and push buttons: The chief engineer's task is reduced to watching the various panels. All the necessary adjustments are made automatically. Boarding ladders also are operated automatically, and cargo handling is almost completely mechanized. Although *The Mississippi Maru* can function with twenty men, it took along an extra complement of eight officers and seamen on its first trip just to be sure.

Is a one-man bridge aboard a ship feasible? Without question, according to the experts, for, in addition to such long standing devices as radar and automatic steering gear, there is a "ship condition" computer that can do in twenty minutes what requires five to six hours of manual paper work. The console includes sixty-seven "clocks," each about the size of a nickel, bearing the numbers one through ten, and each representing tons in various parts of the ship's cargo area. Combining that information with draft as the ship is loaded, an officer can quickly obtain the load limits imposed by cargo placement and can bring aboard cargo once left on the pier because of revisions in load distribution. The "ship condition" unit also gives continuous information on ship stability, fuel supply, and maneuverability. It is evident that the impact of all these devices will be mainly on unlicensed personnel who fill about 75 per cent of the jobs on merchant ships. What the response of the unions has been we shall see later. In the meantime, the ship operators look avidly to the day when they can sail forth with but fractions of the crews they now have.[32]

Loading a ship, of course, has been vastly simplified by "containerization," a technique for consolidating many small parcels or freight items into larger packages. Consequently, only single units have to be handled at the docks or at terminals. Giant cranes controlled by a master console easily lift the containers into the hold. Standardization had eluded the shippers for years, but now it appears well on its way. In 1963 the American Standards Association recommended that van-type containers be built in multiples of ten feet up to forty feet in length and eight feet each for height and width. The suggestion was well received. One shipping line employs a system that ties together two twenty-foot modules: Add a set of detachable wheels, and the huge box can be used for road hauling as well. Even the railroads have been attracted to this idea: The Southern Pacific has eighty containers riding its rails and also has twenty-five rail cars fitted with special cushioning devices. It plans to double-deck its forty-foot containers to increase the loads it can carry. Some containers have fittings to prevent damage to the goods inside; they are, in effect, portable freight cars, which can be transferred without difficulty from dockside into the ships' holds.

All sorts of equipment are available to turn materials handling into a "process": Most striking is a pipe with enough air to "fluidize" a mass of dry materials to make it flow as does a liquid. But there are also powered industrial trucks that move in four directions rather than simply back and forth; lift trucks with belt conveyors mounted on their forks at right angles to the direction of the forks for quick pickup and stacking; vacuum-handling attachments that lift newsprint, drums, and flat corrugated-metal sheets

145

as though they were toys; and remote radio control to direct tractor loads over the preset routes to delivery stations – all these devices are preparations for the time soon to come when a handful of punched cards will do the work of scheduling materials handling and operating fleets of powered industrial-lift trucks. In some automatic receiving systems, particularly suitable for warehousing, incoming materials are placed on conveyors at the receiving docks for movement to master control stations. As the items stop there momentarily, single clerks keycode into computers the part numbers, vendors and amounts received. Within seconds the computers complete the reports by printing out instructions for handling the parts as well as their inventory status. Whereas processing of incoming parts by ordinary methods might require forty-eight hours or more, the computerized conveyor technique does it in less than half that time.

Similar techniques can be employed in loading and unloading railroad freight cars as well. A standard freight car can be equipped with hollow aluminum flooring into which air is piped from dockside compressors or from portable compressors underneath the car. Loads are placed on special pallets with composition-rubber bottoms. The loaded pallets depress small valves in the floor, releasing a thin film of air which creates an almost frictionless bearing surface to support the pallets and allow them to be moved effortlessly in any horizontal direction. Ten pounds of push by a handler would be sufficient to move a ton of freight.

AUTOMATION on the railroads, however, involves a good deal more than handling freight in such spectacular ways. As a *Fortune* writer once remarked, the best way to visualize what goes on in a computerized railroad system is to think of a collection of model trains set up in a basement: The father and his young son know everything, see everything, operate everything. The same omniscience is exercised by a railroad magnate and his 50,000-mile computer control system. Automation may begin with loading the freight car, but the new techniques also enable a yardmaster to spot a car, send out waybills, record departures, make up trains, record payments, and issue holding orders for certain cars with a speed and dispatch hitherto unknown in the industry.

Railroad yards now employ radar, computers, and closed-circuit television for controlling and coordinating operations. There are automatic car-reporting systems that provide visual records of arrivals and departures. One such system would automatically identify cars by atomic radiation. Sources of gamma rays set in a coded arrangement under each car would trigger detectors installed between the tracks at the yard entrance. With a distinct number given to each of the million and a half freight cars, all the freight stock now on the nation's rails could be easily spotted. Furthermore, by grouping the numbers, it would be easy to distinguish cattle cars from tank cars.

Devices are available to monitor speed, engine temperature, fuel supply, and other data on passing trains and to program the switching of an entire train in advance with a switch-list storage system for the computer. Railroad bridges move up and down, wheels are oiled, and mailbags are handled — all automatically. Passenger trains for the Bay Area rapid-transit system now being built in California may operate up to eighty miles an hour as little as ninety seconds apart with the runs controlled by a computer. Railroad men assert that the result will be fewer wrecks and that more money will be available to protect grade crossings. In the automated freight yards, of which some forty-five have been built in the last decade, incoming cars are scanned by television apparatuses to obtain quick readings of car numbers. After this information has been quickly checked against waybills, the cars are automatically sorted. A computer calculates the car's proper speed for the yard from trackside devices, whereas radar notes the actual speed. This system provides the feedback information necessary to automatic retarders, which make the cars conform to the computer's reckoning. The computer also figures how much energy it takes to haul a loaded freight train up a given grade. Furthermore, the work of different yards can be coordinated, so that one master need not load up another: The computer advises them which cars to switch and which to hold. In essence, it is all a form of centralized track control: By 1963, there were 33,000 route miles covered in this

147

manner, more than four times the mileage under automatic systems a decade and a half ago.

One illustration of an automated railroad-control center is the Southern Railway System's $30 million computerized network in Atlanta. Equipment control, power distribution, and policing of yard and terminal performance are handled on a "real time" basis. A combination of facsimile communication units and a microwave system enables yard people to send masses of data to terminals and from there to the control center in Atlanta. Waybill and document information is fed into the computer system and stored for instant retrieval and use, giving immediate data on location, destination, and loading facts for any of the Southern's freight cars. Customers who want to know where their shipments happen to be can be advised quickly; traffic and market conditions can be rapidly analyzed; data for the Interstate Commerce Commission are readily available; and the company can pinpoint practices that drag down performance levels.

Furthermore, crewless trains are no longer science fiction. A remote-controlled engine without anyone on board shuttles regularly on a half-mile of track in Florence, Alabama, hauling coal cars from a siding to barges on the Tennessee River. New York's subway riders have their automated train between Grand Central and Times Square. In West Labrador four crewless shuttles carry iron ore over a six-mile run at a constant speed of a quarter-mile an hour: One man controls the entire operation, whereas eighteen would be needed for a conventional road system. Although crewless engines thus far have been used only for shuttling, equipment makers are promising crewless intercity trains. Should some riders become nervous at the prospect of riding without a train engineer, an automatic pilot can be used that still requires a man, who would function primarily as a conductor. The automatic pilot controls the traction equipment and the two degrees of braking that can bring the train to a halt with a margin of error of less than two yards. It can run the train in "economic time" or "fast running time." Or the choice of the running program can be made centrally for all trains on a particular section of track. The automatic pilot then operates the train in accordance with data on track conditions fed into it by a signaling system in the cab. As O. P. Whitney, a General Electric equipment engineer remarked, the future never looked brighter for the railroads, because they are more adaptable to automation than is any other mode of transportation.

In the meantime, the men who know only railroading are left standing at trackside biting their lips in quiet desperation. For the technological revolution on the railroads has created an occupational upheaval. Total employment dropped from 4,400,000 in 1947 to 800,000 in 1960. A year later it was down to 730,000. The thirteen-year decline almost equaled the loss that occurred between 1920, the peak year for railroad jobs, and 1947. Most of the loss has been attributed to technology — there is little argument among the experts on this point. The elimination of steam by diesel locomotives, which do not need as much servicing, has reduced maintenance jobs. Repair facilities have been combined and some even closed down. Diesels haul longer trains, dispensing with men for operating crews. Between 1948 and 1952, 3,000 diesels replaced 4,000 locomotives each year. Today about 28,000 diesels and 1,000 old steamers, with their picturesque cowcatchers, do all the work. To be sure, there has been a slight increase in some railroad jobs — shop electrical work and signal operations — but the age of automation now threatens these as well.

Commuter service, it is said, will also have to be automated if the problems of urban mass transportation are to be solved. The prototype promises to be the San Francisco-Bay Area transit system backed by the largest single bond issue in United States history — $792 million. It will be operated largely by a computer that will serve as dispatcher, engineer, and conductor and that will monitor the operations of trains, compare their performances, and issue corrective signals when necessary. Even the fare-collection system will be automated, utilizing in all probability magnetic imprints on iron-oxide-coated tickets, which would then be "presented" to an electronic ticket reader at the station entrance.[33]

Not to be outdone, those who prefer to commute by car are thinking of automating this form of transportation. Some engineers have suggested that small electrically powered cars could travel on automated traffic lanes that

Use and Impact

would carry as many as 7,200 cars an hour. The last vestige of direct control that urban man still exercises, his ability to drive a car as he pleases, is now threatened.

WHAT AUTOMATION and mechanization, combined with other factors, can do to an industry is perhaps best illustrated by the history of coal mining. Coal was at one time the standard fuel—until it was displaced in many places by competing forms of energy like gas and oil. Most of the mines that produce bituminous coal are in West Virginia, Pennsylvania, Kentucky, Illinois, Ohio, and Virginia. There are about 8,000 mines and 5,000 companies in the industry: By the middle-1940s it had become a thoroughly sick one. John L. Lewis, then head of the United Mine Workers' Union, decided not to worry about the unemployed at the pits and to help the mine operators become "more competitive." He argued that it was "better to have half a million men working in the industry at good wages . . . than to have a million men working in the industry in poverty and degradation." Lewis agreed to let the operators mechanize and automate, and the payoff is to be seen in the several hundred thousand idle miners in Pennsylvania and West Virginia and a current employed work force of about 125,000. Of course, coal mining is once again profitable, so much so that the businessmen who used to curse Lewis now address him as a "labor statesman."

Horsepower in coal mining—a rough indication of advancing technology—jumped more in the years 1939–1954 than in the previous three decades. The hand shovel was eliminated by mechanized loading and hauling. By 1960 mechanical loading was taking care of 90 per cent of the coal mined. Continuous mining machines became common sights, integrating the cutting and loading in an unending sequence and eliminating the need to drill and blast. A "long wall" unit surpasses some of the present continuous mining devices: It cuts several hundred feet of coal at one time, sends the coal out by conveyor, and provides its own roof supports by hydraulic jacks. When it has completed a job, the machine moves on, shifting the roof supports with it. The procedure eliminated conventional roof propping and does not leave coal behind in pillars to hold the roof. The machine can produce 2,000 tons per shift with an eight-man crew, or 250 tons per man, about seventeen times the present average rate of productivity. An auger drill can be used on a hill, sending its bore a thousand feet into an embankment while a single man operates the electric control panel. A more exotic looking piece of equipment is an 800-ton push-button machine used by the Peabody Coal Company in Ohio. It looks like a miniature multistoried parking lot on giant crawlers; a remote-controlled drilling head is pushed underground, feeding coal onto conveyor cars that unwind from the various "stories." Giant excavators that look like paddle wheels on caterpillars scoop up mounds of earth and coal.

As these methods also bring up refuse and other impurities, the coal must be processed, and then automation comes into its own. Throughout the coal fields, there are now modern plants that employ closed-circuit television to monitor the flow of coal, nuclear density devices to ensure quality, and electropneumatic car stoppers to regulate the loaders and haulers. One new coal-processing factory can produce 5,000 tons per shift, about as much coal as was dug out of the ground by 500 miners in 1959. Only three panel-control operators and twelve maintenance men are required.[34] Punched cards, processed electronically, provide data on cost and performance of rock drills, drill steel, and trucks. Computer techniques are employed to control ore blends and grades, as well as to analyze the results of such production methods as superfine grinding. In fact, throughout all of mining, automatic controls have increased markedly in recent years: Crushing, feeding, blending, bin control, reagent adjustments, thickening, and filtering are all steps that lend themselves without too much difficulty to the new technology. Little wonder that the decline of employment in this segment of the economy has been so precipitous.

EVEN PRINTING, which has a craft history dating back almost 500 years, is not immune to the inroads of automation and mechanization. It too must face the prospect of being surrounded by the mysteries of electronics. No doubt the production of a mass-circulation newspaper in three editions overnight is a remarkable achievement, but even greater wonders are to come. There are photosetting machines that use the punched tape they produce to control photographic units that in effect displace the old hot-metal method in forming type. The machines receive copy from the tape or a typewriter keyboard and convert it into photographic reproduction of lines of type. At the command of the tape, a machine can select any of a thousand or so letters, numbers, or symbols from several different type faces. It can also vary the size of each letter from four points to seventy-two points. The selections are made from a disk in the machine that contains the photographic image of each type character. As the disk spins between a steadily flashing light and a sheet of film, the desired letter is photographed as soon as it lines up with the film. Masters or negatives can then be prepared for engraving.

One such device will be used as the print-out unit for the medical index for the National Library of Medicine. Operating on computer-generated magnetic tape, the machine will set type at a speed of 500 characters a second. In one run it prepared an $8\frac{1}{2} \times 11$-inch page in forty-seven seconds, a pace it is expected to exceed. A similar machine will be used to set telephone directories for Western Electric. Another phototypesetting machine whirls out lines of type on film or photographic paper at the rate of twenty-two newspaper lines per minute. This figure compared with fifteen lines per minute for a high speed hot-metal type caster. Mergenthaler's phototypesetting machine built for the Government Printing Office can handle 1,000 characters per second while turning the magnetic-tape output of computers into film negatives of typographic quality. Its system is built around a high-resolution cathode-ray tube, originally developed for military reconnaissance, and converts data from the computer directly into a form suitable for printing. Making corrections sometimes poses a ticklish technical problem: To avoid messing with the film, some systems produce a typed text before shooting, so that corrections can be made on the punched tape before it is fed into the photographic unit. In other machines, the film is but a thin membrane that can be pulled away easily from its backing to be cut for the insertion of a corrected line. With the high speed these devices provide, the make-up is done by cutting up the film, placing the illustrations in place, and in this manner producing the whole page.

The composing room of the future, then, will prepare a page for the newspaper, from typewritten copy to the finished product, without human hands—up to the point at which it is ready for the press. Linecasting machines can be operated by computers and can do the justification and hyphenation that were once the hallmarks of a compositor's skill. Ordinarily, the linecaster sat at his machine following a typewritten story attached to a copy board. As he operated his keyboard, the linotype cast lines of metal type, each a solid block. As all the lines had to be exactly the same length, the operator had to decide how many words to fit into one line to keep the right margin even. This process is called "justifying" the line: It was done by adding space-bands between words or letters when the line was short and by hyphenating the last word when the line was long. For centuries justifying was the special skill of the compositor— until the adaptation of the computer to typesetting.

The computerized system at one newspaper—the Palm Beach Post-Times—starts with the news stories and classified ads typed on ordinary typewriters. Copy is edited and corrected in the usual manner. The copy is then retyped on paper tape, at which point there is no need to justify lines or hyphenate words. The paper tape is fed into the computer at a speed of 1,000 characters a second. A seven-character message telling the machine what type face and size to use is also fed to the computer. The system's main unit then composes a paragraph at a time, automatically justifying and hyphenating as it goes along. As each paragraph is finished, it is punched on paper tape at 100 characters a second and at the same time printed on paper so that the text can be read as it is produced. The justified paper tape is then transmitted to the linecasting machine at a speed of 1,000 characters a second.

The heart of this computer system is the electronic dictionary, consisting of some 30,000 words from *Webster's Collegiate* programmed into the memory unit, plus the names of local streets and prominent citizens. Justification is done by filling in spaces, but the memory unit's dictionary is the source for rules on hyphenating. If a multisyllable word has to be split, the computer seeks guidance from the 30,000 words placed in storage. Should the word not be there, the computer will break it after the third, fifth, seventh, or ninth letter, according to a predetermined set of rules and leave any error to be corrected by a human proofreader. All this checking is done in minutely split seconds. In another approach, "logical" rules of hyphenation, rather than a "dictionary," are programmed. The computer scans letter sequences to decide where to hyphenate. It can ask itself 150 questions about hyphenation in $\frac{15}{1,000}$ of a second and can justify thirty pages of solid type in one hour.

When IBM announced in 1963 its automatic linecasting system, which involved its 1620 machine, three major newspapers gobbled it up at once, with one of the chief reasons said to be the elimination of any manual intervention. The system has an "on-line allotting capability" and accepts copy in the form of electrical impulses from as many as twenty paper-tape punches. It feeds the output through its circuitry to twenty paper-tape readers attached to twenty automatic linecasters. Copy is first punched into paper tape, which then feeds the information into the 1620's magnetic-core memory. The computer adds spacing to fill out the lines evenly and hyphenates where necessary. The tape then goes to the automatic linecaster.

Another relatively new development is electrostatic printing, already in use for printing address labels without plates. Television-like signals "write" character images on a moving web of dye-coated paper. An electrostatic charge then creates patterns conforming to the shapes of the images laid down on the paper, which is passed through a developer to raise the images. This "nonimpact" technique can print up to 200,000 characters a second. The problem in adapting the method to newspapers is the smearing that takes place at the extremely high runs of the printing presses. Whatever the new method or technique, printing is now an industry rather than a craft. The electronic machines with their typewriter keyboards can be operated just as efficiently, if not more so, by women, and in the typesetting process only unskilled labor has to be employed. The tragic tale of the English hand-loom weavers may be told once again.[35]

As we move from industry to industry, from company to company, and from plant to plant, we thus discover the new technology converting fabrication and materials handling into "processes," continuous, unending, automatic. More than half the approximately 3,500 plants studied in one survey reported that they were using automatic measuring and gauging devices and process-sensing and -control instruments.[36] Almost one-third said they were employing some form of tape and punched-card controls, as well as automatic data processing. And although complete computer controls still represented the smallest category, they had more than doubled between 1959 and 1963. The ingredients for the automatic factory are already in existence: The conversion of industrial materials into a flow; the setting of uniform standards so that output can be treated as a flow; and the use of computers and feedbacks to provide automatic controls.[37]

Even the Post Office is being automated: Machines stack and cancel 30,000 letters an hour; reading devices are being built to scan coded addresses and direct letters through automatic sorters at the rate of 43,000 items an hour; magnetic conveyor systems will distribute outgoing mail in electrically coded trays; and even handwriting will be scanned once present optical reading devices are perfected.[38] Textiles, a notoriously backward industry, is starting to modernize. Faster looms, self-correcting winding machines, and continuous dyeing machines will all call upon the computer for "guidance." Says the Department of Commerce of developments in textiles, "Improvements are directed toward further automation of equipment, more sensitive control methods, fewer workers tending each machine."[39] In one recently constructed mill in South Carolina, fully 10 per cent of the investment in equipment went for instrumentation, compared with the industry's average of about 3 per cent. The various processes are monitored at consoles at fifteen stations. Sensors measure machine speed, temperature, steam flow and pressure, acid-base balance, density, and chemical flows. Departures from required standards are automatically corrected.

Use and Impact

Colors are monitored by an optical scanner, and a computer decides what changes should be made. There are automated garages and elevators without operators. (An official of the Building Service Employees Union in New York said in 1963 that the number of elevator men had dropped in that city from 35,000 in 1950 to about 10,000.) Logging has been made utterly unromantic with mobile cranes, self-dumping barges, and electronically controlled saws for making plywood. Peeling machines strip bark from several cords of pulpwood in an hour or less. Complete harvesting units are being developed to fell, limb, cut, and load a tree in one operation.

IT IS FREQUENTLY said that where human services predominate, as in the retail industry, automation is impossible. Yet there too we discover that computers with feedback mechanisms, as well as electronic data processing, are increasingly utilized. As retailers become aware of the possibilities of these techniques, engineers come forth with devices that can be employed directly in merchandising itself. In retailing and distribution, the outstanding developments are found in prepackaging and automatic handling of materials at both the warehouse and retail levels. Once these devices are connected with data-processing equipment, automation is firmly established.

Here are some of the advances now being made. Shoe chains are adopting data-input devices at the point of sale (cash registers issue punched tape that records details of every transaction); variety chains are working on ordering systems based on a universal code that identifies each item, involving print-punch tickets; drug-store chains are installing computers for merchandising purposes; department stores continue to experiment with point-of-sale devices; apparel chains are using computers in merchandising and inventory control and in preparing documents relating to charge accounts; mail-order concerns utilize computers to control warehouse inventories and to produce order-picking sheets and store invoices; food chains are experimenting with installations that produce punched paper tapes representing daily orders of perishables so that the data can be transmitted by wire to the companies' regional distribution centers; and a number of retail concerns is putting into operation merchandise control and reordering systems based on the use of full-sized punched-card systems.

The motive for automating in retailing is quite the same as elsewhere. One automation advocate writing in a retail-trade journal said, "The machines don't call in sick; they don't talk back; they work early and late and without overtime; they don't get tired; and last, but far from least, they don't line up at the cashier's window every week for a slice of operating funds." The head of another department store made it even plainer, stating that retailing is undergoing an "Operation Meathead" to replace people who are not equipped for the electronic age. To the president of a large Western chain the challenge was to find ways of doing tasks without people.

The back room in the supermarket sector is, of course, a most important area for improved materials handling. It is generally agreed in the industry that "what the boys in the back room" will have is more mechanized equipment. The trend to mechanization is most evident in the handling of nonperishable items. Equipment to speed the flow of stock from truck to shelf has been gaining widespread acceptance among food chains. Although conveyor systems of both the gravity and power types have been used in single-level and two-level stores for many years, the trend is for more automated installations. Full conveyor systems are now in use, in which the line of flow of merchandise is along the most direct line from the truck to the shelf. Alternate flows are built into the system, so that the stock may go to holding areas until needed and then to the price-marking stations.

Supermarkets are installing overhead rail systems for unloading and transporting sides of beef; more power equipment for cutting, grinding, and shaping; more highly powered automatic and semiautomatic wrapping machinery; and more scales that automatically print the prices on the packages. Linked up to these devices are both power and gravity conveyor systems. Wrapping machinery accelerates the mechanization of the various departments, and such machines often require linked-in materials flow systems to keep up with their wrapping capacities. Much of this development heralds the beginning of an automated operation, for what is utilized here is the principle of the transfer machine linking disparate operations. Tie a computer into the operation, and we have automation.

What is important to note is that these devices feed on one another. The trend toward more packaging of produce, for example, leads to more mechanization in the steps both preceding and following the packaging operations. This mechanization, in turn, leads to larger departments, with relative increases in storage and preparation areas. And then this growth creates a need for more materials-flow equipment. This sequence, perhaps more than anything else, is the significant thing in mechanizing retail operations. One step produces another, and in the end human beings become less important in the conduct of business.

When these mechanical devices are linked with electronic control systems, we create the possibility of establishing a completely automated retail establishment in such a way that the customer will be able, with a minimum of effort, to place her order, have the merchandise delivered to the front of the store, and pay her automatically computed bill. In fact, such a system has been developed by the International Telephone and Telegraph Company and is intended primarily for chains of 150 stores or more, all of which would draw merchandise from central warehouses. The system can transmit orders, for example, for thirty-seven cases of eggs, ninety-six bunches of bananas, and a half-ton of instant coffee, which can be delivered automatically to the store. The orders are then transmitted at the store into a telephone. Although the sounds are not intelligible to the ear, they are automatically decoded and fed into a printer and card-punching machine or calculator, which then goes to work gathering the order. The system can be linked to a data-processing computer, so that orders coming in from all stores may be totaled.

In November 1959 the General Telephone and Electronics Company announced a machine that can be placed at supermarket check-out counters where it will read or scan fluorescent stickers on each grocery item as it passes on a traveling belt. This information is passed to a computer, which totals the customer's purchases. Such an automatic check-out operation takes about two-thirds the time now required for manual handling by check-out clerks. Automatic checking thus speeds customer flow, provides more accuracy in totaling orders, and supplies an automatic reorder system for the warehouse. The scanner is connected to the cashbox, where a similar device enables the electronic reader automatically to record prices of the individual items at the check-out stand. Problems of handling items selling for prices in combination, like three for 29 cents, are solved by having the device renumber the first two items at 10 cents each and ring the third at 9 cents.

In the supermarket field all that seems necessary at this time is for one of the giant chains to undertake such an installation and to accustom the public to its use. This step does not seem too difficult a public-relations task. When supermarkets were first started, customers were unwilling to purchase prepackaged meat and insisted on seeing the butcher at his work. This problem was solved by the late Lansing Shields of the Grand Union Company by moving the butcher workman out from the back room and closer to the selling area to do his job behind a glass window. Gradually the housewife became accustomed to prepackaged meat, and today one seldom sees the butcher at his work. Prepackaged meats are placed in attractive displays and counters, and the housewife is quite content. Personal relationships, once believed so necessary to the success of a retail operation, are being reduced to a minimum, if not entirely eliminated.

One of the major problems in supermarket operation is the tendency for customers to queue up during peak-hour operations at the check-out counters. To help solve this problem, one concern experimented with an automatic packaging machine at the check-out counter. As the customer approaches the check-out clerk and places the merchandise on a conveyor belt, the clerk adjusts the machine for the size of the order. While the order is checked out on the register, the merchandise is placed into a loading bin with light and fragile items on the top. As the loading bin is filled, the cashier presses a button, and the bin pushes the merchandise into an open bag, which is then lifted onto a receiving platform while the bin reopens to accept a new load of merchandise. Should it become necessary to resack a heavy grocery order, either at the customer's request or because of injury to the bag, the automatic bagger can do it in fewer than ten seconds by merely reloading the filled bag into the loading bin and starting the loading machine which automatically does the job of repacking. Equipment of this type not only increases productivity in the sense of speeding up the flow of merchandise through the check-out counter, but it also eliminates the need to have an extra employee to do the bagging. Such a device can be easily linked to electronic data-recording and processing equipment for inventory and sales records.

Even change making, important to the completion of a transaction, is being mechanized. Clearly, with the development of automatic vending machines, the possibility of completely automated retail stores is virtually upon us. For a long time, growth in automatic vending was limited by the lack of a reliable machine to handle paper money. After years of work, the Atwood Vacuum Machine Company of Chicago developed a device that, when presented with a $1 bill delivers two quarters, three dimes, and four nickels in change. The Atwood device operates by holding a bill in a perforated screen under a photoflood lamp and then electronically reading the amount of light passing through the perforations. It can be adjusted to accept denominations other than $1 and to deliver any combinations of change.

Said *Architectural Forum* in December 1958, discussing retail automation: "It is too early to say what all this will do to the ranks of service workers, currently the most sharply rising sector of U.S. employment, thus far almost untouched by automation. It may someday pose a problem of no mean dimensions." In the light of these developments, it is not unwarranted to assert that retailing is an area in which jobs can be simplified and made routine so that electronic computers can replace the worker entirely or permit one worker to do the jobs of several.[40]

AND SO WE come closer and closer to a world of work without men. The experts are quite certain that this world is what we shall have in the not too far distant future. E. L.

McLeary of General Electric's program-control division not only told a conference of his peers that entire plants would soon be operated by such methods as numerical control, but also said enthusiastically: "A final step will be to combine automatic handling and automatic assembly. By tying these individual systems together we arrive at a complete piece of automation—all commanded from one central point and producing parts which flow into the streams for complete product assembly. It's fast, it's flexible, it's foolproof—and it's coming."[41] The fact is that present developments in automation represent a combination of various techniques that, taken together, represent a striking breakthrough in methods of production. It must be noted that defense and space research have provided some of the central technological elements that otherwise might have taken years to develop. And it seems evident that even small companies can make use of the many pieces of flexible automatic equipment now available. In fact, one device manufactured by General Mills brought in twice the sales volume from small and medium-sized firms that it did from large ones.[42]

From the cybernetic point of view, the automatic factory is completely feasible. Although no company has yet carried automation to its final technological and logical conclusion, the elements now exist, ready for a new synthesis. The production of metal billets, electronic circuits, and machine subassemblies has already been taken out of the hands of skilled workers and put under the guidance of computers. The fully robotized factory is now on the horizon. After all, the machine or machines represent a purposive system that is deterministic in the sense that its output can be precisely and objectively specified. That is to say, there is little doubt about the purely engineering aspects of the input-output relationships required in an automated plant. There would be feedback mechanisms so that information could flow from operating units to controls and back again in "real time," that is, as events take place; there would be couplings and transfer devices between machines, as well as transducers to convert energy from one form to another, as with quartz-mercury crystals that change electrical energy into sound energy in sonic-delay lines; there would

161

be techniques for handling information in the system so that stochastic or probabilistic and random effects would be minimized; and there would be mechanical robots equipped with memory units and sensors at points equivalent to hips, shoulders, elbows, and wrists to work continuously without human direction.

And with industrial robots no humans at all would be needed. There are, in fact, several industrial robots available, among them the Unimate and the Versatran. The latter uses analogue servos to drive its arm, with command signals recorded on magnetic tape. The Unimate employs digital servos; its commands are placed in a magnetic drum. Each, however, has its particular advantages: The Versatran for jobs in which path control is necessary, like paint spraying or welding, the Unimate when point-to-point positioning is crucial, as in machine loading. These devices can unload die casting machines, operate forging presses, paint auto parts, contour-weld auto-frame parts, load ceramic tile into kilns, load pallets, operate multiturret presses, transfer parts between punch presses, and a good deal more. Also available is the TransfeRobot, which oils clock assemblies as they pass on a conveyor belt, packages chocolates, and places parts inside a welder. Mobot, another such device, operates underwater locking screws for valves and gripping pipes in an oil-drilling rig on a Shell Oil Company installation off the coast of Santa Barbara, California. Mobot does not suffer from the human diver's occupational hazard of the "bends."

Why should not these mechanical and electronically controlled monsters be used when the lost time due to failure is thereby reduced to 1 per cent of total operating time? Furthermore, the investment in a robot is always recaptured through depreciation allowances. The robot is stronger than a human worker; it stands wherever it has been placed; it has a longer reach; it does not tire; it does not suffer from boredom; it can work three shifts, and it can "memorize" a complicated set of motions with only one rehearsal. Furthermore, decision-making capabilities can be built into the robot, and, once computer techniques that simulate human thought have been perfected and attached to the robot, the possibilities will be truly enormous—and

162

frightening. In the factory, the robot could be hooked easily into a central computer, which would shift from one program to another as demanded by the necessities of control. Although the sensory attributes of robots today are still poor, the character-recognition devices or scanning systems can do much to give them eyes, enough perhaps to enable them to "see" the general outlines of a part in ten or fifteen different "views." This "seeing" would allow the robot to select a desired part from a bin in which various items had been jumbled. The engineers who build these instruments happily assure us that man will not become obsolete but rather will be "... excused from drudgery to concentrate on more human endeavors." Unfortunately, the latter are seldom specified.[43]

In short, the factory would become a "black box," based on a sequence of linked individual "black boxes." As far as the engineers are concerned, they would be delighted to automate everything in sight, regardless of cost. One apocryphal tale tells of a designer applauded for creating a $1 million machine that could handle complicated scrap-removal jobs. His triumph ended when someone asked, "Couldn't a man with a wheelbarrow do the job just as well?" The wheelbarrow will have to be replaced, however, simply because one innovation leads to and in fact demands another. Computers, almost 20,000 in number, are already on the scene, ready to engage in process control, as well as in ordinary data handling. The time lag between the development of a new device and its adoption is diminishing rapidly: It took fifty years before the telephone was widely used; the assimilation of television occurred in less than fifteen years; transistors entered into industrial use in five years, lasers in a little over a year. Is the automatic "black box" factory so far away?[44]

Norbert Wiener, the acknowledged "father" of cybernetics, has said:

The automatic factory and assembly line without human agents are only so far ahead of us as is limited by our willingness to put such a degree of effort into their engineering as was spent, for example, in the development of the technique of radar in the Second World War. . . . It makes the metaphorical dominance of the machines, as imagined by Samuel Butler, a most immediate and non-metaphorical problem. It gives the human race a new and most effective collection of mechanical slaves to perform its labor. Such mechanical labor has most of the economic properties of slave labor... *However, any labor that accepts the conditions of competition with slave labor accepts the conditions of slave labor, and is essentially slave labor*... There is no rate of pay at which a pick-and-shovel laborer can live which is low enough to compete with the work of a steam-shovel as an excavator. The modern industrial revolution is similarly bound to devalue the human brain, at least in its simpler and more routine decisions... [In] the second revolution... the average human being of mediocre attainments or less has nothing to sell that it is worth anyone's money to buy.[45]

And elsewhere, he added:

There is nothing which will automatically make the automatic factory work for human good, unless we have determined this human good in advance and have so constructed the factory as to contribute to it. If our sole orders to the factory are for an increase in production, without regard to the possible aspects of this new and vast productivity and without regard to the problems of unemployment and of the redistribution of human labor, there is no self-working principle of *laissez-faire* which will make those orders redound to our benefit and even prevent them from contributing to our own destruction.

The automated filing cabinet   5

The increasing control of industry, as exemplified by the automatic factory, is paralleled in the front office, where handmaidens of the ledger had woven a web of purchases and sales with typewriter and comptometer. In the Fifties and Sixties, however, the computer's high reliability and its capacity to do the work of dozens of bookkeepers, file clerks, typists, and inventory clerks made the machine attractive enough to start displacing women in the office. Clerical work became "labor" to be replaced by equipment, just as the man on the line had been replaced. Data handling, represented by millions of pieces of paper, was converted into a "continuous-flow process," as the remaining office worker, like the remaining shop worker, became caretaker to a machine.

More important, the businessman recognized not only that the computer could handle the routine tasks of book-keeping and storing information but also that, with its capacity to manipulate information in extraordinary ways, it could affect the manner in which business itself was to be conducted. Those who recognized the potentialities of the computer were likely to become innovators, after the fashion of Schumpeter's hero, for with advanced data processing and "communications techniques" they could move more quickly than their rivals. Of course, when the computer could be adopted as a direct substitute for clerical labor, there was no hesitation in using it. To some companies this adoption meant little change in methods other than converting a few documents into punched cards. Others, however, discovered that the computer could be utilized to marked advantage in inventory control, production scheduling, and engineering planning, as well as in shuffling office paper. It was found that customers could be quoted prices and delivery dates within minutes after receiving the orders, and material-control systems began to reduce the need to invest heavily in inventory.

Although not all managements thought it worthwhile to resort to extensive computerized data processing, for such a giant as Du Pont there were few doubts to trouble its corporate soul. This company, one of the true pioneers in applying computers to data processing, has some 5,000 employees involved in one way or another in ADP (automatic data processing). Although the figure does not represent much of an increase in such personnel, compared with 1959, the company is twice as large as it was then, and the amount of information processed through its computers has increased geometrically. Du Pont's more than seventy-five computers evidently pay their way, with each tended on the average by some eighteen operators and programmers. Even the engineers spend half their time at machines.

With automaticity in the factory, the data that flow from the production floor or the shipping platform must be equally automatic—otherwise, the manager's control is incomplete. Furthermore, such control cannot be retrospective: It must rather be in "real time," simultaneous with the event itself. Communication channels needed by management to direct its operations must keep pace with the rapid changes that take place on the production floor. To solve this problem, the experts have devised remote data-gathering systems that tell plant managers the instant a machine breaks down or the moment a critical inventory item has been depleted. Such a system provides a running account of the number of workers on a given task, the tools they use, and the location and progress of the job at hand. And while the computer is churning out reports on these "events," it automatically generates the information for payroll and billing.

How such automation can be achieved in practice is illustrated by Western Electric's electronic-equipment plant near Kansas City. There operations are conducted by an IBM 1401: Data relating to orders, billing, shipping, warehousing, shop orders, disbursements, materials requisitions, inventory records, and general accounting flow through the machine without end. A network of special dial telephones scattered around the shop area enables production men to report the status of particular jobs. Each telephone has a deck of prepunched cards that identify machine tools; another deck is used to identify the orders in process. When a job goes through a given operation, the workman pulls out the appropriate card and "feeds" it to the telephone, thus transmitting a record of order status, machine use, and his own time to the data-processing center. The computer can then check on scheduling estimates. This system has reportedly reduced inventory, machine time, and materials, as well as personnel.

IN SOME OPERATIONS, notably in defense and space work, production runs are relatively short, so that the factory must be organized as a huge job shop, with as many as 50,000 different job orders in progress simultaneously. To check on the progress of a single job lot could be a tedious affair. Now, however, the plant manager merely inserts a card with a description of the order into a remote data unit, which sends the information to a computer. The machine then returns a report telling where the job is located in the plant, the number of parts involved, exactly what work has been accomplished so far, and the estimated completion time. It all takes but a few seconds.[1] The system is especially useful in cases in which numerous parts are used in production, requiring substantial inventories. The remote data units keep track of the materials and of parts requirements, making possible drastic cuts in inventory stockpiling.[2]

In petroleum the men who search for oil no longer wear leather jackets and stand in sand up to their hips. They are "white collar" workers, who, like anyone else tied to a

167

desk, are up to their knees in paper and statistical data. For example, in searching for oil, the history and data on each well are the geologist's main tools. Sometimes there are so many facts on an individual oil well that four or five days may be spent shuffling papers. But now automated data-processing systems for oil wells are available. One such system is the Permian Basin Well Data System at Midland, Texas, in which twelve major oil producers are involved. The basic data included are well name and operator, legal location, description and coordinates, facts on formation tops, drill-stem test information, depths, cores, oil logs, and completion history. All the facts can be processed quickly to tell the geologist what he wants to know.

At Pittsburgh Steel, IBM equipment handles every number in the company, except possibly the address on the letterhead. The company, a relatively small producer, had computerized its complicated incentive-pay system as far back as 1956, and in 1962 its computer system was advanced enough to explore the cost implications of the revised supplementary unemployment-benefits program and the extended vacation plan negotiated with the union for the entire steel industry. The company's data processing has resulted in better control of inventory; it has also halted the growth in its clerical force. In 1956 Pittsburgh Steel had one clerk for every twenty employees; in 1963 the ratio was one to eight. With the computer, this expansion has ceased, and the proportions will no doubt be reduced.

Pittsburgh Steel's technique, based on a "total-systems concept," is essentially a single-entry record file programmed to relate each recorded activity to every other activity on which it impinges and to have each event automatically activate the subsequent one. The variables are quite diverse, stemming as they do from mining, transportation, and metal-working, as well as steel making. If an order comes in from a regular customer—and most orders are "repeats"—only ten variable bits of information have to be entered into the fifty-six-million-character random-access disk file. The other bits are already in storage. The system then makes twenty-one computations: What size ingots? How many for this order? What dimensions for the slabs? When will the space be needed at the mill? Are any slabs of this type already in

stock? Is the customer's credit satisfactory? Which salesman got the business? What is the cost per ton? The computer virtually minds everybody's business. It orders raw
materials, checks on mill spares, records straight-time man-
hours, computes incentives and accumulated vacation time,
tells the sheet mill when slabs will arrive, and records the
fact that a delay in a certain department is to be attributed
to some defective components.[3]

Chrysler Corporation's headquarters, plants, sales
offices, and warehouses used to send one another a million
words a day via teletype and telegram. This now archaic
system has been replaced by a computer that receives and
transmits messages automatically. Under the old system,
in which a Detroit communications center relayed the
messages, a query from eastern Canada to Vancouver went
first to Windsor, Ontario; then to Detroit, from which it
was sent to a relay station in Los Angeles; and finally up
to British Columbia. It took twenty-six minutes. The
electronic system takes thirty-five seconds and eliminates
the stopover at Los Angeles. The new way is much simpler
and is connected to only twenty two-way simultaneous
circuits instead of the twenty-six two-way unidirectional
circuits formerly employed. More teletype stations can be
hooked onto each circuit, and there are fewer circuits. The
computer also supervises some accounting operations.
Every seven-thousandth of a second it checks each circuit's
condition and reports to a human supervisor. It also records
the number of words stations send and calculates the
costs to be assigned to each. At another level is a data-
processing system based on corporate centralization that
would combine the eleven manufacturing groups into three,
employing the transmission of 1.6 billion bits of computer
data a month between plants. An enlarged memory capacity
would store the history of every car sold under the company's five-year or 50,000-mile warranty, so that any
Chrysler sales office would be able to secure within seconds
the complete history of any warranted automobile.

A tobacco company utilizes data-processing equipment
to deal with inventory management, leaf usage and logistics,
smoke analysis, sales data, and credit review. Sorters and
account tabulators handle record keeping for libraries. (The

librarians resent being turned into document retrievers and at the same time are anxious about their own careers.) Magnetic tapes store records of elementary and high-school students and also digest other educational information. Drug-dispensing charges are kept by computers in pharmacy departments of hospitals. Automatic ticket-punching devices, in which the commuters' rides are validated by sensing instruments speed passenger movement on suburban rail lines. And computers and radio signals coordinate traffic lights to regulate the direction and volume of traffic on different streets at different times of the day. In the latter, information on punched tapes is fed into a computer, giving it detailed data on traffic conditions throughout a city. When the morning rush hour starts, the computer sets the signals to allow a rapid flow of traffic downtown. In the afternoon, the signals are reversed. As one expert remarked: "Traffic control is no longer a bunch of lights at an intersection. It's a data processing system."[4]

AS MIGHT have been expected, the computer also has affected the office landscape as well. The electronic desk calculator is essentially a small computer; some units can be rented for little more than it costs to hire two clerks. The Monrobot XI, made and marketed by the Monroe Calculating Machine Company, processes "buy and sell" orders for a Wall Street investment house, sends out confirmation notices to customers on the day's transactions, and balances the books daily. A shopping-center operator uses a similar machine to allocate operating costs to tenants, computing and billing expenses for air conditioning, sewage, and utilities. The business form too has been altered. Although computers have long billed utility customers in the form of post cards, a unique system developed by Standard Register avoids the double pass through the machine by printing both sides of the bill on a sheet of special paper, which is automatically folded, glued, and sliced as it leaves the computer.

As in most technological developments, there were antecedents. Although the first typewriter patent was issued in 1829, it was not until a half-century later that the

Remington Company was able to market it for office use, and even then it did not sell in any appreciable quantities. It was not until World War I that the mechanization of the office started in earnest, triggering a revolution in both correspondence and the sex composition of the clerical work force. In the next twenty years there came the adding machine, comptometer, telephone, bookkeeping machine, duplicating machine, dictaphone, mechanical letter opener, collater, folder, and addressograph. Now there are solid-state electronic desk calculators; electrostatic copiers producing as many as 2,400 copies of an original document; portable dictating machines embodying microminiature components; duplicating machines with automatic sequence controls; and repetitive typewriters that print the same letter over and over again under the guidance of a punched paper tape. All this change clearly represents a new level of technology.

Needless to say, the files are now automated as well. At the North American Insurance Company, fourteen clerks were needed to handle inquiries. Each inquiry necessitated a search through an enormous collection of 3 × 5-inch cards and then location of other documents in one of 12,000 boxes stacked on floor-to-ceiling shelves. Now the cards are in elevator files, which automatically bring them to a clerk sitting comfortably at a desk. The mechanized system—not yet fully automated but on its way—cut the number of clerks needed in half and eliminated over 1,000 square feet of floor space. Remington Rand's Kard-Veyer brings a file to a clerk when a particular button is pressed. Remote dictation equipment, automatic typewriters, and recording systems that take orders over the phone further illustrate the mechanization of the office. And automation itself intrudes on the stenographer's assignment, with IBM's experimental translation system to transcribe notes made on a stenographic machine into typewritten English. With a huge stored memory for grammatical rules and sentence structure, it prints out homonyms like "red" and "read" according to the context. The desk calculator becomes more and more automatic. A billing clerk in a fuel-oil company can preset the price of a gallon of oil on his machine at the start of the day. As the delivery trucks return from their rounds, the clerk enters the number of gallons delivered on the keyboard and pushes the start button. The machine then automatically produces a report on total deliveries, number of sales, and total revenues.[5]

The end of the file clerk is especially signaled by developments in information retrieval. File rooms, with their mountains of cabinets and transfer cartons containing reports, memoranda, and correspondence may soon become a thing of the past. Information-retrieval machines range from a simple reference system costing about $300 to a $2 million monster that can instantly flash a document on a viewing screen and, if necessary, produce a copy. Considering the fantastic flow of paper in business and government today, these devices appear essential. To illustrate, a pharmaceutical laboratory in Philadelphia received 275,000 documents in five years relating to patents and technical papers, with 50,000 being added each year. Socony's New Jersey laboratory must keep track of 140,000 similar pieces of paper. To store all of these data, as well as accounting and sales information, and to extract an item of information when needed require microfilming plus the computer. Systems based on the latter have a larger capacity and are faster than are the older manual techniques. For example, IBM's 9900 special index analyzer can be hooked into another IBM machine, the 7090, in one case, to assemble test results of thousands of records, a method actually employed by North American Aviation and by Du Pont. Special programming, which enables the 9900 analyzer to classify titles by groups, has produced over forty complete summaries of technical literature. Virtually all the indexes issued by the American Chemical Society are developed in this manner.

Microfilming can shrink documents by factors of more than 140 to 1, placing as many as 10,000 pages on a single 8-inch-square film sheet. The saving in space, let alone labor, is phenomenal. In one microfilming system, the images of documents are placed on an $8\frac{1}{2} \times 11$-inch card containing 100 micropage frames. The cards are filed in groups of 10; each drawer contains 10 sections; and each cabinet has 10 drawers. A cabinet thus holds exactly 100,000 frames, and each digit of a document number corresponds to its location in the file. Retrieval becomes a matter of seconds, for "54321" means drawer 5, section 4, card 3, row 2, and column 1. Other retrieval methods include high-speed scanning of titles, identification of documents by binary codes of black and white spots photographed on the document reel itself, and almost instantaneous reproduction of the original.

AUTOMATED RESERVATION SYSTEMS on airlines are perhaps the classic development of data-handling methods that eliminate the human equation. Introduced in the 1950s, they have quickly replaced manual methods. Reservations require three essential steps: checking whether or not a seat is available on the requested flight; tallying the sale against the inventory of seats; and making out the ticket and accounting records. In the old days, about a decade or so ago, the ticket agent would call a central reservation office, where the request was checked against an availability board, a large blackboard listing flights and seats. As the number of flights increased, the manual posting in this system began to run behind, with clerks stepping on one another's toes in an effort to check requests and record reservations. The transfer of information between the sales office and central reservation began to bog down. The computer came to the rescue. Now a reservation clerk can select a small metal plate and insert it into a machine, which activates the circuitry. He then presses a series of buttons, requesting a flight and seat. If the space is available, a green light shows, and a ticket can be sold to the customer; an amber light indicates a "sold out" plane; a red light says the clerk has erred in his request. One such system reduced the man-years of employment in central reservations by 11 per cent. Labor requirements for seat-inventory record keeping were cut by 85 per cent. True, there has been an increase in some jobs on the airlines in recent years, but this increase has come mainly from the growth in revenue ton-miles. Yet the growth in traffic was faster than employment in the years from 1957 to 1962: 8.8 per cent a year for traffic compared with 3.9 per cent a year in employment. In the decade between 1947 and 1957, the increase in jobs had been greater — 6.1 per cent per annum.

Use and Impact

Trans World Airlines began automating its reservation systems as far back as 1958. Its newest system, installed at Kennedy International Airport in New York in 1963, includes four magnetic drums turning at 1,800 revolutions a minute. Availability of seats is recorded on the drums' surfaces at magnetized spots that represent open, closed, wait list, and other reservation data. When "queried" by a sales agent, the steel-alloy drums reply with the appropriate light signal. The memory unit records current transactions, whereas messages received or sent are put on tape recorders, which can hold as many as four million digits of information on a single reel of tape 2,400 feet long. In addition to seat space, the system stores passenger names, hotel accommodations, phone numbers, and meal preferences.

American Airlines' SABRE system is even more versatile. This one started in 1953 aboard an A.A. Los Angeles-to-New York flight, which brought together C. R. Smith, the airline's president, and R. B. Smith, an IBM salesman (no relation). During the long flight, the two Smiths talked about the complications of a reservation system and how it might be computerized. For the next three years IBM's Smith mulled over the problem, and in 1956 the computer maker assigned several engineers to work out the details. The programming began in 1961, utilizing an IBM 7090. The system, which costs about $30 million, works in "real time." It requires more than eight different actions and contains in its consoles and units more than a million instructions. Although it is not so complex as the air force's SAGE, it is undoubtedly the most involved civilian computer operation.

The major problem is to handle the seat inventory efficiently, as a "bumped" passenger is apt to become irate enough to write to the C.A.B. or even to enter a lawsuit. Furthermore, it is important to know when and where a seat has been vacated, in order to sell it to someone else. That is, an optimum proportion of sales to total seats must be maintained; otherwise the airline may lose money. The sales agent enters his reservation request on a small keyboard at his desk; the data and flight number are relayed to an IBM 7090 computer in Briarcliff Manor, Westchester County, New York, where it is checked against flight information in the memory unit. If the seat is available the sale can be closed; if not, the computer automatically supplies a list of alternative flights. The sales data are then returned to the computer, where they are stored in its memory. The SABRE center in Westchester County consists of a variety of units—data correlator, arithmetic and logic units, stored programs, and the like—which receive information from interchange stations and can calculate the numbers of meals and drinks required for each flight. The guesswork is taken out of "overbooking," for the computer can reckon the number of "no-shows" for each flight on the basis of past experience. As full a flight load as possible can thus be assured. Furthermore, it is estimated that 30 per cent of the entire airline staff can be eliminated when the system is fully "operational."[6]

PERHAPS THE GREATEST publicity has been given to bank automation. At first the banks seemed hesitant to disturb the equanimity of traditional ways. But then magnetic-ink character recognition was developed, and appropriate type fonts that could be read by scanning devices began to appear on checks. In fewer than seven years virtually all the commercial banks of the country were issuing coded checks to their depositors. In 1963 some thirteen billion checks were written, and the number was expected to increase by a billion a year. All of them passed through automated equipment for posting and clearing. The numbers on the checks, designed in 1957 by the Stanford Research Institute for the Bank of America, are readable by both humans and magnetic sensing devices. The method was so successful that the American Bankers Association urged all its members to use it. The numbers are printed with an iron-oxide ink, so that the permanent magnet in the machine can magnetize them for the reading head of the machine. As each digit gives off a different signal, the magnetized characters can be used to operate such equipment as sorting machines. Additional numbers for clearance and other purposes may be added by an inscriber. These are the devices with which banks are moving into the second half of the twentieth century.

175

Use and Impact

Obviously, the banks also can use ADP for accounting purposes. When two major New York banks merged a few years back, creating an institution with more than a hundred branches, all the paper work involving demand-deposit accounting was transferred to a single location, resulting in substantial savings. Conventional verification of accounts for audit purposes requires more than 1,100 man hours, but with the computer the whole job can be done in ten hours. Furthermore, the work can be handled after hours, so that by nine o'clock the following morning the branch manager can be supplied with all the information needed on over-drafts, insufficient funds, or stop payments. Even bank examiners have had to become data-processing experts, for transactions that constitute the history of an account are now recorded in symbolic language and are stored on magnetic tapes, drums, disks, or cards, rather than posted in ledgers. One bank computer system developed by the National Cash Register Company consists of master processing and control units; magnetic tape handlers to serve as "files" for installment-loan, mortgage, and checking accounts; a high-speed document sorter able to process 1,620 checks a minute; a print-out unit with a capacity of 720 to 900 lines a minute; and a punched-card reader that deciphers 400 cards a minute. The system is a modular one, allowing the bank to put in additional electronic equipment as its business increases. Today almost every bank with deposits of more than $50 million uses a computer.

Some banks discovered after installing the new equipment that they had more computer time than they knew how to fill. They began to offer smaller correspondent banks in the hinterlands the same computer services they were running for themselves—accounting and data handling of mortgage and consumer loans. One bank in Denver plans to offer its correspondents an "on-line" tie-in, so that no paper has to be transmitted to the central computer. Customers can be provided with account reconciliations and payroll servicing, and billing can be done for doctors and dentists. Royalties for independent oil operators, rentals for real-estate firms, and optimum inventory levels are among the jobs that a number of banks are computing for their clients—all for appropriate fees.

Some of the tellers can be eliminated too, for customers in a hurry can put their transactions through the Banko-graph, a device that looks like an automatic washer with a slot that accepts the deposit slip together with the accompanying checks, paper money, or coins. Developed by Reflectone Electronics, a subsidiary of the Universal Match Corporation, the machine quickly ejects a stamped receipt, and, as the customer hastens back to his parked car, the machine photographs everything he has put into it, processes the film, and neatly wraps film and deposit in a small bundle. Later, at his leisure, a teller checks the film for possible errors and credits the customer's account.

Such "front lobby" devices have been spreading rapidly among the nation's 13,656 commercial banks. They require relatively little investment and can by used by small as well as by large institutions. The Bankograph costs about $5,000, compared with almost a quarter of a million dollars for an automated check sorter. Some bankers believe that fancy equipment draws new customers. One savings-and-loan association in New York paid $500,000 for an IBM 1440 on-line data-processing unit to link tellers via a key-board terminal to the computer, located on an upper story, that would advise whether or not to accept the customer's withdrawal slip and would provide also an accurate balance printed in the passbook. Nine banks in Massachusetts linked themselves to an electronic system to provide instantaneous accounting at the tellers' windows. The American Telephone and Telegraph Company is developing a dialing system to enable a housewife to pay her bills via a telephone line connected to a computer.

In addition, closed-circuit television and pneumatic-tube assemblies speed up drive-in banking, the suburban rage. Instead of outside booths manned by tellers, there are traffic islands on which are placed units that look like gasoline pumps. The pneumatic tubes and closed-circuit television connect the islands with the bank office, and, as the customer drives up and talks to the teller inside via the two-way intercom, his deposit is whisked through the tubes and his receipt whisked back. Again, the novelty is supposed to attract business. In the meantime, the teller on the inside is told to handle several stations at once. The pneumatic system may even encourage banks to open remote-control stations in subways or shopping centers or to establish direct links with controllers of corporations. The Mosler Safe Company, which makes the pneumatic-tube system, suggests that banks in the suburbs will become gardens with drives through them lined with flowers and television banking units. "Mass banking" will thus replace "class banking."

Of course, there have been increases in bank employment. But these increases have stemmed from the greater volume of banking activities. If the number of checks processed is taken as an indication of the latter, then the average annual percentage increase between 1947 and 1957 was 6 per cent. Employment, however, increased at a lesser rate — 4.5 per cent per annum for the same period. With the increase in manpower, bank executives became concerned — hence automation, in the forms of proof and sorting machines, electronic bookkeeping, tabulating equipment, dictaphones, microfilms, and electronic check processing. Without such equipment, the jobs necessary to handle the increased banking load might well double in 1975, compared to 1960, when bank employment totaled 610,000. Of these jobs, 83 per cent were for clerical workers, but of this group 62 per cent, or 314,000 employees, were vulnerable, that is, apt to be automated out of existence. These estimates, based on Bureau of Labor Statistics data, are substantiated by the experience of one major bank in which the number of bookkeepers in demand-deposit work declined 80 per cent over a four-year period, despite a rise of 10 per cent in the number of demand depositors. Another bank told B.L.S. that it expected to eliminate half the bookkeepers in its branches and to assign the other half to other duties. Even with attrition and reassignment, bank automation will eliminate at least half the jobs in demand-deposit bookkeeping, not to mention the probable losses in loan, trust, and time-deposit departments. All told, the *net* loss is apt to be close to one-fifth of the jobs that might have been expected in the absence of automation. In the meantime, the volume of banking activity, as measured by the number of checks processed, will have risen substantially; the number of executive, administrative, and professional personnel will also increase as the banking business booms. This point illustrates one clear purpose of automation: It is intended to achieve the same level of output with fewer workers or a higher level of output without a proportionate increase in employment. In any case, the rate of expansion in office jobs will be dampened over the long haul.[7]

WALL STREET is not far behind its commercial-banking brethren. The Stock Exchange needs "real time" information to overcome ticker lag so that floor transactions can be reported immediately. Automating the big board will eliminate the tedious business of obtaining telephoned bid and asked quotations. A computerized operation, furthermore, would handle 60 per cent more calls a day than the record achieved on May 29, 1961. It consists of an optical reader that speeds bid and asked information and sales reports directly from the trading floor to a computer and voice assembler. The latter can compose messages from a prerecorded electronic vocabulary and can play them over the telephone to brokers, thus cutting the two- or three-minute lag between a transaction and its report on the ticker to only a few seconds. Furthermore, new tickers will print a thousand characters a minute, double the present rate.

Investment bankers want municipalities and corporations to issue registered couponless bonds, as the computer can keep records of interest due more efficiently. Automated coupon clipping would do away with cutting, posting, mailing, record keeping, and burning paid-up coupons. In addition, a registered bond enhances security as it is not negotiable. A lost or stolen bond with its coupons attached has the same chance for recovery by the owner as a wallet full of $1,000 bills. Of course, as investment houses get about a nickel a coupon for servicing bonds put in their care and as this sum is often a substantial part of the earnings of smaller firms, the latter may question the need to automate this fascinating feature of American life. With all these changes in the nation's way of handling its financial affairs, the number of back-office workers—those who handle the records and documents—has been sharply reduced. In some brokerage houses employment in these departments has been cut in half. The savings have paid for the increased cost of the equipment, and, said one broker, as volume increases, savings become that much greater. But, in addition, the objective has been to use automation as a way of tightening control over office operation and to "professionalize" its management.[8]

Data processing by computer has many more applications, including check verification at retail stores, estimating bids for contractors, making decisions on buying policies, forecasting sales, and guiding the complicated steps that have to be taken in building a space missile. In check cashing, for example, a request to the computer elicits information on credit ratings, validity of auto licenses, bank reports, and the like. The machine may also have stored information on checking account numbers of people known to be poor risks. To estimate electrical-contract bids, an index of 45,000 electrical assemblies is stored in a special unit together with data from blueprints. As the required assemblies are checked off with an electrically operated pencil, signals automatically enter the information into the machine. A computer then prepares a summary of costs and a complete bill of materials and labor requirements.[9]

Of course, there have been moments when management's enthusiasm has gone awry. An expediter for a television manufacturer simply threw away his daily tabulation of shipments received because it was always a week old. To obtain current information he had to employ the conventional method of telephoning suppliers and receiving clerks. A purchasing agent in an aerosol company discovered that the ADP reports on purchases that came from the accounting department gave only financial data without the technical descriptions he needed. In an aircraft company, a data-happy programmer issued a performance report on suppliers based on a fancy statistical formula that tied together in one index number prices, delivery records, and quality. No one knew what he or the machine was talking about. These instances, however, are rather rare; in most cases, sophisticated data processing is useful enough to save 50 per cent or more on operating expenses. One company cited in the *Harvard Business Review* (March–April 1964) reduced its personnel by 23 per cent after installing a computerized system in its purchasing department. By applying ADP to its purchasing operations, another corporation substantially reduced its product costs, enough to come close to its goal of a 15 per cent cutback. When the purchasing operation consists of repetitive orders of low dollar volume, the computer can take over the entire routine.

In one such system, the computer is automatically triggered when data from inventory shelves indicate a need to replenish stock. It immediately prints out a purchase order to a preselected supplier for a quantity determined by the computer itself and will also signal the buyer if the item is not received on time. The human buyer is needed only to determine the vendor and to negotiate the price, although the computer may some day do these tasks as well. In any case, some experts would put the whole buying operation into the computer by storing quotations, supplier performance, price histories, quantities to buy at certain price breaks, and price-delivery combinations; then have the machine print the order, check acknowledgments, note the receipt of materials, compare invoices with receiving documents and original orders, and print out the check for payment. It would be a total systems operation, in which neither the office nor the factory would contain humans. Genesco, a major shoe manufacturer, has computerized its handling of a rapidly turning inventory of $1\frac{1}{2}$ million pairs of shoes, made up of about 49,000 different size and style combinations. Its distribution center can receive as many as 50,000 pairs of shoes a day, and it can ship up to 40,000 pairs to 1,500 dealers, including independent stores, leased locations, and the company's own retail outlets. All this work is done with fewer than sixty people. A random-access computer memory contains a complete current record of every pair of shoes on order, on back order, and on hand. The computer knows exactly where each pair of shoes is located in the warehouse. Incoming orders and shipments are processed against the memory file. When there are shortages of certain styles, the computer decides which dealers will receive priorities. There is no paper shuffling — and there are very few clerks. The warehouse is almost empty of human beings, for all records, from order lists to quality control, are generated by the computer. In the view of the "systems" experts this setup would bring middle-management people closer to the top echelons. But what need have the latter of such togetherness when the computer is present?[10]

Consider the Chemstrand Company's decision-making machine. A textile-fiber manufacturing subsidiary of Monsanto Chemical, the company built a spanking new $400,000 building on a four-and-a-half acre tract at Greenville, South Carolina, especially to house its data-processing work. When a customer's order is fed into the equipment it sets off a chain reaction through sales, production, warehousing, scheduling, and traffic. The information is stored electronically, ready for print-out reports for management. The system consists of an IBM 1410 with six magnetic-tape units and a 40,000-unit storage capacity, with a hookup to data-processing sections in other Chemstrand plants linked to it by high-speed teletype. About eighty people are employed in the structure, but the computers have cut inventory by 35 per cent and have reduced capital investment.[11]

PERHAPS THE MOST dramatic use to which computers can be put is in the new management tool called PERT (Program Evaluation and Review Technique). This technique was developed during the 1950s as a way of controlling manpower, materials, and facilities in such complicated projects as building space vehicles or nuclear powered ships. Starting with a joint effort by Du Pont and Sperry Rand to work out ways of checking on engineering work, it was adopted by the navy in 1957 as a method of unraveling the intricacies of the Polaris missile project, which involved more than 11,000 subcontractors. Du Pont cut the time on certain projects by one-fourth, and Polaris was built two years ahead of schedule by applying PERT. With Polaris, research and development supervisors were never certain which component would be ready first and how it might fit into what already had been done or what still had to be worked in. Essentially, the problem was one of complex scheduling, or fitting certain activities and production and completion dates together in a way that would bring gains in costs and time. For example, shipbuilding is based on numerous small jobs that are interrelated. The pipe fitter cannot run his conduits until holes have been cut through plates; the electrician cannot lay wires until provision is made for cables. PERT is a method for figuring out what will be needed when. Stated this way it sounds deceptively simple, but the steps can be sufficiently complicated and numerous to warrant the use of a computer.

The method employs a network or flow chart to show the movement of materials and the use of manpower as the project moves from one "event" to the next. Such "activities" as the outlay of money, the scheduling of time, and the use of equipment may be plotted, showing at the same time the various relationships that develop among them. Most important, the charting enables one to make time estimates involving each "event" or "activity": At last, the project manager can evaluate the data to calculate a completion time and then relate the activities to the time when he is supposed to deliver the goods. The "critical path" on the flow chart is the longest time it would take to reach the project goal. Upon completion, the whole network looks like a diagram of the nervous system of an exotic animal.

Obviously, it is not difficult to calculate the details when the network is small, encompassing no more than say ten or twenty events and activities. One enthusiast drew up a PERT diagram for himself when his wife bore him a child: It took up three large sheets of paper, listing visits to the hospitals, purchases of formula ingredients and bottles, arrangements for diapers and the like. There are small manual disk graphs available to help figure PERT systems for small projects. Designing a diagram or network is something like working out a plane-geometry problem: Knowing the end result, the expert works backward to discover how to get there.

The sequence of operations is set up in a manner that can be fed into a computer, which in turn enables the whole design to become more elaborate. As the chart shows the estimated time between events, the computer quickly totals the figures for each possible path and even computes alternative time estimates. In complicated construction jobs, some operations are done in parallel rather than in sequence, so that a measure of time overlap develops. The computer will take this overlap into account as well. In a sense, it is all similar to planning a party: Food must be ordered and prepared at various points of time, a cake baked, liquor purchased, a maid hired, the hostess's hair set, a table prepared, a closet emptied for guests' coats, and so forth. Like the housewife, the missile maker may discover that it is more expensive to pursue a crash program than a normal one.

PERT became quite the rage, especially when the Defense Department and NASA advised their contractors that it would be a good thing for them to carry out their obligations along PERT lines. A typical PERT program was the one designed by IBM for the construction of the student-faculty center at Stevens Institute in New Jersey. The network included 1,500 activities, but that was no problem for the computer. It showed which work had to be started each day in order for the project to be completed on time. When a shipment of granite from Norway threatened a month's delay, the new information was added to the computer, which specified which other jobs could be accelerated to ensure that the structure would be completed on time. By using PERT on one of its projects, General Precision Electronics was able to reduce overtime work by a substantial margin. General Electric now uses PERT in most of its divisions; Climax Molybdenum schedules its mining operations according to PERT; Olin Mathieson moved an entire division from Baltimore to New York via PERT; and a Colorado hospital has employed PERT methods to plan open-heart surgery. Canadian companies are beginning to apply the technique, and a member of the Soviet Academy of Sciences showed up at an American Management Association PERT seminar in 1963 to learn what it was all about.

PERT planning has been used in the installation of materials-handling systems, ship construction, blast-furnace relining, tooling programs, missile-countdown procedures and computer installations as well. Its proponents consider it an important tool for speeding project completion, controlling projects, identifying problem areas, managing resources, and reporting progress. For some middle-management people, however, it is simply another reporting system. And one builder snorted, "I've been doing that in my head for years." The literature on PERT has become enormous: There are now available articles, reports, papers, manuals, and even books on PERT. The air force recently estimated that by 1963 there were more than 700 works in the field. The experts now talk of "PERT time" or "basic PERT," the original form that stressed expected time requirements for the whole set of activities, as against "PERT cost" and other "multidimensional" forms, which take into account expenditures, manpower, performance, and other variables. There is also CPM (Critical Path Method), which concentrates on that path in the network that would satisfy time scheduling at the least cost. In CPM, there is less dependence on time-probability calculations, a characteristic of the PERT technique. It is this feature that makes the CPM approach more useful in cases in which the technology and processes are better known.

Variants of the technique have proliferated. SPAR is a way of smoothing out work loads; COMET, employed by the Army Materiel Command, emphasizes scheduling; CRAM, the air force's favorite, is totally computerized, with the machine setting the control cycles of "events" and "activities" and purchasing sequences for components and parts; IMPACT is a way of controlling computer systems by estimating programming costs; CRAFT lays out facilities and materials for new plants; and LESS calculates the least cost method for a particular program. And, of course, there are PERT II, PERT III, PEP, PEPCO, and Super PERT. All are ways of turning over the brain work of middle management — those responsible for the operation of factories or sales forces or control of inventory — to the machine. Granted that the major achievement is in the mathematical technique, yet what need is there for personnel when the computer can schedule production, determine manpower needs, establish tool requirements, set shipping quotas, and assign salesmen to territories? In these areas the repetitive, routine nature of much of the work makes them candidates for a computer program. And these areas are the ones that have been computerized.

Use and Impact

Consider the traveling-salesman problem. A salesman wants to visit a certain number of cities, stopping once in each city and then returning to his point of departure. Which route will be the shortest, and which will incur the least travel time? If there are only fifteen cities, the number of different routes that could be followed will reach 1.3 trillion. Even with a high-speed computer it would take centuries to evaluate all the possibilities. Yet the machine can be programmed to provide a fairly close solution for a fewer number of cities, which it achieves in a relatively short span of time. The answer is worked out on an IBM 7094 utilizing 4,500 instructions: The method can be applied to such problems as routing cables or wiring or scheduling production "events," as in a PERT problem.

These methods illustrate certain facets of "operations research," the whole range of mathematical techniques developed since the war to guide management decision making. Most companies with computer installations have concentrated mainly on payroll, bookkeeping, and other routine data-processing tasks. Now that these tasks have been mastered and made routine, they—or rather the programmers in charge—are looking for bigger things to do. And the latter generally consist of the sort of problems just described. Rule of thumb and trial and error are archaic methods for the conduct of business affairs today. The data that now flow out of the machine are sophisticated enough to solve problems that were seldom thought capable of solution. When A. K. Erlang, a Danish mathematician, worked on the problem of waiting lines in military telephony, it was not realized that the theory of queueing that ensued might help solve highway toll-booth line-ups—after the data had been put through the computer. The question of how long it pays to keep spending money pursuing delinquent credit accounts appears as a variation of the World War II submarine-search problem. Sometimes the query to be answered is rather strange—for example, figuring out how to reduce employee consumption of toilet paper (answer: tighten the clips on the side of the roll so that it won't move easily). Or it may be a matter of reusing paper fasteners. But then management has to control all costs of operation.[12]

186

NOT ONLY IS private business deeply involved in automatic data processing, but government too has made extensive use of the new office technology. After all, it was government's need for rapid mathematical calculation that spurred the development of the computer. The first government installation of a computer was in 1949 at the Aberdeen Proving Grounds to solve ballistic problems; in 1952 the Census Bureau acquired the first UNIVAC; at present there are more than 1,500 automatic data-processing systems in all Federal agencies, making the government the largest single customer in an ever growing industry. The result has been "substantial changes in the conduct of Federal programs and administrative and scientific operations," plus "significant modifications in the occupational structure of the affected departments," to quote the wonderfully bland comment of a Labor Department report.[13] From a mere forty-five machines in 1954, the government's complement of computers rose to 1,770 ten years later; by 1965 the number had increased to 1,946 machines; and by 1966 it was expected that 2,140 would be in place. Between 1961 and 1963 alone the increase of computers in the Federal government was twice as great as that of the number of employees required to operate them. And in departments that had only punched-card equipment, employment was down by 8 per cent, although there had been virtually no change in the number of machines. Despite the proliferation of new programs, the computer has helped hold Federal civilian employment to around 2.5 million for over a decade, and it will no doubt check any further increase.

Government personnel do not therefore appear to be immune from the consequences of advancing technology. As far back as 1959 the House of Representatives Post Office and Civil Service Committee inquired about job losses caused by ADP installations. There were then a mere 400 computers in use in the various agencies. In check-writing and check-reconciliation operations, it was discovered that between 1956 and 1959 the number of employees involved had been cut almost in half, while the output per employee, that is, the number of pieces of paper each worker handled, had jumped 120 per cent. In the General Accounting Office and in the Treasury's check division, only 23 per cent of those employees affected by the computer held on to their jobs: Fifty-three per cent had to find work elsewhere, whereas the rest had resigned, retired, or simply were laid off. In the New York and Chicago offices of the Bureau of Public Roads, computer installations resulted in layoffs of 36 per cent of the workers involved in a fifteen-month period, with "quits" taking care of another 18 per cent. Some retraining was attempted, but, of 410 persons who were tested for such a program, only 77 were selected, and 23 ultimately assigned to caring for the electronic equipment.

Or one might look at the experience of the Internal Revenue Service, which started to computerize its data processing in 1959. It was hoped that layoffs, downgrading, and compulsory relocation would be avoided, yet 5,000 routine jobs were scheduled for liquidation. The Atlanta office was the first target: Of 1,000 jobs involving the processing of tax returns, half were slated to be gone by 1966. This distant date was set because I.R.S. wanted to be humane: Jobs were to be eliminated via the attrition and retirement route. Although jobs for computer work increased —for programmers, console operators, and tape librarians —most of them were centralized in Martinsburg, West Virginia, where I.R.S. had placed most of its machines. Only thirty-two such jobs were allocated to the Atlanta office. Furthermore, it was unlikely that displaced clerks could qualify for these specialized posts: Most of them had had only high school education and were over forty-five years old. Furthermore, I.R.S. found it difficult to get anyone to take a new job in another city because employees did not want to sell their homes or because the spouses had jobs or because people just didn't care to go to strange towns. I.R.S. had not been aware of the psychological and emotional roots that people are apt to sink in a community.

No doubt ADP is required by the government. It must maintain personnel records and statistics, make out payroll, keep inventories, take censuses and surveys, process intelligence reports, keep track of satellites, pay insurance to veterans, and test new plane designs in wind tunnels. I.R.S. itself handles 400 million documents a year. In 1930 there were only 6 million tax returns to check; by 1970, 114 million returns are anticipated, not counting all the ancillary pieces of paper that must be handled as well. All I.R.S. data processing will now be done at its National Computer Center which will have a master file of 80 million business and individual taxpayer accounts stored on magnetic tape. Each account will contain tax information for several years and will be updated to give access to the taxpayer's current status. This system requires that each taxpayer be easily identified: Hence the use of the social-security numbers on all forms.

But the effect on jobs is apt to be of enormous proportions: Half of about 11,000 employees will have to look elsewhere, will quit, or will be forced into retirement. That employees are advised what is in store for them seems small consolation to a clerk unprepared to do anything else but shuffle papers and check a taxpayer's arithmetic. Furthermore, the Atlanta experience suggests that attrition alone is a most unsatisfactory solution. Although four-fifths of the affected employees were women — among whom turnover rates are generally higher than among men — attrition accounted for only a quarter of those separated from their "pre-automation" jobs. Clearly, automation threatens to slow down job expansion in government, which in recent years had been the major growth area in a generally stagnant job market. During the decade ended in 1962, government contributed half of all new jobs — 2.7 million — but automation is posing a serious problem for the politician, for it might imperil the foundation of patronage, the business of giving jobs to loyal followers as rewards for service. What this change might do to a political machine is unimaginable.[14]

WE MAY CONCLUDE then that the office, like the factory, will be computerized, particularly where there are such machines available as automatic electric typewriters operated by magnetic tape, on which data can be stored, revised, and reused and which are able to type 180 words a minute. Suitable for copying the same material over and over, such devices eliminate much drudgery in a secretary's job, but they may also eliminate the secretary. In one such unit, made by IBM, sentences and paragraphs can be deleted or added by a search procedure that examines the tape at a rate of 900 characters a second to locate the spots to be corrected. The machine electronically checks its own work for accuracy and even makes several logical production decisions, involving respacing and repositioning particular words, for example. And the tape can be coded to stop the typing for manual insertion of names and addresses.

Such instruments are grasped as a way of getting people out of the office. Business men, long accustomed to desk-top machinery, are hesitating less and less to pay twice the cost of standard equipment to obtain four times the output of paper and ten times more data that they may or may not use. But their primary concern seems to be people – who are only in the way. "You'd be amazed at how many useless white-collar workers there are," said one corporation president. "We're going to get rid of them." In one insurance company there were 539 people employed in the commercial department prior to the installation of automatic methods. Yet, with only electromechanical devices, 133 people, plus about 60 old-fashioned machines, were replaced. A 1964 Department of Labor study concluded that electronic data processing in one insurance company eliminated more positions than it created. A wholesaler displaced 150 tally clerks with a computer and 10 workers. A retail chain eliminated 100 employees from its home office and well over 1,000 from its stores by installing computers, with savings of $4.75 million a year. And in the telephone industry, more than 750,000 operators would have been required in 1960, instead of the 225,000 actually employed, had there been no increase in automatic dialing since its inception in the 1920s and had there been no change in productivity. Of course, there have been job increases since 1911, but they have been mainly the results of expansion. Yet from 1952, the peak year for the employment of operators in the major telephone companies, to 1960, there was a drop from 262,000 to 192,000. These companies – the Class A group – account for the bulk of telephone employment.[15]

We are frequently told that there is no cause for concern: The white-collar work force increased from 20.1 million in 1947 to 29.9 million in 1962. Four new white-collar jobs, it is said, were generated for each blue-collar and farm job eliminated by the new technology. But we are apt to forget that the largest increase was in the professional and technical category, which swelled in a most spectacular fashion in those years — 112 per cent. It is unlikely that a displaced clerk can become a draftsman or an engineer. Furthermore, Census data indicate that women form the bulk of the clerical work force, and in fact by 1970 women may constitute perhaps one-third of all workers. They will constitute an older work force and will perhaps be better educated, in the sense that most will have had at least high school educations. But they will be precisely that part of the total work force most likely to be hard hit by automation in the office.

In one Labor Department study of office automation, it was revealed that, on the average, one-fourth of 2,800 jobs affected had been declared redundant. Employment in particular firms remained steady or perhaps increased somewhat only because management thought it could use the vast quantity of information pouring out of the computer. All this growth, however, merely served to mask some "unsettling consequences for employees," as one industrial-relations consultant put it. The fact is that many of the employees affected by office automation discover that there is no room for them and that they must quit, retire, or transfer elsewhere. As in the I.R.S. and Veterans' Bureau, most such employees have been doing simple, routine tasks. The new jobs created by the machine must be filled by college-trained young men: On the average, only 6 per cent of the new openings can be filled by the displaced. Finding new spots for long-term employees and excess supervisors becomes the most difficult adjustment of all.[16]

There seems little doubt now that the fit of the white collar is changing and that for many an office worker it promises to become increasingly tight as machines continue to replace them. Few managements recognize that the result is a breakdown in the traditional relationship between themselves and their office staffs, for a white-collar worker cannot consider himself part of the management "team" if he has no decisions to make and is in fact isolated from the decision makers. The result is an increasing "proletarianization" of the office force and the imposition of work standards not unlike those of the factory. Work analysts take movies of office operations to discover ways of establishing "output" criteria in the office. Stop watches time the removal of paper from a typewriter (it takes 3.528 seconds) and the separation of typed copies from carbon paper (which takes longer — 6.984 seconds). When such studies suggest that office workers take too much time to do their tasks, management is apt to turn to the machine. The latter does not require coffee breaks, nor does it go off to powder its nose. In a Philadelphia pharmaceutical house, a combination of improved techniques, including work measurement and new equipment, wiped out 21 of 157 jobs in one department. Similarly, a large insurance company eliminated more than 1,000 paper-work jobs of a total of 3,400 in its regional service centers and sales offices in a period of about two years, saving some $4 million a year.

There is thus ample encouragement for management to computerize the office. After all, the latter is an area in which Parkinson's Law — that work expands to fill the time available for its completion — operates with marked éclat. It is not surprising then that the rate of growth, at least in the routine clerical jobs most easily taken over by the computer, has slowed down. Bureau of Labor Statistics data reveal that clerical employment increased by only 0.6 per cent in 1962–1963, as compared with a 2 per cent increase the year before and almost 4 per cent the year before that. Even the expansion in professional and technical personnel has been slower: a 2.7 per cent gain in 1963, contrasted with 4.4 per cent in 1962 and an average annual growth for the decade 1950–1960 of 6.6 per cent. It is evident that this decline cannot be attributed to any management fears of economic trends: Sales and profits have been too good to be the causes of the retardation in white-collar employment. Rather, there is abundant evidence that automation in the office is a major cause. The Hanover-Manufacturers Trust Company acknowledged in 1964 that new machines and new systems explained the drop in its staff — almost all white-collar workers — from 10,345 to 10,080 in one year, after a decade of steady employment gains. Employment in Manhattan's financial concerns — the white-collar capital of the nation — slipped to about 322,000 in 1963 from a high of 324,000 a year earlier. These alterations in employment patterns have been masked by the now normal "A & P" method — attrition and pregnancy. Computers were expected to cause a drop in the Mutual Life Insurance Company's staff of about 236 by the end of 1964. And among bank workers, the number of whom had jumped from 411,000 after the War to 730,000 in 1963, there was a perceptible slowdown: A 5 per cent gain in 1960 was reduced to 3.1 per cent in 1961, to slightly less in 1962, and to only 2.2 per cent in 1963. Continued expansion of electronic data-processing equipment was cited by one banker as the reason for the cutback. It is generally estimated now that the number of white-collar workers displaced by computers has grown from virtually zero a decade ago to as high as 100,000 people a year, perhaps one-half of auto-mation's toll.[17]

All this change should be little cause for concern, say management proponents. Those who will remain in the office after the new technology has become universal will enjoy a veritable utopia. The tedium of office tasks will have been eliminated, and white-collar workers will have acquired new skills and will be engaged in more interesting and more vital work. If these notions are accepted, they will form another twentieth century myth. Even with the machine, most jobs remain tedious. And upgrading, which we shall discuss in greater detail later, is equally a myth. The routine nature of many jobs associated with the computer — aside from those that involve programming and the like — make it possible for the clerks that remain to adapt without too much retraining. The greatest likelihood for the future is the creation of two main groups of workers in the office. At the top there will be a few highly paid, highly trained people working closely with the computer itself. Their work may be interesting, and recruitment will come mainly from the colleges. At the bottom there will be a somewhat larger group, comprising mostly women, doing routine work, which will demand even less skill and will be even more monotonous than conventional clerical activity. There will be little circulation between the two groups. Each will be governed by the requirements of the machine, and each will be controlled by the boss at the top.

The trauma we await 6

The almost natural reaction of the worker to advancing technology is fear, for what he sees immediately, and often for the duration of his own lifetime, is the abolition of jobs (unless a war intervenes). The most important "property" he possesses in his capacity to work, and anything that threatens that is bound to elicit reservations, if not hostility. It is rather difficult to convince someone faced with the prospect of joblessness that a machine can make more work or that it will brighten the factory: Even if it did, it would most likely happen only during the life of his grandchildren. As an ordinary human being, a workingman's horizon is apt to be limited to the present: He understands Keynes's quip—"In the long run we are all dead"—much better than does the economist. The long view is a luxury he can ill afford, for his children must be fed now, and the landlord must be paid now.

In the eighteenth century the worker found himself compelled to go into the factory; it was a prison, and he hated it as much for his loss of control over his own work as for the brutalizing, filthy, and oppressive atmosphere. The reluctance of the first generation of workers to become part of an industrial anthill no doubt led manufacturers to draw on women and children, especially the parish paupers, for their "labor supply."[1]

The American worker is no more convinced than was his eighteenth-century ancestor that he ought to wait for the long run. If technology creates a "problem," he hopes that the solution can be discovered in time to make his own life somewhat easier. But when an exasperated labor leader asserts that automation can be a curse, the head of the United States Chamber of Commerce responds that he is a Luddite. In the spectrum of views, of which these two are but polarized examples, there are those who suggest that the situation would be better if birth control were practiced, those who assert that "disemployment" is an inescapable economic law, those who hanker for a preindustrial golden age, and those who look to history's next stage to take care of the exploiters. All these views evade the need to confront the realities of one's own time.[2]

THE IMPACT of technological change stems not only from automation per se but also from rationalizing techniques, locational shifts, and even mergers—in fact, from anything that alters the so-called "production function," the relation of input to output. When Packard and Studebaker merge or when the latter closes its lone American plant, the effect on the worker is the same as what occurs when numerical control and the computer displace skilled machinists. Although automation can be distinguished from other types of technological innovation, in practice it is rarely intro- duced alone, simply because it demands a redesign of plants as well as further mechanization. One step leads to another; a change up front requires shifting equipment about in the rear. As in the supermarket, the innovations feed on one another. Such an admixture makes it difficult to disentangle the effects of automation from the effects of mechanization. Yet even the Labor Department, in a typically incurious report on displaced workers, conceded that technology was a major factor in the five cases of shutdown it had reviewed. There were other elements present also, like shifts in con- sumer demand, but new labor-saving devices and the replacement of old equipment and methods appeared to be most significant.[3]

Advanced technology is essential for economic growth,

and growth has become a cardinal precept in the new political eschatology. But the more we advance, the more difficult it becomes to find enough jobs for the unskilled and semiskilled. Productive capacity continues to mount, and output per man-hour increases steadily, yet the number of jobs necesssary to provide the wherewithal for everyone tends to lag. In recent years unemployment has affected large blocs of families in the land. In June 1961, 14.5 per cent of the families interviewed in a nation-wide survey had at least one member each who had been unemployed during the year; in 15 per cent of the families someone in each had been out of work twice; and in 13 per cent, one member each had been unemployed three times or more. In the more advanced plants, a worker will comment: "Every time a new machine's put in two or three jobs are gone. If you don't have seniority to beat it, you're a dead duck." With the automatic factory, seniority may not help either.[4]

What has been happening in the meat-packing industry illustrates the dilemma of America. From 1956 to 1963 there was a loss of 39,700 jobs, a drop of more than one-fifth from the monthly average employment since the start of the period. Meanwhile, output per man-hour increased by 53 per cent, and production labor costs declined by 11 per cent. (It is noteworthy that total wages plus fringe benefits account for just over 8 cents of the sales dollar in the meat-packing industry.) In order to recapture the market position won by smaller companies after the war, the Big Three — Armour, Swift, and Cudahy — have been closing their larger, older plants near stockyards in big cities and have been building smaller, specialized meat factories in small cities. The new machinery, virtually all of it automated, had cut the number of packing-house jobs — from 200,000 in 1955 to under 160,000 in 1962. Furthermore, the companies can escape the trade unions and pay lower wages than they did in the larger communities. It is not surprising that the Packinghouse Workers' Union has exclaimed: "American industry is undergoing a technical revolution and the result is massive unemployment. By accepted business standards reaping bigger profits is all the justification that is necessary. Managements optimistically pretend to believe that the job 'slack' will be taken up in the 'service industries' and by retraining... they figure that 'surplus' workers can be dumped first on unemployment compensation and finally on relief."[5] Furthermore, there is enough evidence to show that it is the older worker who faces the greatest difficulty once he has lost his job: Prospective employers complain that the older man or woman raises pension costs; that the man over forty-five is not so efficient; or that he may return to his old job to keep his seniority alive. The Negro worker is victimized even more — once displaced, he receives little consideration. Constituting a significant part of the semiskilled and unskilled work force, he has even fewer chances in a world where machines easily take over the job he used to have. But most unbearable of all is the silent, puzzled stare of his child, the shame and the sense of inadequacy, the destruction of self-esteem and the loss of "face," and the deterioration of what the social worker describes as "mental health." The situation may not be pathological, but it is one in which attitudes are altered and morale shattered.[6]

Improvements in the unemployment situation may occur, as in the most recent period, but joblessness for Negroes, youths, and the long-term unemployed continues without much abatement. The unemployment rate for teen-agers during the first half of 1964 remained at about 15 per cent, and it was evident that gains in employment did not help the Negro as much as they helped the white worker. Then in early 1965 the United States Department of Labor detected an improvement in the employment situation. Its surveys indicated that employment had risen by 700,000, contrasting sharply with the record of the previous four years. Factory workers, it was said, were the chief beneficiaries, and even Negroes enjoyed some gains, albeit their joblessness remained twice what it was for whites. The headline writers failed to notice, however, that the major gains in employment were for nonproduction employees; production and maintenance jobs for the blue-collar worker increased less rapidly. And the figures for hard-core unemployment (seasonally adjusted) were up. In fact, the jobless rates worsened for Negroes, teen-agers, and young men in the twenty-to-twenty-four age bracket.

Furthermore, the improvements may very well be

deceptive, not only reflecting mid-year shifts in labor-force participation because of school-year starts, but also and perhaps more important reflecting intensified military activity in Asia. The increased outlays for the war in Vietnam clearly have provided extra business for a wide range of companies, while the increasing draft calls have been taking more youths out of the labor market. Obviously, unemployment can evaporate very quickly in a war, as it did during 1940–1945; a reasonable question is whether or not war is indeed the only way in which our society can solve its unemployment problem. What is more, the male teen-age participation rate in the labor force — 54 per cent in 1947 — is now down to 43 per cent. And several thousand young men have been "drawn out" of the labor force by the poverty program. In the absence of the latter, they would have been classified as unemployed.

Yet there have been some doubts that the momentary trend could be sustained. Said one Federal Reserve Board economist in September 1965, "The big question is whether the economy can continue to absorb job seekers, unless military manpower needs rise substantially." Complicating the situation was the increase in inventories, which forced investment up in relation to consumption. Inventory build-up in steel prior to the 1965 strike deadline may thus have had a salutary effect on employment in that industry. But concern with excessive inventories led other companies to undertake control measures. This control could only have had a dampening effect, with the consequence that some industries showed improved job situations, whereas others exhibited poorer records by mid-1965 — food, petroleum, and tobacco were cases in point. The impact of inventory build-ups was precisely illustrated by the experience of the steel industry. Once the 1965 settlement had been achieved, employment dropped, and the drop was expected to gather momentum in subsequent months, unless other factors could intervene. Overtime work vanished, and many steel workers were put on short time. It was difficult to say at what point the artificial effects of inventory stockpiling would wear off: It was more than possible that thereafter the impact of technology would be less obscure.[7]

Another critical element in the situation was the patent

fact that productivity continued to outpace wage gains. Output per man-hour in manufacturing continued to rise at an annual average rate of about 4 per cent; wage gains, including fringe benefits, were still moving along at 3 per cent a year. Although this rate presumably introduced stability in unit wage costs (though other evidence suggests a decline), it seemed that the prospective gain in consumpton would lag substantially behind investment. All these data suggested some validity in the views of those who have questioned recent euphoric forecasts.

Let us consider the electronics industry: The rate of growth in the number of workers in this industry — the one with the greatest promise — was 8.4 per cent in 1958–1961, certainly an expansion of no mean proportions. Yet it is expected that, for the balance of the decade, employment will slow down to less than a 4 per cent rate. Furthermore, the projected increases in the dollar value of shipments per worker are higher than those of employment: The rate for shipments will probably be 6.8 per cent for the remainder of the 1960s.[8] There is less need for semiskilled workers when testing components is done by machine. Industry people employ a rather strange logic to excuse the current situation: If demand increases in the long run, they say, the production worker will be taken back. This idea suggests that preautomation techniques would be utilized to meet such higher demand, a most unlikely contingency, as in all probability industrialists would simply resort to more automation to fill any large orders. To assert that businessmen would employ more primitive methods is a strange sort of logic.

Similar effects are visible in the railroad industry. True, the relative position of railroading in American transportation has declined through the years: In 1947 the railroads accounted for two-thirds of intercity freight; in 1957 their share had dropped to half, even though the decline in freight ton-miles was only 9 per cent. Yet during the same period capital outlays by the railroads averaged more than $1 billion a year, with half of that sum spent on new equipment. The job loss caused by this investment was extraordinary, but productivity climbed. Between 1947 and 1953, output per man-hour, measured by freight ton-miles plus twice the passenger miles, had increased by 14 per cent. Up to 1951 employment increased, but it began to drop thereafter. By 1959 productivity had jumped another 32 per cent, accompanied by a similar drop in employment. Of course, some jobs increased in number: There was an increase of some 24,000 jobs for electrical shopworkers, yardmen, and executives. But this gain was far outweighed by the elimination of about 170,000 jobs, with heaviest losses suffered by engineers and foremen. The total job loss in railroading from 1953 to 1959 was more than 390,000: Laborers, engineers, and carmen were reduced almost in half.[9]

OFTEN A PLANT closes for reasons other than automation, but the effects on workers are quite the same. When the Packard Motor Company closed its Detroit plant in 1956, more than one-fifth of the displaced workers were unable to find any other work at all by 1958, and more than half the Packard workers were jobless long enough to have exhausted their unemployment insurance. More than half the 500 or so workers were past the age of fifty-five, and they had to take jobs, when they found them, at lower rates of pay than they had received at Packard.[10] When the Pressed Steel Car Company closed down in Mt. Vernon, Illinois, in 1954, more than 12 per cent of the more than 1,500 shopworkers were still unemployed two years later. About 11 per cent had obtained part-time work, whereas 9 per cent had "left" the work force entirely. The Murray Body Company had to lay off 5,000 workers in 1954 when Ford automated its stamping plant. True, the latter hired some additional workers to handle its increased output, but a year later almost 30 per cent of the Murray workers were still jobless.

The shock sustained by a community once dependent upon a particular plant is incalculable. In virtually none of the meat-packing plant shutdowns was adequate advance notice given to the workers. The burden of the change and of the move to another city was simply dumped onto the workers and the town. Most of the men were semiskilled or unskilled; they were generally past the age of forty-five, married, with two or three dependents. Under the best of circumstances they would have had difficulty locating new work, but their lack of broad experience, their ages, their poor educations converted handicaps into almost insuperable barriers. For the Negroes it was even worse.[11]

Perhaps the most dramatic plant shutdown in recent years was the closing of Studebaker in South Bend, Indiana, in December 1963. With a history dating back to the carriage-making days of the 1850s, the company decided to move all its auto-making facilities to Canada, leaving behind some 6,000 workers to shift for themselves. Ten years prior to "Black Christmas" the future had looked bright for Charles Snead, a Studebaker worker: He had had thirteen years of seniority and was reasonably well paid. He had purchased a ranch-style home and, like other American fathers, hoped for college educations for his children. Eight months after the South Bend catastrophe, he and 1,700 others were still unemployed. Snead could not even sell his home. "We've thought of moving, but we'd have to give this house away," said he. Unemployment insurance was bound to run out, and the thought of relocating was difficult to entertain, for the company had had three generations of families at work in South Bend: The roots were too deep. To save expenses, such pleasures as movies and week-end trips were eliminated. Said Snead's wife, "We'd go crazy if we didn't have television."

John Berlin was a forty-five-year old trim repairer who had worked almost a quarter of a century for Studebaker. After the shutdown he searched for work in South Bend and in Chicago, but he discovered that he was "too old." Then he took a forty-eight-week air-conditioning course, meanwhile supporting his family on savings, $36 a week in unemployment compensation, and surplus foods. He had never believed that the corporation would ever really leave South Bend—the city where he had been born, owned his home, and was employed. He felt demeaned and degraded whenever he collected government surplus food and was bitter about personnel directors older than he, who would not hire him for reasons of age. Nor was he certain that he would find work as a refrigeration and air-conditioning man: The search for a job carried him far beyond South Bend.

Use and Impact

Although the town did not openly express resentment against Studebaker for withdrawing its $1 million weekly payroll and dumping its workers on the community, the main Studebaker dealer preferred to display Valiants and Chryslers, and the Studebaker stickers saying "Made in South Bend" were scraped off bumpers. Worse yet, the company's vaunted pension plan turned into a hollow joke. Snead had twenty-three years of service when the plant closed, entitling him to vested pension rights. The fund had to go first to those already retired, however, and then to those eligible for retirement. When those men had received their paid-up annuities, the $24 million pension fund would be exhausted. The pension fund's assets, administered by the Chase Manhattan Company, were to be liquidated, and, once that was done, Snead, who was not yet fifty years old, would become the holder of an empty pension claim. The company's response was, "Millions of dollars were paid into the pension plan, while Studebaker stockholders were losing millions on their investments." Stockholders, however, had some recourse, but the workers had none, unless it was the public relief rolls.

In the meantime, unemployment in South Bend, a long-standing problem, was intensified. About a decade ago a Singer Sewing Machine plant had left town, and the frequent Studebaker layoffs had not provided much stability. After the latter's last gasp, the unemployment rate hit more than 9 per cent of a work force of only 91,500. By the spring of 1964 it had slipped to somewhat less than 7 per cent, but by June it was back to about 8 per cent. Of the nearly 9,000 workers who lost their jobs at Studebaker, perhaps fewer than 1,000 were young enough or had sufficient training to find new jobs quickly. The most were hampered by lack of skills and job-seeking experience, by age, and by color. Production workers average fifty-four years of age, and one-third of South Bend's Negro work force (in a population that is 5 per cent Negro) had been employed by the company. Negroes suffered the double blow of age and color.

Much was made of Studebaker's effort to find customers for its South Bend plants. True, several companies did come to the town: Kaiser Jeep, Cummins Diesel, Allied

Products. The total number of jobs these firms could provide was less than 1,000, with a promise of another 800 jobs within a year. This figure barely dented the direct and indirect losses caused by the shutdown. Only retirement and leaving South Bend for other, more active cities prevented a catastrophe like that of the Thirties. Of course, the problem could be solved statistically: Retirees and those tired of looking for other jobs are simply not counted among the unemployed.

It is not only the displaced but also the "new" entrant to the labor force who is affected by technology in an economy developing an underground of unskilled. The Negro "new entrant" — a statistical euphemism for the teenager — is perhaps hardest hit. In the second half of 1964 a staggering 25 per cent of Negro male teen-agers who were in the labor force were out of work. In addition, the rate, which was only slightly higher than that for white youths a decade previously, was nearly twice as high as for whites. Perhaps this disparity explains in part what happened in Harlem, Elizabeth, and Rochester in the summer of 1964 and in Los Angeles a year or so later. In more prosperous years — 1953, for example — the percentage of unemployment among Negro teen-agers had been 7.1 and that for white boys 6.3. By 1955 the jobless rate for Negro lads had soared to 17.7 per cent; by 1958 it had reached 24.3 per cent; and it continued to increase to more than one-fourth of the Negro-youth work force. Population growth does not account for this extraordinary condition, for both white and Negro groups have grown in the same proportion — about 50 per cent since the late 1940s. Nor can lack of skills or family problems explain the wide disparity in employment. Are there changes in the character of the economy that lie at the roots of these difficulties?[12]

But now, we are told, there are built-in stabilizers to cushion the blow of joblessness — unemployment insurance and a variety of so-called "transfer payments." Unemployment compensation is soon exhausted when the empty days pile up week after week, however, and in some states a displaced worker does not receive that much because he may have obtained severance pay as a result of a collective-bargaining agreement. In Oklahoma City disqualification periods for unemployment insurance ran from eighteen weeks to nine months because workers had been given severance pay in the Armour shutdown. Furthermore, at an average of $30 to $40 a week, unemployment compensation is not a very soft cushion. Seldom can unemployment insurance or severance pay be stretched over one year. And R. C. Wilcock and W. H. Franke, two University of Illinois economists, report that in the Armour cases most of the severance money went to pay company credit-union loans, which were called in immediately after the shutdown. In six instances studied by these writers about half the severance money was used to pay accumulated family debts; in East St. Louis the proportion was closer to three-fourths. Creditors began to press for repayment; insurance policies were cashed in; some personal belongings were sold; and living scales had to be reduced, with food, clothing, and medical care cut back sharply. Frustration and humiliation were visited upon men who believed that they had become permanent members of the affluent society. They withdrew from lodges, bowling clubs, and even churches as the long night of unemployment intensified their sense of isolation. They became blighted men.[13]

The white-collar worker may fare somewhat better when he is displaced, but his reaction is not unlike that of his blue-collar brother. On November 7, 1960, *The Detroit Times* sent telegrams at 3 a.m. to some 300 employees advising them that their services were no longer required. The *Times* had closed. A fifty-two-year old circulation worker said bitterly: "Twenty-six years down the drain... At my age I won't find anything [as] good." Another worker wondered why the telegrams were not sent collect. "You would think that after 15 years, they could at least tell you in person." But these people were white-collar workers with some skills and some education. Six months after the shutdown, more than 80 per cent had found other jobs. Of course, those who were older or those whose education was inadequate had a rather rough time. Still they were able to secure new employment more quickly than had the workers in South Bend. And their wage rates were almost the same as those they had received on the *Times*. Clearly, only the educated and trained have a second chance in our society.[14]

Job hunting itself can be a searing experience. Workers walk from plant gate to plant gate or seek out friends who may have heard of an opening somewhere. Employment agencies, either public or private, are of little assistance: The former are incompetent, and the latter will refer only the young and experienced. Frequently, the worker in search of a job is offered a temporary one or one in another industry for which he has no aptitude, taste, or skill. Furthermore, the displaced worker seldom knows where to look for work. The realization that he has suddenly become old or incapable is often traumatic. Transfer to a new city is not relished, for to leave a town where one has grown up and where one's friends are can be painful. In that sense, these men are not mobile, nor can they be made mobile while they lack resources. They are on their own, and, when finally they do discover jobs, they generally earn less pay than they had earned before. We must observe too that severance pay and unemployment insurance do not delay the search for work. Such was the incontrovertible evidence in the Wilcock and Franke study, contrary to the claims of such journals as *The National Observer*.[15] The best that severance pay does is to help a man resist offers of low-paying jobs. But eventually even that protection is dissipated. In the Armour situation, the pay losses were drastic: Whereas the old jobs had paid $2.20 to $2.33 an hour, the new ones ranged from $1.37 to $2 an hour. In Oklahoma City, 14 per cent of those who found new jobs earned less than $1 an hour. The displaced are downgraded by a society that gives them paltry skills to start with.

This experience is repeated throughout the land again and again. A Department of Labor study issued in 1964 summarizing the experience of workers affected by shutdowns in such disparate industries as petroleum refining, automotive equipment, glass jars, floor coverings, and iron foundries revealed quite similar impacts. One striking disclosure was the fact that the average displaced worker was a white male: In no case did "nonwhites" exceed 7 per cent of the total. And in most instances, the majority of workers had not completed high school. Again, the workers were reluctant to move elsewhere because of seniority, pensions, or simply devotion to their home towns. When American

Viscose closed its Roanoke, Virginia, plant in 1958, the cast-off workers were simply thrown upon the already strained resources of the community. Once more it was the unskilled who suffered most severely, and even the skilled could not adapt to other industries. Five years after the Viscose plant had shut down, 13 per cent of the workers were unemployed, and 30 per cent had "withdrawn" from the work force. Of the unemployed group, approximately one-third had not worked since 1958. In East St. Louis, where Armour closed its plant in 1959, the proportion of displaced workers "still in the labor force" three years later who had not worked at all was 30 per cent. Some would never work again.[16]

THUS ARE BORN the "depressed areas," the South Bends and the one-industry towns like Donora, Pennsylvania where the permanent shutdown of the steel mills in 1962 created an unemployment rate of almost 80 per cent. More than 2,500 people in Donora had to go on the relief rolls; 3,200 people were receiving surplus food from the government. When the U.S. Steel Company offered transfers, the men had to give up their seniority. Said one worker who transferred to the Fairless Works near Philadelphia and was furloughed shortly thereafter, "I gave up 25 years of service for five weeks of work." The difficulty stemmed from the patent fact that the Donora works were part of the industry's excess capacity. When sales were high, the blast furnaces and open hearths worked around the clock. But improved capacity elsewhere and new mills operated by computers in other parts of the country made Donora useless. The steel company saw no reason for modernizing the mills. Said one steel magnate, "You just don't buy grandfather a new set of rompers." Roger Blough, head of U.S. Steel, intimated at the time of the shutdown that more liberal depreciation allowances might have encouraged the corporation to rebuild at Donora: In the absence of such underwriting by the government, the people of the town would have to do without the mills.[17]

It has been argued that the regional uniformity in unemployment rates between 1950 and 1960 demonstrates that there was no serious structural change in the economy. The diffusion suggested by the state-by-state figures, it was said, revealed that only demand deficiency had been at the root of persistent unemployment.[18] As industry itself, especially autos and steel, has decentralized, however, the lack of variability in unemployment rates offers no persuasive argument against the effects of structural shifts. Obviously, deficient demand is an important element, but it alone does not explain why the affluent sector of the economy was unable to absorb into itself the nonaffluent — without the stimulation of war. As Charles Killingsworth has said:

> To be sure, changes in employment opportunities in particular sectors of the economy are nothing new. To cite the most familiar example, agriculture once absorbed 75 per cent of our labor force and today absorbs only 10 per cent. In recent years, there has been a decline in the absolute number of farmers and farm laborers. This basic change in the structure of our economy was accomplished without any major upheavals, although we do have a chronic "farm problem." Some of those who recognize that automation and other technological changes are affecting the structure of manufacturing employment have argued that the changes will be of modest proportions; that job loss in some industries will be replaced by jobs in other sectors of manufacturing... There is now reason to doubt the validity of this argument. The percentage of the labor force finding employment as *production workers* ... has been declining.[19]

The problem has been with us since the early 1950s. To be sure, there are variations: Recovery from the 1948–1949 recession brought the unemployment rate to a postwar low in July 1953. After the economic downturn of that year, unemployment moved up to 3.9 per cent in early 1957. A 5 per cent rate was the best we could achieve in February 1960. More recently it has hovered about 6 per cent. And now the unemployment rate has dropped to 4 per cent, unquestionably as a result of artificial stimuli. But hard-core unemployment does persist, and opportunities for "new entrants" are restricted. Why? Perhaps what happened in a Bayonne, New Jersey, wax refinery offers a partial explanation. There the old presses were replaced by a multimillion-dollar solvent de-oiling unit and a fractionating tower. Wax molds and sweating apparatus were removed to make places for new machines and filtration equipment. Conveyor belts and automatic packaging completed the change-over. Wax refining could then be done by a few dozen men instead of a few hundred. The displaced were well along in years with no potential for retraining. Most of them had to "retire"; some went into a general labor pool for use on construction projects. In all such instances, the wages were less than the workers had been receiving.[20]

It does seem necessary then to face up to the question of structural change, at least in the sense that in any dynamic economy there will be continuous changes in technology, consumer tastes, plant location, composition and utilization of the labor force, and the very mix of industry itself. Such conditions may exert a cumulative force, resulting in a residue of stubborn joblessness, which may tend to increase with each cyclical ebb of business. In fact, it seems possible to assert that the official figures contain at least some percentage points attributable to structural causes. And if one were to add the "invisible" unemployed — those who no longer search for work and those working part time because that is all the work they can obtain — then "real" unemployment, as Leon Keyserling calls it, rises substantially.[21]

The presumption that structural unemployment can be a serious matter is sustained by the data on long-term unemployment. This fact could not be discerned in the early years after World War II, but it became undeniable in the later 1950s and the first part of the 1960s. Nor could the shift from goods-producing industries to services provide enough jobs to take up the slack. By mid-1963 the proportion, among the unemployed, of those out of work six months or more had risen to 15.8 per cent; a decade earlier the figure had been only 3.7 per cent. In mid-1965 there were still more than 600,000 long-term unemployed workers.[22] Between 1948 and 1963 the number of part-time workers grew by more than 50 per cent; it was expected that by 1970 this group would become 25 per cent larger. To admit that this sort of unemployment hits older workers, youths, and Negroes the hardest does not make it evaporate.

Furthermore, it is more than likely that the work force in 1970 will show increased proportions of women, especially middle-aged women, and of younger men. The ability of most of these groups to adapt to the new circumstances engendered by technology is doubtful. Says Alfred Tella:

> ...it appears that an unprecedented situation is developing which suggests that the degree of labor force adaptability in the past may not be sufficient to fully adjust future shifts in labor supply to labor demands...There will be sudden sharp acceleration in the working-age population of young persons of both sexes. These are the same groups who have displayed a considerably greater than average cyclical sensitivity in their labor supply, who also have the highest unemployment rates currently, and who are least likely to qualify for employment... because of their general lack of skill and experience...Young persons will require at least two-fifths of the 12 million increase in civilian employment that will be needed in the remaining 1960s in order to bring down jobless rates to minimum acceptable levels...[23]

From 1957 to 1961 the number of production workers in manufacturing had declined by 1.1 million. Output had gone up by 8 per cent and output per man hour by 18 per cent. What evidently happened was that higher productivity accounted for the elimination of 747,000 jobs and that declining demand in certain industries cost 576,000 jobs: A total loss of 1,323,000 jobs in the four-year period. This loss was counterbalanced by a gain of 229,000 new jobs, leaving a net decline of 1.1 million. To be sure, there has been an increase in jobs since 1961, but it had not overcome the earlier losses. From 1953 to 1964 employment in manufacturing was virtually stagnant (it increased 50,000, to be exact) while the production-worker component dropped by 960,000. The major gain thus took place in nonproduction jobs, emphasizing the enormous shift of the work force out of manufacturing into trade and services. Furthermore, one must again stress that the advances in employment in 1965 were to be attributed to an expanding war effort, hardly indicative of the internal resilience of the economy.

It was estimated that by 1965 the work force would be seventy-nine million. This implied a need to add more than six million jobs, not counting openings for the teen-agers seeking employment. As one writer put it, "A relatively full employment goal by 1965 presupposes sustained employment gains beyond the experience, not only of recent years, but of the postwar period as a whole."[24] The prediction was accurate: Even with special stimuli full employment was not achieved.

Most of the new jobs prior to the Asian affair were supplied by government—federal, state, and local—and for the 1953–1963 decade, it is more than likely that *private profit-making industries contributed to unemployment rather than to employment.* During those ten years the civilian labor force increased by 8.9 million; employment by 6.6 million; unemployment by 2.3 million. The net increase in people at full-time work was 2.5 million, whereas people working only part time increased 3.2 million. There were some 900,000 people on vacations and various leaves at the end of the period; if they had been prorated between full time and part time, the totals would have been 3.1 million full-time and 3.5 million part-time employees. The increase in government employment, mainly in state and local government and virtually all of it full time, was 2.8 million. Full-time private employment was up perhaps 500,000. But private nonprofit organizations supplied 1.5 million jobs. If only half the latter had been full-time jobs, they would have absorbed the 500,000, an indication of a substantial drop in full-time jobs offered by private profit-making enterprises.[25]

There is little consolation for the factory worker in the expansion of government employment (which resulted primarily from the assumption of more tasks), for he does not possess the requisite transferable skills. In 1962 government employment totalled 9.2 million, of which 3 million consisted of professional and technical workers, half of them teachers; 2 million were clerical employees; and almost a million more were skilled craftsmen. Only a little more than one-third of government employment thus consisted of semiskilled and unskilled "service" jobs—the most likely openings for those forced out of private industry. And what is more, further growth in the number of Federal jobs seems doubtful, whereas the needs at the state and local levels are for teachers, nurses, social workers, and hospital employees.[26]

To add to the problem, whenever the computer in government is applied to physical processes particularly, jobs are eliminated just as in industry. The Civil Service Commission reported a net loss of some 1,900 jobs in agencies using the computer for tasks other than data processing.[27] Even in the latter area, a significant impact could be discerned. In 1959 there were 403 computers in Federal-government agencies, involving 24,400 man-years; by 1964 there were 1,767 computers requiring 53,600 man-years of attention. The ratio of man-years to computers dropped from sixty-to-one to thirty-to-one, while the number of computers in use grew considerably faster than did the number of man-years employed in their operation. An absolute loss in employment in Federal employment might have taken place had it not been for the labor-hoarding indulged in by some agencies using armies of clerks to check what the computer does and were it not for pressures from congressmen to prevent layoffs. For the fact is that each computer can put thirty-five people out of work and can alter the jobs of about 100 other workers. With anywhere between 3,500 and 5,000 new installations each year, the "disemployment" results come quite close to the Labor Department's estimate of 200,000 jobs "affected" each year because of automation.

THE INITIAL IMPACT of automation on the white-collar work force is often imperceptible, leading to the superficial view, as Ida R. Hoos has observed, that technological change has no serious effect. The influence of automation on white-collar workers is disguised, however, first, by ordinary business expansion, which tends to absorb some workers who might otherwise have to search for new jobs, and, second, by increased maintenance and perhaps a temporary increase of the work force during the installation of a computer system. But once the system jells and is operating at full strength, growth in the work force is halted and may even decrease, a phenomenon noted by both Hoos and Bright.[28] As far as white-collar work is concerned, then,

211

there may be no immediately observable mass displacement, but the work force is gradually eroded nevertheless. Instead of "chopping heads off the payroll," the computer is allowed to cut "a hole in floor"; jobs are simply not filled when girls transfer or quit. For example, between 1960 and 1962, the New York Life Insurance Company wiped out more than 1,000 of its 3,380 jobs at regional service centers and sales offices by just such procedures. The firing, in a sense, is silent, quiet, and unnoticed.[29]

And so our situation represents a persistent paradox. On the one hand, jobs are easy to get; on the other hand, they are hard to get. At seventy-two million people, the number of Americans at work in June 1964 represented a record. The list of employed increased by 850,000; yet at the same time 1.1 million lined up at unemployment-insurance offices, if they were eligible, or simply joined their fellow unemployed to walk the streets. Despite a pool of surplus labor, the Labor Department listed, in that month, sixty occupations in which there were shortages of workers: accountants, auditors, chemists, college presidents, professors, engineers (certain kinds only), librarians, doctors, nurses, social workers, draftsmen, detectives, and policemen. All these vocations, of course, demanded skills that the unemployed did not possess. And meanwhile, twenty-six million more youngsters will be looking for work in the decade of the Sixties. By 1970 the labor force is expected to reach some eighty-five million workers; yet the rate of increase in jobs promises to leave nine or ten million of them without work—an unemployment ratio of 11 or 12 per cent —unless the war effort can absorb them.

And the promise of jobs for the educated and skilled may have an empty ring, for, with alterations in defense and space-research programs, large numbers of engineers, scientists, and skilled workers may also be wondering about the shape of the future. In July 1964, the Engineers' Joint Council reported that the demand for engineers had "eased" over the previous two years. Its findings were based on data from 543 companies and government agencies employing more than 250,000 engineers. Automation tends to exacerbate the problem; a chemical manufacturer's response to community rejoicing at the construction of a new plant revealed the dilemma. Said he: "True, several hundred jobs are added where the plant structure is going up. But when the plant is finished and in operation, it [will] come as a shock to learn that a dozen men can run the whole thing."[30]

As one expert described the employment situation in the early 1960s, about 200,000 jobs each year were "affected" by automation. The range of occupational changes was said to have been enormous, running from a one-million increase — 13 per cent in three years — among professional and technical people to about a third-of-a-million decrease among farmers. Among unskilled laborers, jobs fell 200,000 in the three years between 1960 and 1963, whereas 80 per cent of the net increase in jobs was among white-collar and service workers. These groups will continue to increase at a rapid rate of 25 per cent for the decade of the Sixties — in finance, insurance, real estate, trade, and state and local government. Such shifts in the work force stem in the main from the new technology. It is this that explains a high unemployment rate for the unskilled and untutored, compared with the tiny unemployment rate for the professional category.[31] Yet, when he moves into a service industry, a worker displaced from a factory or a young entrant may discover that he can obtain only part-time work or a lower-paying job. Furthermore, he frequently must compete with a housewife whose family is "complete" or who has become a secondary wage earner to keep the household budget in the black. Let us consider part-time work: It represented half the new jobs created between 1953 and 1962. Most of the expansion in non-governmental jobs was in occupations that offer less than a full week's work only; retailing and domestic service are the outstanding illustrations. In 1962, about one-third of those engaged in selling worked part time; so did about half the domestic workers; and, among gas-station attendants, bus boys, janitors, waiters, and barbers, the proportion was more than half. In many instances they were required to work a short week, not for reasons of their own choosing, but because that was all the work they could obtain. For example, full-time, year-round jobs in trade declined from 54 per cent of the total in 1953 to 48 per cent in 1962. The expanding sectors of the economy do not appear to be offering many viable employment opportunities.[32]

The consequence is, as Secretary of Labor Wirtz once admitted, that we risk piling up a "human scrap heap" of thousands of people, many of whom do not even appear in the statistics. The proportion of nonparticipants in the labor force — those who have given up looking for work — *among men in their prime years* increased from 4.7 per cent in 1953 to 5.2 per cent in 1963. For Negroes the nonparticipation rate leaped from 5.3 per cent to 8.2 per cent over the same period. Indeed, if adjustments were made for nonparticipation, requiring some shift in statistical definitions, the unemployment rates would be a good deal higher than the Federal figures show. When California officials made such adjustments for both part-time employment and nonparticipation in the work force, they came up with an unemployment rate for the state more than twice the figure issued by Washington. Of those who will enter the labor force in the late Sixties and in the Seventies, perhaps ten million will not have high-school educations and three to four million will not have completed elementary school. For them our technology will have made no room. And it may have no room either for those with seemingly extensive education and training, for there is no assurance that automation will require the well-educated in very great numbers.

True, high skill requirements tend to rise with increasing automation but, as Bright has demonstrated, only up to a point. After that, the demand for skills levels off, affecting also the need for well-educated staff. After all, why invest in automatic controls if one must then attach expensive labor to them? The point is illustrated by a training program sponsored by the Datatrol Corporation under the Manpower Retraining Act to teach people with "average" educations how to set up problems for a computer. Some of those in the program were former meat cutters, librarians, landscapers, and office sweepers. In a steel mill a master roller no longer controls the operation by manipulating levers but rather feeds punched cards into a computer. An ordinary mechanic can be trained to operate a numerically controlled machine tool. Clearly, some of the displaced will be taken into automated factories, but it is equally clear that they will be the fortunate ones. Most will be outside the gates looking in.[33]

IN THE MEANTIME, productivity and the capacity to produce have mounted. Productivity measurement, of course, can be a complicated affair. In its simplest form, it is an attempt to relate the rate of output to the rate of input, usually expressed as an index-number series. A common measure is output per man or per man-hour, but some experts believe that this measure is somewhat simplistic and that the index ought to be weighted to reflect the different components of man-hours of labor. Then there are those who insist that the inputs comprise both capital and labor, arguing that this combination offers a more effective measure of economic efficiency than does labor alone. But in evaluating the influence of technology and automation, it seems more useful to limit the denominator of the productivity fraction to labor input, as one is interested essentially in changes in labor requirements. Of course, increases in output may arise from a number of factors – speed-up and "rationalization" are only two of the more obvious, if frequently primitive, ways of getting more goods per unit of labor. Yet today it seems evident that advanced technology is the major consideration. And at the same time enhanced productivity results in job losses, about 165,000 a year in the 1957–1961 period.[34]

From 1909 to 1947, output per man-hour in private industry increased by 2 per cent a year. In the fifty-three-year period up to 1962 the average rate of increase was 2.4 per cent. It is therefore fair to conclude that in the postwar years, especially from 1957 to 1962, productivity gains were more rapid than in earlier periods. After a dip in 1963, the productivity figures began to rise again in 1964 and 1965. In manufacturing, in both 1961 and 1962, output per man-hour rose 4 per cent a year. But output, which must rise faster than productivity if jobs are to be created, went up substantially less – 3.6 per cent in the 1957–1962 period. Says Leon Greenberg, productivity expert for the Labor Department: "We seem to be experiencing high rates of productivity increases in manufacturing in the face of smaller gains in output. This implies a relatively higher impact of technological change ..." That is, automation has finally begun to bite in.[35]

That this trend will continue seems incontestable. A growing share of investment is now allocated to automated equipment. Whereas only 11 per cent of capital investment was employed to install automation of all kinds in 1955, this figure rose to 12 per cent in 1959 and 19 per cent in 1963, reaching a total of $10 billion in 1965. This rise should not be surprising, for automation has a "... pronounced capacity to reduce labor requirements." Furthermore, "Increasing numbers of trained people are graduating from universities and seeking employment in consulting firms and operations research teams where their main task is to survey existing operations systematically to determine where savings can be made through the application of new techniques and equipment."[36]

The results of our new technology have been truly fantastic. However, the impact has been somewhat obscured, by the relatively slow growth in effective demand, causing a certain amount of excess capacity and enforcing a lower rate of productivity gain than would otherwise have been the case, particularly in the second half of the Fifties. Nevertheless, the gap between actual and potential productivity has narrowed, occasioned mainly by the spurt in manufacturing, a spurt that moved productivity up 4 per cent in 1962. In virtually all industries, not only in manufacturing, the growth in output in recent years has exceeded the growth in employment. Only in concrete products and footwear was this disparity not present.[37] Such rates of expansion in the capacity of private industry to produce will not slacken; they will accelerate as automation spreads and as research and development efforts are intensified. Labor Secretary Willard Wirtz underscored these trends in testimony given to the Senate Finance Committee in January 1964. Said he: "For such large productivity gains to be sustained over so long a period has been unusual. Technology may be giving us a new dimension of growth." But, he added, "Unless we have a sharply stepped-up demand ... such gains ... as do occur may not be large enough to forestall a decline in job opportunities."[38]

IN THE MEANTIME, what about those who may remain in the plant or office? How will they fare in the new computer utopia? According to some authorities, automation promises to create a veritable paradise. Not only will it end for all time the drudgery of the factory, but also with robots doing all the heavy work and moving materials around the floor, it is said that there will be no more accidents. Fewer workers' fingers will be severed, fewer feet will be crushed, and fewer men will suffer hernias. Ford has claimed that accidents decreased by 60 per cent in its automated Cleveland plant over a four-year period. In petrochemicals, automation reduces the exposure to toxic materials, substantially improving the health of the workers.

Unfortunately, the elimination of fatigue and accidents will not create the perfect work environment, for automation tends to generate its own peculiar pathology. The strains engendered in an automated plant or office may differ from those of the older, more conventional factory, but they exist nevertheless. Workers who must continually match panels and lights develop fatigue just as much as does the auto worker, although it is fatigue of another type, a neurotic fatigue apt to end in gastric ulcers. The World Health Organization reported in 1959 that 40 per cent of employees in automated offices were irritable, suffered from insomnia and headaches, and were likely candidates for coronary attacks. Even such optimistic researchers as Floyd Mann and L. R. Hoffman discovered a higher incidence of tension in an automated power plant, compared with that in a traditional installation. Automation may provide steadier employment—at least for those fortunate enough not to be displaced—but it also requires shift and night work, as the machines must operate continuously to be economic. In fact, the sense of loneliness in computerized plants has led some British unions to ask for "lonesome" premiums. Automated work can be utterly boring: At least there was some satisfaction even in the repetitive cycles of the traditional factory. Walter Buckingham tells the story of a Coca-Cola inspection line that was so dull that an occasional 7-Up bottle had to be inserted to keep the inspectors awake.[39]

In a country like Japan, the strain can become even

greater than in the United States. Tea drinking and knitting in the office are no longer possible, and the noise of the machines is so disconcerting as to become disturbing. The chairs, built for long-legged Western females, are uncomfortable for Japanese women. Consequently, leg troubles develop with great frequency in automated Japanese offices. Key punchers, who must handle unstandardized documents and even check figures on abacuses before preparing them for the machine, acquire "keypunch neurosis," a paralyzing sensation in the hands and fingers. According to a Tokyo physician, this neurosis reflects a feeling of hatred for the equipment with which the girls must work. To a Japanese girl, a mechanized office is not unlike a factory, a reaction that plays hob with her sense of status. Yet a Japanese worker is less likely to quit than is an American, for she feels the need to succeed on the job quite keenly. She is honor-bound to produce for her company; to leave would mean a loss of face and is therefore unthinkable. Suicide appears to be the only way to call attention to an intolerable situation, and it is not surprising that self-destruction has in fact taken place.[40]

A 1961 O.E.C.D. report on office automation suggested that the traditional relations between management and clerks were coming to resemble those existing in the factory. The looseness that once pervaded the office—the coffee breaks and the idle chatter around the water cooler—has been tightened, for the computer can function well only in an environment in which tasks are made thoroughly routine and rigid. Again, the speed, the need for close attention, and the reduction of work to repetition duplicate the boredom of the assembly line. In time, the white collar becomes tinged with blue, and the sense of status that once sustained the office worker in his endless shuffling of papers and ledgers evaporates. While those responsible for programming and computer operations assume a managerial outlook, promotion into their ranks from below becomes virtually impossible; it is unlikely that a card puncher will learn the esoteric techniques needed to extract reports from the machine. The office becomes a paper-processing factory, with workers tied to the machine.

THE AUTOMATED FACTORY in the United States is even worse. In an automated auto plant the ears are assaulted by the noise of power wrenches bolting cars together. The rapid "clack-clack" sounds as if pellets were pounding a sheet of bullet-proof glass. Car bodies move along the line with a noise that suggests the hammering of metal into junk. The heat is intense and often intolerable, and the men work with an unrelieved concentration that can arise only from the inescapable necessity to serve an automatic line. Sometimes a man must do several things almost simultaneously. Drive shafts weighing twenty pounds are lifted 600 times a day and inserted through axles and transmissions. And the speed is so great that men working a few feet apart are seldom able to talk to one another. The line itself controls the speed at which the men must work, so that speed itself is converted into a skill.[41]

The effect of the new technology on man and society is so different from what prevailed in the past as to constitute a significant qualitative change. Values and attitudes are undergoing alteration, and, as Donald Michael has urged, these may be more important than the economic changes that are so clearly visible. The uncertainty engendered is marked: We can no longer affirm that change really constitutes progress. For what is the nature of the worker's identification with the new work process? What essentially does the new technology do to man as man, and what does it do to his persistent and noble effort to comprehend his environment? Unfortunately, many of the studies of worker reactions to automation are not terribly helpful, for they all too often tell us that some percentage of the respondents "perceived" change, after the fashion of an opinion poll. Yet, despite the limitations of these investigations, we do learn that workers have lost control over the pace of work; that they no longer know what skills they need; that they still suffer fatigue, albeit different in character; that they are rapidly losing the capacity to know their fellow workers; and that the rigid-ities imposed by automation demand formal relationships quite unknown in the older technology. These relationships are now part of a vast automatic apparatus in which human contact on the floor is replaced by machine action. Whereas workers once formed close groups whose élan was often sufficient to sustain the spirit in a dreary environment, not even this small consolation remains. The worker is no longer able to josh his partner or engage in mutual oaths hurled at a passing foreman. "Verbal interaction" is impossible: Sometimes a special sign language is invented to warn one another of a supervisor's approach or to advise how close the clock is getting to quitting time. Says Floyd Mann:

> Computer systems mean more rationalized organization, more integration, greater interdependence, a curtailed distribution of job grades, more centralized decision-making, higher performance standards, more accuracy in deadlines, greater coordination, more responsibility, greater job variety . . . [but also] less job security, more pressure, less promotion opportunities, a drop in employee and supervisors' satisfactions and mental health, changes in relations between company and its employees . . . This all implies a heavy spending from the employee "good will bank."[42]

Of course, not all workers react in quite the same fashion. There are those who accept what seems to be in store for them and resign themselves to fate. As Ida Hoos describes them, they are the "clay pigeons." When transfer to another city is proposed, they prefer to stay put, consumed by anxiety and participating in "going away" lunches for their fellow workers, knowing that next month or next year they will be the honored guests. Some workers do not believe that automation can really affect their jobs: Their work, they believe, is too essential, and no amount of button pushing can match their production. Workers in oil refineries, on railroads, in machine shops, and in accounting offices are the ones most apt to voice such self-assurance. Their tragedy is all the greater for their rejection of reality. And then there are those who, like the proverbial eager beavers, rush to take cookbook courses in mathematics and programming for which they are ill prepared, in the hope that they may emerge unscathed when the computer takes over.[43]

The over-all effect of automation, then, appears to be an intensification of the sense of alienation. To assert that workers in an automatic factory regain control over the work process, as Robert Blauner suggests, seems unwarranted in the light of experience. Perhaps some workers felt this way in 1947, the year for which Blauner obtained his data, but it is doubtful that they would have the same reactions today. Mechanization and automation convert crafts into processes, as in the printing industry, and impose upon work an unremitting bureaucratic structure in which meaninglessness is apt to be intensified. Not that the emptiness of work did not exist before the advent of the computer: In many an industry the worker always has been only an interchangeable part in a continuous line. Under automation, however, lower tolerance for disturbance requires an even further elevation of the machine. The need to watch dials and gauges and to react instantaneously creates a sensation that the "machine is on top of you." When humans are "in line" with the machine, they are necessarily absorbed by it,[44] just as an oyster is absorbed by a starfish. At best the relationship between man and machine becomes ambiguous, for, although a few become more "powerful" by virtue of their control of production, workers in general become less powerful. This loss of power stems from the limitations imposed by the new technology. Furthermore, unemployment and the declining significance of direct labor cost in the totality of industrial operations emphasize the loss of status sustained by the human being in the machine process. We can only speculate on the sort of society that will be created.

For one thing, skills, in the old sense of the word, become quite redundant. With the elimination of craft, it is entirely unnecessary to train new generations of workers. Trades atrophy: There are no plumbers, no shoemakers, no house painters, no carpenters to respond to the urgent call of the housewife for elementary services and repairs. In Georges Friedmann's words, the link between the general culture and occupational knowledge is severed, leaving a chasm to be filled by hordes of amateur "do-it-yourselfers." And in the plant, promotion does not really advance a man's knowledge of work and skills, for it appears too often as mere movement from one semiskilled post to another; nor does it restore the value of work for the worker. Vocational education also fails, for all too often it is society's way of filling time for alleged misfits and delinquents. Ways of creating skills in a culturally meaningful manner have changed profoundly, and we are none too certain that they help us grasp and control our environment.[45]

Back in 1955, Peter Drucker, perhaps the leading apostle of today's management philosophy, predicted that automation would lead to the greatest surge of upgrading that labor would ever experience. Routine jobs, he asserted, would become a thing of the past and only technical, maintenance, and professional occupations would constitute the work of the future. Neither in the plant nor in the economy as a whole, however, has this seemingly reasonable forecast come about. For one thing, such new skills as are needed in the automated plant and office are displayed by entirely new personnel; the older workers are simply shoved aside. Furthermore, as James Bright has demonstrated, many of the maintenance and technical jobs are transitory. And in a survey of workers in an automated metal-working plant cited by Walter Buckingham, only 27 per cent of the remaining workers thought that higher skills were being required than before; 43 per cent believed that the new equipment demanded less skill than that in a conventional plant! Will there perhaps be more programming jobs? Says Ida Hoos, "Once the team has developed a library of programs to cover the company's transactions, the addition of more [installations] to cope with expanded business does not entail the hiring of more members."[46]

The notion that automation will necessarily upgrade the work force was thoroughly smashed by Bright. In his investigations he found no upgrading, for, as the object of automating was indeed to replace humans, lower skills appeared sufficient for the jobs that remained. "There was more evidence," Bright has said, "that automation often had *reduced* the skill requirements of the operating work force and occasionally of the entire factory force, including the maintenance organization."[47] The reason is clear, for with increasing automaticity control over machines is exercised by machines, measurement is done electronically, there is self-correction, and decision making in production is mechanized. Consequently, the prospect for labor requirements is a *lower* level of skill. Furthermore, no great mental effort has to be exerted, for sensing apparatuses and gauges provide the data, which merely have to be recorded.

Responsibility? Then why the feedbacks? In fact, the reality of the factory points toward a larger slice of the line to be attended by each employee, a none too subtle form of "stretch-out" in a work process that will have been largely trivialized. To be sure, the initial stages in automation may call for some advanced skills, but, once the new technology has come to flourish, circuitry experts and maintenance men also can be reduced in number. For it is evident that the early calls for these skills appear to have been more reflections of novelty than of continuing industrial need. And such high skills as may be demanded under automation are apt to be sparsely distributed. The greater likelihood, then, is downgrading for the larger number of workers, and, as automation requires fewer people, the small gain in the employment of skilled workers that may develop must be counterbalanced by the unemployment of an army of unskilled and semiskilled workers.[48]

Here then are the first two myths of automation—that it upgrades workers and produces as many or more jobs than it destroys—and, because they tend to assuage our concern, they are vicious. The third myth is that automation advances but slowly. As Willard Wirtz has said, these statements are opiates dulling our awareness of the need to control the machine. "The comforting myth that we can always pull the plug . . . out of the wall disregards the fact that we won't. And the companion piece about 'nothing coming out of machines except what men put into them' disregards the fact that this is probably no more true now of some machines than of some men."[49] In fact, machines now exhibit at least the equivalent of a high-school education, in the sense that they can do the work of a high-school graduate, and, as they do not line up at the paymaster's window for weekly paychecks, they get the work assignments. Considering the advanced state of computer technology, may not a robot some day arise and say: *Cogito et facio*?

223

THREE

Anxiety and Response

Slow road to Erewhon 7

When President George Meany declared to the 1963 A.F.L.-C.I.O. convention that automation is "... rapidly becoming a curse to this society ... in a mad race to produce more and more with less and less labor without any feeling ... what it may mean to the whole economy," he was not being merely truculent. His attack reflected a state of panic among many union officials over the visible job-displacing impact of automation. They were concerned, deeply concerned, despite their public commitment to technological advance. Even Secretary of Labor Willard Wirtz, who rejected such "solutions" as the shorter work week, conceded in his address that "... robots — mechanical men that work at wages which wouldn't feed a family — are the uninvited delegates at this convention."

An Opinion Research Corporation survey found that two-thirds of the labor leaders questioned believed automation to be labor's most serious concern. Perhaps Mr. Meany was not ready to lead a new band of Luddites against the machine; perhaps he was addressing himself rather to the government to take heed that an intractable social problem was in the making; perhaps he knew better than most that collective bargaining had been able to deal with automation in but piecemeal fashion. For it was evident, not only that the creation of an underground of the displaced could threaten the wage standards built by collective bargaining, but also that displaced workers would eventually look upon the union movement as a protective institution for those with jobs against those with none.[1]

It was an uncomfortable situation for the unions. Despite a gain in factory jobs of about a million from 1961 to 1964, so well advertised by such journals as *Fortune*, the fact remained that over the long haul the number of production workers in manufacturing had declined.[2] There seemed little question that automation had cut into the ranks of those workers who make up the bulk of union membership, and the likelihood was that it would continue to do so. It was once estimated by the U.A.W. that in a fully automated auto industry 200,000 men could do the work now done by the entire union membership. Furthermore, the shift of the work force to white-collar and service occupations posed additional problems for the unions, for the patent fact was that they had not yet learned how to organize such workers effectively. The white-collar worker had an ingrained reluctance to join a union, believing himself superior to the blue-collar man. Supporting this attitude was a sense of identification with management; at any rate, management was evidently more successful in fostering such sentiments among white-collar people. Often the white-collar worker believed that individual effort was the key to achievement, and he was supported in this belief by his education, advertising, and the popular literature.

While academic analysts and corporate executives insisted that the effect of automation on jobs was no different from that of ordinary technology, the unions remained unconvinced. Despite fluctuations of one-tenth or two-tenths of a percentage point, unemployment in the early 1960s remained high and could be brought down only by massive war outlays. To bring joblessness down to manageable peacetime levels would have required a $4\frac{3}{4}$ to 5 per cent growth rate, yet the best the nation had done under normal circumstances was 4 per cent. The greatest pressure from automation and unemployment was in manufacturing, mining, and transportation, areas of traditional union strength. While, for the moment, the service trades seemed immune, it was small wonder union chiefs were disturbed.[3]

YET FOR ALL the inventiveness in bargaining, which was described in some circles as "creative," the various devices left much to be desired.[4] Adjustments to enforced erosion of the work force through technology were limited to advance notice (presumably to give the worker a chance to find something else); attrition (which closed down jobs after retirement or quits); early retirement (necessitating more funds in pension reserves to make it meaningful); severance pay (generally used to pay off accumulated debts); and other arrangements like retraining, automation funds, and human-relations committees. The cumulative weight on the bargaining process was enormous: In fact, collective bargaining as we had come to know it in the United States was not designed to handle all the problems stemming from automation. Therefore the "solutions" sooner or later evolved as gimmicks that failed to supply meaningful answers for *displaced* workers.

Furthermore, automation threatened to dissolve the one weapon available to a union—the right to strike. This was especially evident in the oil industry, where production in struck plants continued uninterruptedly despite the picket lines outside the gates. In 1961 the Oil, Chemical and Atomic Workers' Union took out all the production and maintenance workers at the Gulf Oil Corporation's Port Arthur, Texas, plant. Yet, manned by only 600 supervisory and technical personnel, the refinery turned out gasoline, fuel oil, and other products at 65 per cent of the prestrike pace. After seventy-two days, the union caved in: Its search for "job security" for its members failed, and all it could obtain was a promise of sixty-day advance warnings of layoffs. As if to drive home the nail, the company also won flexibility in making job assignments.[5] Today it would be most difficult for the union in the telephone industry to conduct a strike, for it would require a prolonged dispute before service would be markedly interrupted. The strike in an automated industry is obsolete, and the unions are able to worry only about protecting the jobs that are left. Or they can insist on "buy-outs" to compensate for those jobs that have become outmoded.[6] As John Herling, a noted labor reporter, once said, the nature of the problem was economy-size, and collective bargaining offered at best retail help for a wholesale condition.

Anxiety and Response

In the meantime, management insisted that automation was nothing more than the means for providing the efficiency needed to survive in a competitive world. Although it sometimes acknowledged that some social problems might have to be dealt with, management's primary concern was to protect its major prerogatives, control of production methods and control of the work force. Management, it was said, is a trustee for everyone involved in the corporation — stockholders, suppliers, workers, and customers. As an extension of this concept, collective bargaining was merely an opportunity to move labor relations toward "solutions" without in any way surrendering managerial authority. Any such notion as that advanced by William Gomberg, that a job is a property right involving notions of equity, was deemed to be otiose, if not subversive.[7]

The struggle was often manifested not only in bargaining but through arbitration and grievances as well. Illustrating the problem was the case of an automated drilling machine installed in an auto plant. The task of programming the machine had been assigned to engineers not in the bargaining unit. The U.A.W., however, protested that the work now done by the tape had once been performed by toolmakers and therefore the programming job belonged in the unit. The arbitrator agreed, holding that the toolmakers had a vested right to the work. Management was chagrined that anyone should believe that a contract created a property right to a job. They strongly objected to the principle that work done by employees in a bargaining unit prior to the installation of automated equipment should stay in the unit after automation. And the courts were remanding disputes to arbitration, rather than trying to settle these questions themselves. Yet the fact was that, beyond questions of defining the scope of a bargaining unit, most collective-bargaining agreements could not deal with automation problems: If a skill had been completely eliminated there was not much the union could do, unless special arrangements had been provided in advance. The National Labor Relations Board itself was uncertain on these matters: In the 1959 Litton Industries case, technical and nontechnical workers were kept apart, but the 1961 Sheffield case placed such employees in a single bargaining unit.[8]

IT HAS BEEN suggested by some observers that unions affected by automation should be merged, as perhaps ought to have been the case with the flight engineers and airline pilots. Although some mergers have been carried out, they have not always been simple matters, for not only has it been necessary to distribute officials' posts, but promotion and seniority lists and work rules have had to be merged as well. When specialized skills were involved, the problem became exacerbated, as the downgrading enforced by a new process was apt to be resisted with some bitterness. In several instances the prospect for certain organizations was a future of "ghost unionism," top-heavy with officialdom, well financed, but reduced in size and national influence. They came close to representing an entrenched but dwindling minority and appeared to be cut off from—if not violently at odds with—the poorer strata of the working class. Affluent shells of their former selves, they resembled the United Mine Workers, once a major social force in American life but now with little influence beyond the confines of the coal fields. Perhaps the alternative might be some sort of amalgamation cutting across industrial lines, just as in the Thirties the C.I.O. cut across craft lines. But Walter Reuther's suggestion to his colleague James Carey for precisely such an amalgamation was rejected with disdain. Nor did Reuther have much success with his National Coalition of Conscience, an abortive attempt to organize the poor. Yet as Dr. Margaret Chandler of the University of Illinois has said, unionism now needs to be organized around a *process*, in a kind of superunion covering a complete industrial flow, a complete technology.[9] This kind of organization would be a natural response to management threats to move elsewhere or to subcontract some of the work: The superunion could overcome such whip-sawing tactics by organizing all the inside and outside workers in an industry.

Still, serious organizing problems would remain. Although automation shrinks plant employment, organizing costs for the unions do not drop proportionately. The Oil, Chemical and Atomic Workers' Union states that it costs as much to organize 100 men as 500 men. And, as the units are smaller with automation, the union must spend more

231

on servicing and enforcing contracts than do other unions of comparable size. For example, whereas the Rubber Workers' Union has about 350 contracts to negotiate and service, O.C.A.W. must handle 1,600 different agreements. The amalgamated structure with company-wide agreements would do much to ameliorate the problem.[10]

For the present, however, most of the affected unions could think only of work rules as a protective device. They were only a defensive measure, resulting all too often in screams of "featherbedding." As technological change was introduced, management was often able to play one group of workers against another. In one such instance, cited by George Strauss, the company announced its intention to lay off some workers and then proceeded to grant pay increases to a few senior workers in excess of what the union had asked for the new jobs. The maneuver effectively split the workers and turned them against the union. Maintenance work is often subcontracted, generating marked hostility, as employees see their own jobs given to others while the union is unable to protect them. A strike at the Pennsylvania Railroad in September 1960 stemmed from the subcontracting of locomotive-rebuilding jobs; and in the auto industry in both 1958 and 1961 a key question was who would do the modernizing work in the plant.[11]

All such problems are by no means merely side shows, for the central issue in collective bargaining today has become job security, and all the measures employed to meet automation's threat are directed toward that single objective. So-called "automation funds," "progress-sharing" schemes, extended-seniority work rules, supplementary unemployment benefits, sabbaticals, shorter hours, and human-relations committees are all intended to provide protection for workers too old to work and too young to die. The unions insist that a property right does inhere in a job and that if that right is destroyed it entails some *quid pro quo*. Granted that the high road to total security for the worker lies in full employment, even that condition of bliss would not fully assuage his sense of unease. Some companies expand, but others decline; technology wrenches traditional occupational patterns out of shape; and certain areas experience losses in jobs while others gain. From the union point of view the struggle to achieve security is ever present.[12]

Although workers may be aware that adjustment to automation can be made through attrition or retraining, much of their immediate concern is rooted in a fear of changed job content and work rules. If the same amount of work is to be done by fewer men, what will be the nature of the individual jobs? If some jobs are less risky than others, who gets what work? As the work force diminishes, how are seniority lists to be handled? Furthermore, can attrition operate quickly enough over time to reduce the work force to levels management says are optimum, or will outright firings have to be utilized? The question is not an idle one: The Canadian railroads and the Locomotive Firemen and Enginemen agreed as far back as 1958 to an attrition scheme, estimating that about 5,000 jobs could be eliminated in this manner in about ten or fifteen years. Now they say that at least another decade will be required to adjust the work force to the newer technology. By 1963 only about one-fifth of the jobs scheduled to go had been eliminated through attrition. The pressure may now grow to lop off the jobs without waiting for "quits," retirements, and death.[13]

It also has been suggested that early retirement would help cut down the work force. Workers have an enormous interest in all the private pension schemes that have burgeoned since World War II: More than twenty-two million employees are involved, and the assets of these systems total more than $60 billion. Yet in an automated economy some workers may not stay on jobs long enough to earn pension rights. They may have to move from job to job, even from one industry to another, to find employment. The solution to this problem ought not be too difficult — let the pension credits follow the worker. That is, pension rights ought to be as portable as savings accounts. The banks and insurance companies could easily develop the requisite mechanisms. But *early* retirement — how shall it be paid for? About $13,300 is required at age sixty-five to give a man a pension of $100 a month. If he retires five years earlier, the benefit is cut to $66 a month, and there is no Federal social security to supplement his retirement income at that age. If early retirement is to be meaningful,

233

the benefit would have to be increased or the gap "bridged" with an adjustment at the time social security does take effect. But to provide a $250-a-month benefit at age fifty-five, with a social-security adjustment ten years later, requires a reserve of about $35,000. The contributions would have to run about 40 to 50 cents an hour, compared to the present 10 to 15 cents an hour. One wonders if there are many companies around prepared to undertake such a cost.

Nevertheless, there seems to be an increasing tendency toward early retirement, despite the lack of any adjustment for decreased benefits. In 1961 30 per cent of the men over age sixty-two who were eligible for social security elected to retire before reaching sixty-five. The proportion rose to 48 per cent in 1963 and zoomed to 56 per cent in 1964. This increase may not be unrelated to the employment problem: The A.F.L.-C.I.O. suggests that older workers are retiring early because they have to, not because they so desire. Early retirement under private plans can sharply reduce pension income: Retirement at age sixty can mean a 20 per cent cut in the normal (at age sixty-five) pension. That some unions are seeking to correct this deficiency is worth noting, but the technique of "bridging," or similar devices, is not yet widespread.[14]

Of course, some firms are generous. The Humble Oil Company offered the mariners in its tanker fleet an early-retirement program under which a seaman with fifteen years of service could retire at fifty years of age. This offer was part of a plan to reduce crews by 16 per cent in order to minimize the effects of installing automated deck-maintenance and tank-cleaning equipment. The workers were not offered much choice: For every early retirement, said the company, one less employee would have to be laid off. At age sixty-five, a retired employee was to receive 96.4 per cent of full benefits; at age fifty-five a retiree would have 72 per cent of what he would be entitled to if he could work another ten years. And various other companies help their employees plan their retirement beyond advising him what his benefit rights may be. North American Aviation has automatic retirement at age sixty-eight. But on his fifty-fifth birthday the worker gets a letter and a couple of "look-ahead" pamphlets. More literature is sent out on his sixtieth birthday and on the sixty-second; at age sixty-three he is interviewed and given a budget book and a personal-property record form. At age sixty-four he is given a health-inventory checklist and a Kiplinger article telling him how to buy a cemetery lot.[15]

AND WHAT OF automation funds, quite the rage these days in some industries? After studying their functioning in the coal-mining, longshore, meat-packing, garment, and musical-entertainment industries, Thomas Kennedy concludes that such funds have ". . . provided little or nothing in the way of benefits for the workers displaced by automation."[16] None of the funds adequately protected the accumulated rights of those displaced, nor did they provide the assistance that might have been necessary to tide them over to new jobs. Nor could the funds be used effectively for retraining because of restrictions arising from state unemployment-insurance laws. As Kennedy remarks, automation is often a way of meeting a competitive situation; it is unlikely that firms seeking to automate would be willing to assume an added burden unless required to do so. At best, an automation fund may provide some share of the savings for the workers who remain. Furthermore, when the financing of such a fund is based on so much per hour of work, management has an inducement to automate in order to reduce its contribution per unit of output. Of course, the unions are easily attracted to these schemes because they promise benefits to members in the future, but in the general excitement of creating a new instrumentality, the over-all benefit program is all too often fragmented. The major use of automation funds has been evidently to provide little more than a public-relations device.[17]

The most controversial item on the agenda of adjustment is the shorter work week. Opponents argue that not only would it increase costs of production, assuming no change in hourly rates, but also that geographic and occupational patterns are more rigid than shorter work week advocates presuppose. Furthermore, the relationship between men and machines in many industries is said to be rather rigid, posing difficult technical problems in absorbing additional workers. The response, however, seems obvious: If enough men were reabsorbed, industry could readily resort to multiple work shifts, thus overcoming discontinuities in production. The warning continues, however: A shorter work week might seriously affect productivity; and the work pace would be intensified with harmful effects on workers.

The key issue at this point, and the one most difficult to establish, is the optimum relationship between the length of the work week and output. Although there will be some point in the work week at which output will be at a maximum, this point will vary from industry to industry and even from one location to the next in the same industry, depending on weather, raw-materials availability, the state of mind of the worker, or the irascibility of the foreman. Presumably, optimum hours per week can be longer, the shorter the total work period. On the basis of such rough and inelegant concepts, corporate executives will argue that a forty-eight hour week is optimum, a "calculation" generally ridiculed by organized labor. The latter insists that shorter hours reduce absenteeism and industrial accidents – and enhance total output. But, say opponents, it is a fair presumption that the length of the work week that maximizes profit is longer than workers are willing to put in. If the typical marginal analysis is modified, as is done by C. E. Dankert, then the optimum point for the length of the day from the firm's point of view would be defined by the intersection of marginal *hourly* cost and marginal *hourly* revenue. It is likely, however, that the supply curve for labor at any given hourly cost will begin to bend backward prior to the optimum point, resulting in a smaller profit for the firm. The solution to such a dilemma, it is suggested, is to reconcile workers' and employers' work weeks by applying "human engineering" to convince employees to put in more time, or perhaps to increase their wants through advertising and salesmanship so that they will work for more discretionary income. In any case, one can always appeal to sputnik.[18]

We may note that, from 1860 to 1960, average weekly hours dropped from sixty-eight to forty-one, or about fifteen minutes a year. The sharpest decreases occurred between

1900 and 1920, with New Deal legislation during the Thirties cutting the work week still more. Total work time, however, has not declined so sharply, owing in all probability to the larger number of part-timers and the greater number of holidays, expanded vacations, and the like. Labor Department data indicate that 90 per cent of the workers in manufacturing are on a forty-hour schedule. Although shorter schedules in manufacturing are uncommon, the proportion of workers in major metropolitan areas who work shorter schedules increased from 6 per cent to 10 per cent between 1953 and 1962. Short schedules are widespread in the printing and women's-apparel industries, retailing, construction, and offices. It is evident that the short work week is not unknown in American industry.

Arguments at the turn of the century favoring shorter hours were based on considerations of health, the need to diminish fatigue, accidents, and the like. Employers insisted on the cold logic of economic science: As wage rates were set by marginal productivity, any increase in rates occasioned by shorter hours would be inflationary unless the countervailing forces of high productivity were to prevail. Furthermore, such higher costs would induce a substitution of capital for labor. Although it is difficult to establish the precise relationship, it is nevertheless clear that, historically, reduced hours have not depressed productivity: In fact, they may have enhanced it. Could it be that the point of optimum marginal productivity never had been attained? But, of course, this esoteric concept is simply a technical term for labor demand and is a much more complex element than the concatenation of marginal outputs and costs makes it seem. The consequence is that rules of thumb are apt to be the guiding principle in decision making: On this score, the worker's thumb does not differ appreciably from the employer's,[19] and if he deems the shorter work week to be a desirable goal we ought to hearken to his reasons.

As summarized by Edward T. Chase, the case for a shorter work week rests on the following considerations: A broader and more equitable sharing of jobs would ensue; an increase in purchasing power would take place as a result of maintaining the same hourly rates; and the service industries, especially recreation and education, would

237

benefit from the greater income. A progressive reduction in the work week of fifteen minutes per year, the historical trend, implies the creation of about 400,000 jobs annually. Add to this figure the roughly 600,000 jobs produced by normal growth and the 500,000 jobs that could be created by vigorous retraining, relocation, and other "structural" measures, and the economy could conceivably reach the 1.5 million new jobs required annually. One illustration of the possibilities of a shorter work week was supplied by the electricians' union in New York, which obtained a five-hour day in 1963. For this gain it was savagely flayed by editorial writers for selfishness and lack of patriotism. The union insisted it was only "spreading the work" and that it had long had a thirty-hour week anyway. Any tendency toward higher costs was held in check by increasing the number of apprentices; staggering shift hours; providing lower rates for residential-maintenance repair jobs; and stressing greater productivity and efficiency. In the meantime, about 1,000 new jobs were opened up.

But what about the cost factor? It seems to pose an insuperable barrier, for cutting back from forty hours to thirty-nine with the same wage rate means an increase in *labor* costs of 2.6 per cent; cutting back to $37\frac{1}{2}$ hours implies an increase of 6.7 per cent in cost; and a thirty-five hour week with no change in wage rates will cause labor costs to jump by 14.3 per cent. Such increases, we are told, would be inflationary, would squeeze profits, would stimulate more automation, and would create unemployment.

But the arithmetic falls far short of a complete analysis, for it ignores the ratio of labor costs to either total costs or total revenues. Suppose labor costs were about one-third of total costs, as seems to be the case in many a manufacturing industry. If this ratio were present, then the increase in total costs occasioned by a one-hour reduction in the work week would be less than 1 cent an hour! A $37\frac{1}{2}$-hour week would raise total costs by exactly 2 cents an hour. Add such factors as productivity gains, induced-cost savings, and the impact of more intensive use of plant on overhead, and the shorter work-week idea does not seem so wild. The difficulty with all the contra arguments is that they assume "other things" will remain the same. They seldom do in a dynamic economy, and the response is apt to be such as to make it quite feasible for American industry to handle the "burden" of a shorter work week.

Of course, one might adopt a transitional scheme, as suggested by the United Auto Workers. This scheme would maintain the forty-hour week whenever unemployment was less than a specified percentage of the labor force; a reduction would occur only when unemployment went above the indicated ratio. The procedure would be reversed as soon as unemployment declined. The funds necessary to maintain take-home pay as the work week was reduced would be supplied by a special "adjustment fund" accumulated through a modest payroll tax. In effect, the fund would operate as a stabilizing device. Unfortunately, there has been little public discussion of this striking idea. Yet, clearly, manipulation of weekly hours is one of the devices that can be used to deal with unemployment. In effect, unemployment may be described as a function of the labor force minus the ratio of gross national output to the product of productivity in man-hours and hours worked per year. As the latter is equivalent to output in man-hours per year, the entire ratio in the second term of the equation is equal to the number of men at work. Therefore, if productivity or hours worked per year are high, fewer men will be working; if the national output is larger with the same productivity and hours, then more jobs are created; and with the same, or a slowly growing, output reduced productivity or *hours* would provide more jobs.

The A.F.L.-C.I.O. has estimated that a million new employees would be needed to provide the same number of work hours should one hour be cut from full-time work. A reduction to 37½ hours would require 2.7 million added workers. Of course, there are limitations to these gross estimates, and union economists acknowledge them. A uniform reduction in all industries might not be feasible, part-time workers would have to be brought up to the new hours specifications, and geographic and skill factors might impose constraints. These arguments are supported by A. J. Jaffee's statement to the Senate Labor Committee on September 26, 1963. Said Professor Jaffee: "If by 1970 the length of the work week should decrease by four hours, and more people should have paid vacations – and longer vacations – the number of employed could rise significantly. Indeed, such a curtailment in the length of the work week by itself might bring employment very close to 83 million."[20]

WHEN AUTOMATION COMES, the consequences are such that dissension among unions is often the result. As jobs are abolished, occupations realigned, and tasks mechanized, a scramble ensues to see which union will exercise jurisdiction. Clearly the union most affected by technology is apt to be the loser, as in the case of the Flight Engineers' International Association, which cannot even take consolation in the sort of survival enjoyed by the Journeymen Horseshoers (290 members employed at race tracks) and the Cigar Makers (4,700 members making specialty smoking items).

When jets came to the airline industry, fewer pilots were required. Seeking to protect its members' jobs, the Airline Pilots' Association decided to seize jurisdiction of the engineer's seat in the cockpit. In 1957, A.L.P.A. tried to have the F.E.I.A. charter revoked by the A.F.L.-C.I.O.; failing, it then decided that the third man ought to be a pilot also and sought to appropriate the seat through bargaining. By mid-1961, five of the airlines had agreed to complete pilot control of the seats up front. When Eastern Airlines decided in 1957 to go along with A.L.P.A. also, trouble ensued, only to be calmed temporarily by employing three pilots and one flight engineer. But this scheme was hardly a feasible solution. Meanwhile, A.L.P.A. insisted that the third man have pilot training to help in emergencies – the "fail-safe" principle – while F.E.I.A. was equally vocal that he be a mechanical specialist able to inspect, adjust, diagnose difficulties, and make routine repairs while in the air. The pressure was on the F.E.I.A. however; Federal commissions and Administration officials sided with the companies on the point that a jet needed only three men and, as an afterthought, agreed that they might just as well all be pilots. The engineers responded with a strike. But with everyone arrayed against them they were bound to fail, and fail they did. As Albert A. Blum says, "... not only [were] the trends in technological change against the flight engineer in the

struggle for jobs (and the various arbitration awards indicate this) but the power structure [was] also against
[them]."[21] Few other unions responded to their call for help
against Eastern. Even the Machinists, who were sympathetic
at first, began to walk through the picket lines. Assisted by
a mutual-aid pact among the airline companies, which
brought Eastern $200,000 for the duration of the strike,
the usual government subsidy, and defecting F.E.I.A.
members, Eastern was able to get back into the air after
some seventy days. The real winner, however, was the
A.L.P.A.[22]

Perhaps the flight engineers should have exited from
the stage with the same grace exhibited by the navigators.
The 1961 agreement between TWA and the Air Line
Navigators' Association provided for a virtual elimination
of navigator jobs: The men were to be replaced by automatic
devices. Severance pay ranging from $10,000 to $25,000,
depending on length of service, was provided. In addition,
the now unemployed navigator was to receive $400 a
month for three years. He retained his group-hospitalization
benefits and his rights in the retirement plan were vested.
Furthermore the navigator and his wife received lifetime
passes on all TWA flights. He could roam the four corners
of the globe in search of work.[23]

THE PRINTERS, with a history of craftsmanship going back
almost half a millennium, must now also face up to the on-
slaught of automation. Their struggle for job security and
the effort to deal with technology's impact have been long,
beginning with Mergenthaler's linotype machine in the
1880s. Yet the frustration of the newer labor organizations
would be compounded if they were to look to the printing
trades for solutions. The latter's only answer so far has been
reproduction, or "bogus work," a form of nonwork that
the printer dislikes intensely as an insult to his pride of
craft and that is to be traded off sooner or later for another
coffee break.[24] Still, when newspaper publishers can
visualize composing rooms of the future that will automatically compose copy from the typewriter to the finished
page without human hands, the printer has ample cause to

241

worry. Although the union's attempt to control the work process is bitterly attacked as featherbedding, the choice, as Paul Jacobs says, is between that and no work. In the absence of work the featherbed is to be preferred. And, dragooned into doing something he dislikes (on some newspapers, "bogus" has piled up for years — it is simply ignored), the worker cannot be faulted for concocting a rationale. Furthermore, there is always the management featherbed and management make-work to provide a model.[25]

Again, the inability to achieve an effective solution culminates in work stoppages, often of long duration, as in the New York newspaper strikes of 1962–1963 and 1965. One result of the settlement in the first dispute was the formation of a joint board, modeled after the human-relations committee in the steel industry, which at least began joint discussions of job security, efficiency, and the impact of technology. Representatives for the employers have tried to demonstrate that the two most highly mechanized newspapers — *The New York Times* and *The New York Daily News* — have shown gains in man-hours of work. Yet the closing of *The New York Mirror* after the 1962–63 strike far outweighed the supposed gains, in any case achieved through expansion. But the newspapers did agree to share some of the savings from automation — in this instance, the use of tape for setting financial tables — by paying something into a special union fund. The problem of job displacement by machines was by no means solved, however. After the strike both *Times* and *Daily News* installed high-speed machines to cast metal stereotype plates for their rotary presses. The reduction in the number of jobs ranged from 15 to 20 per cent. And the various newspaper unions appeared to have become reconciled to the reduction in the number of available jobs: The important thing was how many openings would be available in the future and the amounts of the payoffs to those displaced. The unions also wanted a share in the savings, but the publishers were reluctant. Most significant, however, was the suggestion that new entrants be cut off from the industry.

Some of the union leaders in the printing trades have realized that a new organizational structure may be needed to meet the problems of automation. Elmer Brown, President of the International Typographers' Union, told the delegates to the 1963 convention that technology and company mergers made union unification a matter of survival. The employers, as might be expected, were disturbed at the prospect of dealing with a larger, stronger union. If the five major unions—Typographers, Pressmen, Paperworkers, Lithographers, and Photoengravers— were to merge, the new organization would become a powerful force of more than 425,000 members. The best likelihood was that the last two would merge, as they did in 1964. But this merger still left out the others, plus the Electrotypers, Newspaper Guild, and Bookbinders. As has already been suggested, merging disparate unions is not a simple task: A craft outlook must be fused with industrial unionism, official posts must be redistributed, voting rights must be adjusted, and the various union funds must be commingled. Despite the difficulties, it is evident that such changes are essential if unions are to face up to the impact of an everchanging technology.

Yet when negotiations for a new contract opened between the typographers and the New York newspaper publishers in late 1964, none of the crucial problems had been solved. The employers agreed that automation was the central issue: The need for increasing productivity was "desperate," they said. The union was prepared to accede to computerized typesetting, provided there was "mutual advantage." Quite simply, they meant controls on the rate of introducing automated equipment and a share of the savings achieved from new machines. In addition, the union was willing to accept early retirement, provided that it was properly financed—and they insisted that it could be, through an automation fund based on a 5 per cent tax on gross annual payroll. Alternatively, a fund might be accumulated through payment of a sum of about 60 per cent of the salaries of the displaced workers for some five or six years, with decreased payments thereafter, ending in fifteen years. From the union's standpoint this plan seemed the only way to provide an attrition guarantee to those presently employed. The publishers, on the other hand, insisted on complete freedom to mechanize, an attitude the union has described as "hopeless." With the contract due to expire at the end of March 1965, the New York Typographers' Union was authorized to strike by a membership vote of 1,978 to 28.

Later in the year *The New York Post* attempted to automate its typesetting operation but was forced to abandon the idea when the typesetters objected. The automation issue then spilled over into the editorial departments, as the Newspaper Guild, refusing to give first place to the printers, asked for a veto on the introduction of automating devices into areas serviced by its members. The Guild argued that an automated system would cut across departmental lines once it was used to "read" proof and bill customers. A twenty-three-day strike in September and October did not resolve the issues: The settlement provided for "safeguards" in job jurisdiction under automation but did not get the Guild any veto over the installation on the new equipment. The publishers, meanwhile, were convinced that they had erred in giving anyone the right to say what machines they might use.[26]

IT SEEMS EVIDENT that the only answer to automation through collective bargaining is to take care of those who are inside the plant: Little can be done for the worker already shunted aside and even less for the younger worker who wants to get in. Nowhere was this point emphasized more dramatically than on the West Coast docks, where labor relations were once a stormy and frequently bloody affair. A violent strike in 1934 gained control of the hiring halls for the International Longshoremen's and Warehousemen's Union: It was an important victory, for the hiring hall had been a vehicle of brutal exploitation. Between 1934 and 1948 there were no fewer than twenty major port strikes and thousands of quick stoppages as the union fought for control of work conditions on the docks. For the 15,000 or so "fully registered" A men, 1,500 to 2,000 B men, and 10,000 casuals, the I.L.W.U. was a savior. The work rules were far from mere featherbedding: At least the longshoreman insists so. He had freedom to select the days on which he wanted to work in accordance with rules established by the union. Frequent rest periods with one gang "spelling" another were common, justified on the ground that there was no compensation for time spent at the hiring hall. And the worker knew that sooner or later such practices as placing a load on the dock before it could be moved aboard would cease.

Mechanization in some places may move slowly, but, as with the gods grinding their mills, it moves exceedingly well. By the late 1950s Harry Bridges, long-time leader of the I.L.W.U., had concluded that the force of technology was irresistible and that he would have to "adjust" to survive. He was determined to take care of the people in his union. Besides, the shipowners were beginning to mutter that they would take their cargoes elsewhere, though it was not clear where. In 1958 Bridges advised the steve-doring companies, represented by the Pacific Maritime Association, headed by Paul St. Sure, that he would agree to mechanization, provided the workers shared in produc-tivity gains. It was a bald hint that the union could be bought off. St. Sure offered a million dollars to demonstrate management's willingness to cooperate. Bridges suggested that the earnest payment be increased to a million and a half. When asked where he had obtained his figure, Bridges replied: "The same place you got a million."[27] By 1960, the P.M.A. was ready to buy out the union — it was as simple as that. The employers agreed to pay $5 million a year for five and a half years into a trust fund, the benefits of which were exclusively reserved to the A men. This sum was nothing more than a $29 million bribe to eliminate working conditions that had been in effect on the docks for years. A handsome pension was made available to those who would retire. The union member's share in the benefits was $7,920. Each longshoreman had two options: He could retire at age sixty-two and receive $220 a month until age sixty-five, when the benefit would be adjusted for social security, or he could retire at age sixty-five and take the $7,920 in a lump sum or in installments, plus the normal pension and social security.[28] There was also a guarantee in the plan that the pay for regular longshoremen would not be allowed to drop below the equivalent of thirty-five hours in wages per week because of more efficient operation.

The guarantee, however, does not apply to reduced hours stemming from economic conditions. Harvey Swados, who talked to union officials, workers, and employers on the West Coast docks, reports that all parties privately admit that the arrangement was a "payoff."

Yet labor costs did not increase: The employers obtained enough extra work for each labor dollar to absorb without strain a 20 per cent increase in costs. Why not? By 1963 the number of tons of cargo handled per hour increased 23 per cent over that in 1959. Six longshoremen can now unload a cargo of copra in nine days by hoisting the oil-laden material into a vacuum tube that shoots it into a conversion plant. A few years ago, it would have taken twice that number of men two weeks to accomplish the job; the saving in man-hours is 70 per cent. It used to take as much as two weeks to remove a load of passenger cars: A ship can now dock, unload, and be back at sea in seven hours. Where loading of cargo containers once might have required a fourteen-man gang working twelve shifts, with mechanization all that is needed is a ten-man gang working only two shifts. This figure represents a saving of more than 80 per cent in man-hours.

Of course, the steamship companies were quite delighted, as the new arrangements permitted quick turn-around and saved them days of port charges and seamen's wages. But the burden of displacement was placed on the shoulders of the B men and the casuals—the latter contemptuously dismissed by the union as moonlighters from other occupations. It is the B men who have really borne the brunt of the adjustment, for the "historic" agreement gave them neither jobs nor benefits. When the A register was opened recently, about 2,200 men were admitted, chosen from among ten times that number of applicants. Yet the total number of "fully registered" dock workers has shrunk from about 14,500 to about 12,000. And for those who work, it is no longer a matter of choice. They must do everything asked of them by the stevedoring boss. The old work rhythm induced by the allegedly archaic work rules, a rhythm that allowed equalizing tasks and help for the older men in the gang, is gone. The men on the docks have now been tied to the machine.

The B men and casuals—the unregistered and those waiting for regular jobs—can only express their frustration by fruitless picketing of Harry Bridges's headquarters. The B man must pay dues and assessments, but, unlike the A member, he does not possess full union membership and protection. Furthermore, he is generally assigned the worst available job, for most of the B men are Negroes. It is not surprising that there is opposition from the ranks, particularly when employers can use the "performance and conformance" program to root out ostensibly undesirable work practices. Interestingly enough, Bridges has turned his back on locals that have tried to resist the P.M.A.'s "performance and conformance" rules. In one case, 82 B men who had applied for A status when the latter's ranks were opened found themselves "deregistered," or fired, for alleged past violations of the rules. Many said they were innocent: In any case, they told Paul Jacobs, they had not been given a proper opportunity to defend themselves against the vague charges. Furthermore, they were denied unemployment insurance and lost their vacation pay and health and welfare benefits. An unemployment insurance board appeals referee restored their right to unemployment insurance benefits, saying that they could not be held liable for "misconduct" supposedly committed years ago. The men even had the temerity to go to court to protect their rights against union and employer, for which they were characterized as "finks."

That a fair number of I.L.W.U. members are disillusioned is not surprising. To make sure that the antistrike clause of the mechanization agreement would not be violated (payments into the fund cease until the strike is over), Bridges and the P.M.A. negotiated a separate agreement directed at the San Pedro local, which had through the years acquired a reputation for militancy. The officers of the San Pedro local described it as a "yellow dog" agreement, under which the employer could blacklist a worker without recourse. In April 1964 the members of the San Pedro local voted unanimously to contest the agreement in the courts. Said Curt Johnson, the San Pedro president, of the Bridges–P.M.A. agreement, "We gave away too much for too little." Many agreed with him that the worker's birthright may have been sold for a mess of pottage.

Anxiety and Response

In the meantime, Bridges joined John L. Lewis among the ranks of labor statesmen. He is now abundantly praised by employers. "I used to think he had horns and a tail and long fangs," said the vice-president of a shipping company. "But now I must say his word is good . . ." A labor-relations executive remarked, "He's one of the few labor leaders in the country who has embarked on a program to tackle the problem of the machine." Bridges and Paul St. Sure tour the countryside to explain the "historic" agreement to labor-management experts. Invariably, Bridges will admit that unemployment can be a serious social problem. But he adds, "We don't want to get into revolutionary theory today, do we?" Harry Bridges, one time radical, resents the appellation "labor statesman": He tells reporters not to assume that he has become a cheerleader for the free-enterprise profit system. It is just that he works for the profit system without any endorsements. If the discharged dock workers were to stare through the windows of San Francisco's Commonwealth Club and the Mark Hopkins Hotel, they could look from Bridges to St. Sure and St. Sure to Bridges and not know which was which.[29]

THE WEST COAST experience now worries the longshoremen in the East. They have an inescapable feeling that they are next on automation's agenda. Bridges and St. Sure freely criticize their Atlantic and Gulf Coast counterparts for not following their example. Not that mechanization is a stranger in the East and South. As far back as 1959, the International Longshoremen's Association, then headed by William V. Bradley, gave in to conveyor belts, containerization, and palletized cargoes. According to the Arthur D. Little firm of management consultants, as much as 75 per cent of the cargoes moving in North Atlantic trade could be moved by containers. But much more mechanization was wanted by the employers. Alexander Chopin, chief employer negotiator in the Port of New York, searches for a "moment of truth," by which he means the exclusive right to determine work conditions. The January 1963 strike in New York may have brought wage increases, but it did not solve the question of manpower utilization. It did result in a special

Labor Department study of work conditions on the docks, and when the results were out the employers were quite pleased: They revealed that featherbedding plagued the waterfront. All the I.L.A.'s president, Thomas W. Gleason, could do was to plead that "progress which excludes the worker is a fake." The union could stall by asking for more data, but it knew what was to come in the end.

According to the Labor Department report, there were too many workers on the New York waterfront. It therefore recommended "decasualization," essentially the Bridges solution. One of the issues involved was the twenty-man work gang: The employers wanted a more flexible ruling, and they offered in return a guaranteed annual wage recommended by a presidential panel in 1964. This would provide no less than 75 per cent of a longshoreman's annual gross income in the years 1963 through 1965. But some union officials asserted that reducing the gang size meant a loss of at least 3,000 jobs. Gleason had argued that the registry of dockworkers in New York had already dropped from 51,000 to 27,000 in the last decade. Even at that, he said, the number of jobs available on peak days was at most 18,000. Rather, continued the union, dockworkers needed strengthened job security, which might be supplied by granting the men a guaranteed seven-hour day with eight hours' pay. The only work-gang flexibility the union was prepared to accept would be to shift individual members from one job to another. The issues were too complex for anything other than stalemate and strike.[30]

While the eastern dockworkers still resisted job erosion, the seagoing unions — National Maritime Union; Seafarers' International; Sailors' Union of the Pacific; Marine Engineers; Masters, Mates and Pilots; and Radio Officers — seemed paralyzed with frustration, anguish, rivalry, and nameless fear. The major breakthrough for the steamship companies came in August 1963, when the National Maritime Union, headed by Joseph Curran, agreed to cuts in crew sizes on automated ships; shortly after, the Marine Engineers had to follow suit. But these ships were subsidized: The agreement was, in part, Curran's way of hitting back at his rival Paul Hall of the Seafarers', whose members work mainly on nonsubsidized vessels. The ship lines agreed to establish an "employment security fund" for Curran and to pay 25 cents per man-day to retrain land-locked seamen. They also acceded to twenty-year retirement regardless of age.

The bickering, however, continued. The shipowners are not averse to employing automation as an excuse to speed up those who remain on board. In the protracted bargaining session with the N.M.U., the employers suggested that two men instead of three be stationed on deck as lookouts after sunset. Usually, three men rotate a night watch, with one out for a coffee break: The companies thought that two men and a thermos bottle would be sufficient. The N.M.U. wondered if this change too was automation. Nevertheless, the agreement broke the roadblock to automating the ships. The United States Maritime Commission, which in 1963 paid out $227 million in subsidies with 84 per cent used to equalize wage rates, hoped to make a substantial reduction in its payments. The General Electric Company asserted that half the subsidies could be eliminated on an automated ship that it manufactured, by utilizing centralized operating systems.

Meanwhile, the operators were looking avidly to the day when they would sail forth with substantially less than half the men they used to have. On the West Coast, the P.M.A., which bargains for the shipowners (and with its longshoreman's contract in mind), magnanimously said that it was "... prepared to provide the necessary funds ... over a five year period to permit a reduction of the total work force ..." The Sailors' Union of the Pacific wanted to know how the total number of men might be reduced without injury to those registered on its books and "without ultimately destroying the union." Nevertheless, Morris Weisberger, head of the union, was prepared to negotiate "for some sort of compensation for the loss of jobs," as, by refusing, continued Weisberger: "... we [might] maintain the status quo in manning for the lifetime of our present contract, another two years, and maybe for another two years of fact-finding after that. But what then?"

Meanwhile, Curran pledged to his members that work conditions, safety, and security would not be impaired through automation and that "adjustments aboard ship are

to be shared fairly by all the unions involved." In the same
breath, his statement, reminiscent of John L. Lewis's signal
to the coal operators, called for a sharing of long-range
gains achieved by automation. Before the Lykes Bros.
Steamship Company would lay the keel for a highly
mechanized cargo ship, it received a commitment from
Curran agreeing to a reduction of fourteen men from the
forty-two required on a conventional vessel. On the West
Coast, the P.M.A. hoped for a 30 per cent reduction in
manning requirements, eliminating 6,000 jobs within five
years on the 120 ships for which it bargained. Even the conventional ships will have smaller crews. Paul Hall too has
accepted the inevitable: He was concerned though that
the shipowners would not be too unreasonable. The shift
to automated vessels is now moving smoothly: Even the
government, which had expected trouble, is pleased. Said
one union official recently: "What the hell, it's progress.
It's a gradual thing anyway. It'll work out." In the last
analysis, the unions can do nothing.[31]

Mechanization and automation, however, have their
most immediate effects on local plant problems, something
that national bargaining can deal with but tangentially and
ineffectively. The consequence is a dissatisfaction in the
ranks that frequently leads to a rebellion against the international officers. Although Gleason may obtain a settlement he thinks is "the greatest in the history" of the I.L.A.,
the rank and file believe otherwise, and they strike all the
ports along the Gulf and East Coast. Local union leaders
decide to negotiate their own agreements in order to deal
with local work conditions. Similarly, the U.A.W. hierarchy
may work out a national agreement with the auto companies,
but General Motors and Ford are struck for a month because
the workers are unhappy over local work conditions. The
men on the line make their sentiments known in unmistakable
ways at union conventions. So well do they love their jobs
that they want escape from the monotony and mindlessness
of the computer-controlled assembly plant. They want an
end to speed-up, they want more coffee breaks to relieve
fatigue, and they want a halt to television monitoring of
toilets. And for them the ultimate answer is early retirement,
release from the filth and dirt of making "insolent chariots".

What this attitude suggests, of course, is an utter loss of hope of ever creating a work process with human meaning. Knowing in his bones that man serves the machine, the auto worker wants to get to that fishing rod just as soon as he can.

BUT IT IS to the coal mines that one must go to witness the final frustration of the unions in dealing with automation and mechanization. Let us go with Harvey Swados to St. Michael, Pennsylvania, to see the men standing on street corners as they have stood since April 1958, when Maryland Shaft No. 1 closed down.[32] They wait for unemployment insurance or relief checks when the insurance has run out. They then lack even the dignity of a cipher in the monthly unemployment count of the Federal government. St. Michael has new industry attracted by the town fathers, but it consists of garment shops employing women, enforcing a reversal of roles in the home. The men do not leave the town because they cannot abide the asphalt of the big city, and they hope for a few more years in the mine to qualify for U.M.W. pensions. Meanwhile, the operators and the union have nothing but praise for the new technology. The businessmen who used to curse Lewis now call him a "labor statesman." They know he has been their savior. But ask a U.M.W. official, as Swados did, how many miners have been displaced, and you will be greeted with silence.

Furthermore, Lewis actively sought to push the miner out of the fields, as was revealed in a Tennessee lawsuit brought against the U.M.W. by the Phillips Coal Company in 1961. In addition to giving a "go ahead" signal for mechanization, the U.M.W. had acquired a controlling interest in one of the largest coal-mining operations in the country: The union was itself in the business of mining coal. To permit U.M.W. members to learn that their president had advocated a policy of machines before men was unthinkable. So the arrangement was kept secret. The investments of the welfare fund and other union monies were also secret; members were unaware of a $35 million loan to Cyrus Eaton, a coal industrialist. The U.M.W., through its control of a major Washington bank, had poured millions of dollars, not only into coal mines, but into railroads and utilities as well. The latter were especially important, for the largest single demand for coal comes from electrical generators.

Lewis is now honorably retired: All the problems of the industry have been passed on to his hand-picked successor, W. A. Boyle. By 1964, however, Boyle was beginning to have second thoughts about traditional U.M.W. bargaining policy. Perhaps it was the virtual civil war in such towns as Hazard, Kentucky, that impelled the present union leadership to think of shifting ground. Whereas at one time the bargaining stress was on better wages, in his 1964 negotiations Boyle sought more "job security." Contending that automation had cut the work force as low as it could safely go, he tried to obtain a job freeze in the bituminous fields. The operators, however, continued their plaint that even more advanced equipment was necessary if they were to stay in business.

To exacerbate the problem for the union, there are the tiny "dog hole," mines to which the displaced workers flock as jobs with the larger operators disappear. These mines are nonunion shafts, which pay perhaps $1.50 an hour and send no royalties to the U.M.W. health and welfare fund. Their safety standards are nonexistent, and union organizers roam the countryside trying to close them down or to get the operators to meet the requirements of the contract, especially the royalty payment. As A. H. Raskin says, the union becomes an "enforcer for the machine." But when a contract is extracted from a small operator, he is often told that full compliance is not necessary: The U.M.W. believes that it can in this way control the output of nonunion coal and that the big operators can be made to believe that their competion is being cut off. Furthermore, the man who works in a unionized "dog hole" receives substantially less than the union scale, although he pays the same regular monthly union dues. In the tradition of the hills, the issue has been frequently settled with rifles. But the dog-hole mines now supply 28 per cent of total output. Even the unionized mines do not at times pay the royalties. In 1962 more than 400 organized companies paid less than $300 into the health and welfare fund. Royalties received by the fund were equivalent to only 72 per cent of the soft coal mined in that year. But the U.M.W. officials in charge of the fund are unconcerned. In August 1962 they withdrew benefits from the miners whose employers failed to pay their proper share. Even some of the union-supported hospitals were closed. Violence erupted as the miners struck to regain their benefits.

The issue of job security, however, has remained paramount. U.M.W. dissidents in western Pennsylvania and the northern sections of West Virginia have said: "A wage increase is not justified. We make enough money. But we do want fringe benefits, job security and safety." In the 1964 negotiations, Boyle did obtain some gains unique for U.M.W.—mine-wide seniority to protect older workers facing layoffs, higher overtime rates, more vacation, and more safety protection—but many of the locals were dissatisfied, and they struck, for they had no guarantee of even the present level of employment. But they were striking against the International Union, not against the employers: Boyle's claim of better seniority, holidays, and control of crew size seemed to them vastly exaggerated once they had read the fine print in the contract. Meanwhile, the operators continued to introduce automatic machinery: Such machines were "management prerogatives" deemed inalienable.[33]

The resentment of the men in fields exploded at union meetings in no uncertain terms. The 1964 contract was called a "step sideways," and the international officers were labeled "lovebirds with the coal operators." For the fact was that the rank and file saw little by way of fringe benefits in the negotiated agreement: The International was still trying to solve its problems by obtaining higher wages. That this emphasis would encourage the industry's already relentless push to increase automation and to displace workers seemed unquestionable. The attempt on the part of the dissidents to secure a greater voice in union affairs by expressing their views at the 1964 convention was promptly suppressed by Boyle's fist-swinging supporters. When one of Boyle's opponents tried to reach a microphone, he was attacked and led from the hall bleeding while the band struck up *The Star Spangled Banner*. Demands by locals for more autonomy were met with silence. And although the Department of Labor had murmured that it would act under the Landrum-Griffin Act to enforce autonomy, nothing has yet happened.

It may be charitably said that these failures are manifestations of the union's inability to cope with the issues of automation. One wonders, however, if the U.M.W. officials are genuinely interested. When Dan Wakefield asked one of them in 1963 whether or not national headquarters would assist the Hazard, Kentucky, strikes, the reply was "not under the present conditions." When Wakefield inquired if the hospitals might be reopened, he was told, "We are not in the hospital business." Asked if the U.M.W. would undertake job retraining for its displaced members, the union officer referred the matter to the Federal government. Clearly the U.M.W. has become the model for "ghost unionism." In fact, it has virtually abandoned many areas along the Appalachian plateau. Technology now takes its toll in the hills unceasingly.[34]

ONE UNION OSTENSIBLY thinking of what it might do by way of responding to automation is the International Association of Machinists. That it cannot succeed in saving jobs in the machine shops and aerospace plants in other than a wartime economy is obviously not its fault. With about 64 per cent of the country's machine tools more than ten years old, the situation is ripe for automation. Several years ago the Machinists recommended to their local lodges certain collective-bargaining demands for dealing with the effects of advancing technology. These recommendations urged advance notice, transfer rights, moving allowances, retraining at full pay, severance pay, early retirement, and "equitable distribution of the gains resulting from greater productivity through general wage increases." All of these demands are standard, but in the absence of action by the whole society they remain palliatives, at best delaying the arrival of doomsday.

At any rate, the Machinists' Union was willing to think about automation, and it has—together with U.S. Industries, a manufacturer of automated machinery. The latter announced in 1962 a company-financed foundation to help workers displaced by automation. With a staff of a half-dozen psychologists, engineers, and economists, the foundation promised to deal with human problems and to develop ways to ease automation's impact on displaced workers. Some studies were sponsored, conferences were held, and proceedings were presented at press luncheons. Of course, all this activity has been to the good, for it has helped "arouse" people. But, like a puppy discovering its tail, the discussion went round and round, and no one knew what to do. Beyond that the Machinists have done nothing.[35]

Will Walter Reuther break the circle of frustration? That too remains to be seen: The U.A.W. has prepared no public material on automation since its first pronouncements in 1955. At that time Reuther's speeches all but embraced the computer, so high was his regard for technology, so powerful his belief in growth and progress. But the best the U.A.W. has come up with was its 1961 "progress sharing" plan with American Motors. The progress was shared through a fund based on approximately 15 per cent of the company's profits, with two-thirds available for wages or fringe benefits and one-third for the purchase of company stock to be distributed in cases of retirement, lay-off, or illness. The plan was started with a $3 million transfer from existing insurance funds. During the first year American Motors' 27,000 workers obtained $3.3 million worth of stock, about seven shares each. Improved fringe benefits absorbed another $6.5 million. The plan provided, however, that a sum equal to 10 per cent of the company's investment was to be deducted from pretax earnings before the employees received anything. As a result, 5 per cent less was available in the second year, as the A.M.C. investment increased markedly. About two fewer shares of stock were credited to each worker. But the company's net profit jumped by more than 10 per cent.

The workers began to fret at a scheme that was really profit sharing and that had little to do with meeting the problem of automation. When asked about it, local union leaders said, "No comment," or "Don't talk to me about it." Furthermore, the shares were worth no more than their market price, and, when the latter dropped, all the workers could see was their gain disappearing. By June 1964 the value of the first block of about seven shares had dropped from \$129 to \$100. This sum was equivalent to one cent per hour. And in the workers' view, they were in fact paying for the fringe benefits through the fund. At the next negotiation round, the union team and management were ready to forget the whole thing. They did not reckon with Walter Reuther, however, who, though preoccupied with other affairs, insisted that profit sharing was good for the workers' souls. The scheme was modified and became an outright bonus. Reuther was still proud of his "profit sharing" plan.

The U.A.W., too, has sponsored retraining programs for its members under the Federal Manpower Act, with mechanical drafting, modeling of new cars, and other white-collar skills as the main courses. Whether or not this re-training would meet the needs of the displaced auto worker depended on conditions far beyond the union's control, but at any rate it was one small way of confronting a difficult situation. More important, it signified a slight shift in the thinking of the union hierarchy. Up to that point, Reuther and his very capable brain trust had placed all their faith in raising the level of aggregate demand as the only way of halting the erosion of jobs. They were reluctant to believe that changes in technology could leave permanent gaps in the automobile industry's labor force. The structural argu-ment — that economic strata shift and can threaten an earth-quake — was for them another Jeremiad. But pressures from the men in the shops evidently impelled them to reconsider somewhat their earlier positions. As a consequence, later bargaining demands included such items as advance notice of automation; retraining to be paid by the companies; trans-fer, where possible, of blue-collar workers to white-collar jobs; relocation allowances; better severance pay; and, above all, "income security," meaning annual salaries for line workers. But what these gains might do for a man already out of work was not clear: This question was beyond the present scope of collective bargaining. No one has yet come up with the idea of "bargaining" for those outside the gates.

Some consideration also has been given to a phased retirement program. One version of the plan is to have substantially longer vacations for workers over sixty, so that by age sixty-five they may be getting several months off each year. At the same time, a kind of "reverse seniority" would be applied: During layoff periods, older workers would go on short work schedules instead of the younger men, as is now done. Alternatively, men over sixty might share jobs, say six months each. During the phase-out period, the workers would receive supplementary unemployment benefits. On the other hand, alterations would have to be made in the unemployment-insurance laws if income, at least enough to reach the 65 per cent of normal take-home pay specified under S.U.B., were to be provided. Interestingly, the idea is not new: It was recommended by the Council on Aging, and here and there a private company has operated its pension program along such lines — Prentice-Hall, Wrigley, Cannon Electric, and several others. But whether or not such schemes create *more* jobs seems to be moot.

In any case, as already indicated, the trend toward early retirement seems to be well established. Liberal benefits do encourage earlier retirements and become an important means for opening jobs to young people entering the labor force. In the auto industry itself, about 35 per cent of the 6,400 hourly workers who retired in 1963 from GM, Ford, and Chrysler were under sixty-five; in 1960 the ratio was 18 per cent, and in 1953 it was 4 per cent. The new U.A.W. contract will undoubtedly accelerate the trend: Benefits were increased more than 50 per cent; the permissible age limit was reduced from sixty-five to sixty-two; and some "bridging" was provided for those retiring between the ages of fifty-five and sixty-five. As a consequence, a man and wife may receive as much as $300 a month when he reaches sixty-five. Nevertheless, the cost necessarily rises, perhaps to as much as 8 per cent of wages, an adjustment that makes other industries balk at the idea.[36]

Yet early retirement on improved pensions and profit sharing and sharing in cost savings protect only the worker who is in; they do little for the worker who has been shunted aside and even less for the younger worker who wants to get in. What happens to those pushed out by automation is revealed in the experience of the displaced meat packer. When Armour suddenly closed a number of plants in the

Midwest, the workers had no time to think about what they might do. Granted the plants were obsolete, yet the burden of the shutdowns was simply dumped into the laps of the employees and the social-service agencies of Oklahoma City, East St. Louis, West Fargo, and Columbus.

One year later almost half the displaced workers in two of those cities had not yet found jobs. Three years after the shutdowns 30 per cent of the East St. Louis Armour workers were still unemployed. Between 1959 and 1962 Armour's production and maintenance force had been cut by 40 per cent. Not even the vaunted automation fund, established in 1959 by agreement with the Packinghouse Workers and the Amalgamated Butcher Workmen, was of much help. A human-relations committee was set up and considerable publicity generated to show how advanced collective bargaining in the industry really was. Yet the fund did little more than pay for a few studies by university professors. No real benefits accrued to the workers, and the plant closings continued without abatement. The 1961 negotiations provided for some benefits from the fund — relocation costs, improved severance and retirement, and some retraining. The value of the last, however, appears to have been quite limited. By November 1963, only 220 of some 2,500 eligible workers had been "retrained." And in virtually every case, the "new" skills brought a lower-rated job with less pay than had been earned at the old Armour packing house. In Oklahoma City, 431 workers had been displaced; 170 took the tests for retraining, and seventy were accepted; forty-seven completed the course, and twenty-one found new jobs, of which five were totally unrelated to the subjects studied. A retraining program in Fort Worth gave to those who secured jobs $1.61 an hour on the average, compared to the Armour average of $2.60 an hour. In the meantime, about 10 per cent of the automation fund went to pay administrative costs, including salaries for the impartial chairman and the executive director.

Little wonder that Ralph Helstein, President of the Packinghouse Workers' Union, described the automation fund in 1963 as nothing more than a "publicity gimmick" for the company and a cloak for "a ruthless program of mass termination." Since the fund was established, Armour has

Anxiety and Response

closed at least one plant a year, leaving thousands of workers
to shift for themselves. According to Helstein, the company
has built replacement plants in complete secrecy, often in
southern towns not notably hospitable to union organizers.
Whenever the union has discovered new construction and
insisted on transfer rights, the company has refused. The
Armour Automation Committee, which administers the
fund, was hailed as a pioneer effort to deal in a statesman-
like manner with the effects of a changing technology, but
its behavior has been odd, to say the least. Payments into
the fund were halted in 1963; of the $500,000 that had been
accumulated, more than half was still lying idle. The simple
fact is that little direct help has been extended to employees
who have been displaced.[37]

AND ON THE RAILROADS automation has already loosened
the desperate holding action of the Brotherhoods. These
unions, once among the country's most powerful are caving
in before technology and politics. In 1959 the railroad companies wanted to lay off all firemen working on diesel locomotives in freight and yard service and insisted on an un-
restricted right to set crew sizes. This right would have
meant the abolition of almost 60,000 jobs. The five on-train
operating unions immediately threatened to strike if the
work-rules changes were carried out, for they insisted that,
not only was train safety involved, but also firemen's posts
were needed to provide training for future engineers. The
companies screamed "featherbedding" in full-page newspaper ads throughout the land. Few listened to the plaints
of the workers or their unions.

In October 1960 a presidential railroad commission
was created, which produced several immense volumes of
statistics that sounded the death knell of the firemen. The
fifteen-man tripartite body held hearings, listened to experts
of all sorts, and in ninety-six days produced 15,000 pages of
transcript and 20,000 pages of exhibits. It studied the pay
structure on the railroads, employment trends, age distribution of the workers, retirement rates, and unemployment benefits and examined experiences in other industries.
The commission then concluded that "a gap had developed

between technology in the industry and the work compensation rules"—that is, that there were too many workers around and that the railroads were right in trying to get rid of them. The few who might remain were to be rewarded with a 2 per cent wage increase.

Needless to say, the unions rejected the commission's proposals. An emergency board under the Railway Labor Act then proposed retraining, special allowances for redundant workers, and arbitration of displacements disputed by the union. The operators were ready, but the unions once again stalled: They were biding their time to hit the railroads the only way they knew how—with the strike. But, as usual, President Kennedy understood full well what was in their minds, and, armed with the Council of Economic Advisers' prediction that six million workers would be out of jobs one month after a rail strike and that the ensuing depression would endanger the national security, he asked the Congress in July 1963 to forbid railroad strikes for two years and to compel the operators and the Brotherhoods to keep talking to each other. Congress, however, went further and imposed compulsory arbitration—which the President accepted. It was one of the few bills that moved over the Hill to the White House that year with more than deliberate speed. On November 26, the arbitration panel established by the statute ruled that up to 90 per cent of the contested fireman positions could be eliminated—a crushing blow to labor that few noticed in the agony of the President's death. When the Supreme Court refused to question the constitutionality of compulsory arbitration, another nail was driven into the automated coffin carrying the Brotherhoods to their doom. The railroad operators immediately announced the layoffs: Fifteen thousand jobs were to be eliminated before the arbitration law expired in January 1966. But the operators moved with almost indecent eagerness: By April 1965 about 15,700 firemen, 42 per cent of the total, had been removed from freight and yard service, and more than 6,000 jobs were scheduled for elimination in 1966. The one saving grace was that a fireman with ten years' seniority might receive up to $8,000 in severance pay if he chose to leave. Although no one knows how many men are still unemployed, even the industry has conceded that more than 10 per cent of those laid off were still without work by mid-1965. The union contended, however, that the figure was higher than that—closer to 30 per cent. At any rate, the operators could offer these men the consolation of unemployment insurance at $51 a week.

The unions—particularly the Railroad Trainmen—decided that they might just as well go for wage boosts rather than for job security, as the latter was down the drain anyway. They tried road-by-road negotiations in a campaign to split the operators' solid bargaining front. The operators refused unless work-rules changes were part of the agenda. The unions made vague threats of a strike, driving the operators to court for injunctions. Nothing had been settled in all the jockeying, however, except that there would be fewer jobs for railroad workers. It never occurred to the unions that an effective consolidation of their efforts and perhaps of their organizations might help them achieve a better position *vis à vis* the operators. They might strike here and there, as against the Chicago and North Western in August 1962 and the Florida East Coast in January 1963, but to not much avail. Despite the "settlement" announced by President Johnson in April 1964, the situation remained an uneasy one. Some jobs were given up by the unions, whereas management agreed to more holidays and a few wage increases. The President temporarily had solved the bargaining impasse with a bit of characteristic arm-twisting.

By mid-1965 it was patent that the Brotherhood of Locomotive Firemen and Enginemen, almost a century old and once boasting 120,000 members, was expiring. It had fought for five years against the railroad companies' demand to wipe out jobs, and it had lost the battle. Few new firemen were now hired: The union had lost members as well as income, the latter at the rate of $360,000 a year. The "full crew" laws that once protected railroad jobs in some fourteen states were being repealed at a rapid clip, so that the arbitration ruling could be applied there as well. Meanwhile, the Engineers' Union, repeating what the Airline Pilots had done, deciding that "there's no sense fighting a lost cause to save the firemen." Indeed, the Engineers appeared to be trying to quicken the Firemen's end by raiding it for the few members who might have kept their jobs. To be sure, the Firemen will probably insist at the end of the arbitration period that the old contract is still in force. This insistence may throw the whole affair into a legal no-man's land; nevertheless, it is more than likely that when the smoke of battle has been dissipated, the Engineers will join the Horse Shoers' Union as a fossilized curiosity among labor organizations.[38]

IT IS SOMETIMES said that the most effective solutions are those developed in the steel industry. The situaton there, particularly in the U.S. Steel Corporation, has been for a long time quite complicated, with technology exerting its impersonal pressures on available jobs and established work standards. Complex local work rules, chiefly to forestall speed-ups, have been part of the collective-bargaining agreements ever since Benjamin Fairless and Philip Murray signed the first contract in 1937. Yet this protection in no way solved the problem, for there have been frequent disputes between local unions and lower-echelon management over crew sizes, seniority, layoffs, incentive payments, and lunch hours. Finally in 1960 a settlement provided for setting up a human-relations committee to deal with the exacerbating issues stemming from the changing character of work in the mills. Subcommittees met, discussions were amicable, yet observers wondered at the lack of accomplishment. Steel-company representatives hesitated to commit themselves for fear that their statements would return to haunt them at the bargaining table. Furthermore, the arrangement in no way inhibited U. S. Steel from introducing new equipment and new techniques. Job attrition in steel went on unabated. Severance pay and supplemental unemployment benefits did not give the protection that in better times it had been thought they would offer. The union felt it necessary to employ its local work rules embodied in the original contract's Section 2B, a set of practices that made management howl "featherbedding!" Nevertheless, it was clear that without Section 2B, job destruction would have been even more rapid. The union was engaged in a holding action; it was hard to predict how long it could maintain its desperate grip.

The two men who sit in comfort and silence in an air-conditioned pulpit astride a roll conveyor in a rolling mill have a measure of skill, but they will soon be obsolete, displaced by a process computer. For the fact is that skills in the steel industry are disappearing and the work force dwindling. The U.S.W. is resigned to the shrinkage of its membership in basic steel, a membership that represents the core of the union. It hopes to offset that decline by gains in unorganized industries and in white-collar occupations: For the latter alone, the ratio in steel of white-collar to blue-collar jobs rose from one to nine in 1934 to one to four in 1964. In a sense, the U.S.W. hopes to diversify. Although this strategy may save the union as an institution, it does little for the steel workers, whose jobs never reached again the half-million or more annual average for the decade 1947–1957.

The goal in steel is to move closer and closer to computer control of production, linking isolated plant units in one continuous process requiring little or no manual operation. The continuous hot-strip mill of the 1920s and 1930s eliminated the old hand mill roller; the oxygen furnace may now eliminate the open hearth. In the process men, if they still remain in the mill, may be given new kinds of jobs, but often in lower classifications. The shutdown of U. S. Steel's open hearths in the Duquesne works cost the jobs of 250 men: Some are to be retired or assigned elsewhere, but about 10 per cent will be out permanently. The number of workers required per ton of steel has declined at the rate of 2 to 3 per cent a year since 1940; by 1975 the number of jobs available in that industry may be well under 400,000. A more dour prediction by a U.S.W. economist is a 40 per cent cut in steel's work force by 1975; this man estimates prospective peacetime employment at somewhat less than 300,000.

As an old Russian writer once asked, "What Is To Be Done?" Perhaps the Kaiser Fontana plan offers a partial answer. In March 1963, the union and the Kaiser Steel Corporation, a maverick among manufacturers, agreed to "share the progress" at the latter's plant in Fontana, California. The scheme included a guarantee that no worker would lose his job — at least for one year — because a machine had taken his place. If no other job were available, he was to go into a reserve pool and was assured of his income even if placed in a lower rated position. Furthermore, all the workers were to share in any cost savings achieved through greater efficiency. Such savings might come from anything that helped reduce the cost of steel — elimination of waste, working harder, or finding a new way to turn a dial on the control panel itself. During the first year, workers submitted more than 900 cost-cutting ideas, 80 per cent of which were good enough to be adopted. The share going to the workers is 32.5 per cent, a formula derived from the proportion of labor costs to total costs. The scheme is plant-wide, so that everyone can help make the pie bigger. In the first year the monthly bonuses averaged about $65 per man. In August 1965 the employees' share was 45 cents per hour worked; the distribution, however, amounted to 17 cents an hour, as the balance had to be placed in a reserve to pay for future increases in wages and fringe benefits. That is, the worker paid for his own benefits to come. And with each dollar of the bonus, Kaiser saved two. The company was hardly playing philanthropist. The workers began to think of the company's money as if it were their own. Cable lengths used by overhead cranes, which used to be junked when they snapped, were retrieved and cut into smaller pieces for smaller cranes. Old nuts and bolts were hoarded as a housewife saves twine.

Yet the plan is still a "buy-out": It has neither halted the advance of automation in the Fontana plant nor controlled its pace. An automatic scarfer, a machine that burns blemishes off unfinished steel, replaced not only the workers who used to do the job with oxyacetylene torches but also the cranemen, hookers, and inspectors as well. The displaced go into the labor reserve pool: At one time there were several dozen men in the pool awaiting reassignment; fortunately, they had been reabsorbed by the end of the year. Although the bonus has gone as high as 66 cents an hour, for the last seven months of the plan's initial year it dropped steadily until in May 1964, it hit only $14 for each of the 5,000 workers participating in it. As a result, enthusiasm for the scheme declined sharply: The incentive workers who used to average $50 to $60 a month in bonuses above their base pay were particularly bitter.

Part of the reason for the drop was apparently the company's installation of certain cost-cutting operations outside the plant, displacing work formerly done inside, and, as the sharing applied only to Fontana, the workers lost out. Not without reason, they charged the company with chiseling. Kaiser, on the other hand, countered that raw-materials prices had gone up and that improved fringe benefits—the cost of which was charged to the saving fund—ate into the amounts the men otherwise might have received. In addition, the company felt that the union ought to have relaxed its stubborn grip on Section 2B, the work-rules clause.

The fact is that in 1964 the Fontana plant was able to operate at full capacity with 1,400 fewer workers than it had used a few years before. Kaiser believes that the normal 8 per cent turnover in its work force will keep down the number of bodies accumulating in the reserve pool: Union leaders are not so sure, but they hope it will. As a key problem in automation is not so much the one fired, although that is troublesome enough, but the one not hired, the Kaiser plan, interesting as it is, offers no answer to the question raised by the 1.5 million young people who enter the job market each year. Can the social effects of automation indeed be handled via the ritual of collective bargaining?

The steel union thinks that its thirteen-week vacation plan negotiated in 1963 can supply an answer: It estimated that the "sabbaticals," which give the senior half of a mill's employees a quarter-long vacation once every five years, would open up 20,000 to 25,000 new jobs. There were some doubts about the accuracy of this optimistic prediction: Some analysts asserted that the extended-vacation plan would provide no more than 5,000 openings. If the latter is indeed the case, then the net decline in steel jobs would run at about 9,000 per year. Furthermore, the mills were scheduling the vacations to be timed with seasonal slowdowns, maintenance shutdowns, and other short-run fluctuations in manpower needs. And automation was not overlooked. They were using the ancient practice of having nonvacationing employees carry the load for fellow workers on holidays. In one mill, schedule and job juggling enabled management to give sabbaticals to forty-one men instead of eighty a quarter and to replace those on vacation with only sixteen new workers. The men who received the vacations were not overly enthusiastic: Except for the fact that they thought they were making room for unemployed buddies, they disliked the plan because it destroyed their vacation flexibility. Often they had to sit around because it was the wrong time of the year to go away. These drawbacks have made the plan quite unattractive to other unions: The U.A.W. has simply ignored the whole idea.[39]

BY URGING an expansion of retraining, relocation aid, and area redevelopment, the A.F.L.-C.I.O. itself has acknowledged that the burden of automation is too great for collective bargaining. The particular approaches of individual unions are at best holding actions and at worst helpless rhetoric. The U.A.W. wants to compel management to respect the dignity of the worker and urges its locals to resist the erosion of its bargaining units. Although the Machinists' Union recognizes that automation poses problems, all it can think of is another conference or perhaps better severance pay. The I.U.E., the Rubber Workers, the Retail Clerks, and several other unions have asked for joint study committees, but there has been no answer from the corporations, which continue unhampered in substituting machines for men. The Mine, Mill and Smelter Workers and the Railroad unions, too, call for higher wages to be paid whenever new equipment is to be installed, a response sure to be used as an excuse to bring in more machines. The Packinghouse Workers want a year's notice on plant closing, transfers for the displaced, more separation pay, and a shorter work week. The fact is that the unions have no answer to the predicament posed by the new technology.

Is the likely future of the trade unions one of declining power and influence? If that were to be the case, then we should all be the worse for it: The patent fact, despite the many strictures leveled at them, is that American unions have made the material lot of the ordinary workingman, and indeed of all of us, far better than it would have been had they not existed. For some craft unions automation is not yet a burning problem: For the industrial and even white-collar unions it is. And the unhappy consequences are magnified because it is precisely the latter, those most vulnerable to automation, that generally have been the more progressive and socially responsive.

Big brother tries   8

The world's largest user of computers is the Federal government. It accounts for well over one-fourth of the volume generated in the computer business, buying, renting, and maintaining almost 2,000 machines. These machines make out virtually all paychecks, keep track of armed-services inventories, record the movements of ships on the high seas, and review income-tax returns. As we have observed, the state has a vested interest in advanced technology, an interest that has been manifested in various ways through all the ages of time. Indeed, the modern computer originated in the war needs of the state: Mark I and ENIAC were used primarily to calculate weapon trajectories. So important have computers become that, if by some accident all the plugs were to be pulled at once, the nation's business would grind to a halt: Plants would close; government projects would cease functioning; the banking system would collapse; and we should be helpless against enemy attack.

IN INDUSTRY, the computer and automated technology continue to spread inexorably. Said *Time*, "If U.S. industry were to automate its factories to the extent that is now possible—not to speak of the new possibilities opening up each year—millions of jobs would be eliminated."[1] Even that magazine had to concede that American society would have to undergo major economic and social changes if those displaced by machines were to lead productive lives. But it has taken a long time for these questions to reach public awareness. After its 1955 hearings on automation, the Joint Economic Committee expressed the belief that only a small fraction of the total work force would be directly involved. The Committee was being cautiously optimistic. The tone of its report appears to have set the pattern for later reactions, even as the effects of the new technology were becoming more and more visible.[2]

The next important government pronouncement was the report of the President's Committee on Labor-Management Policy, issued in January 1962. The Committee had been established by President Kennedy in February 1961 to deal with collective bargaining, national-emergency disputes, wage and price policies, economic growth, foreign competition, and automation. It tackled the last item first because it was supposed to be easiest and least controversial and then took eleven months to arrive at a "sense of common purpose." The twenty-one-member committee, comprising representatives of management, labor, and "the public," spent an hour with the President offering its findings. Afterward, a Committee member described it as a "darn good bull session."

The Committee's report echoed the concern of the President for young people seeking jobs and for displaced older workers. It recognized that the net effect of modern technology was unemployment and suggested that something might have to be done.[3] At that, Henry Ford II and Arthur F. Burns, who had been Eisenhower's chief economist, dissented, for it seemed to them that any sort of government action might be oppressive to free enterprise. Burns also rejected the notion that automation could cause unemployment. At the same time, the labor members were disappointed that the Committee stressed programs to raise aggregate demand in preference to a shorter work week.

As far as official policy was concerned, full employment was to be achieved mainly through such fiscal measures as tax cuts. To be sure, the Gross National Product appeared to have benefited from the gain in "discretionary income,"

270

but this gain had failed to give jobs to foot-loose miners, unemployed packing-house workers, laid-off railroad men, and all the others whose skills had become unwanted. The unemployment rate remained at around 5 per cent, despite occasional fractional wiggles downward. A persistent down-ward movement came about only with war expenditures. Nevertheless, the Council of Economic Advisers argued before the Senate Labor Committee in 1963 that there exists a "proven capacity for a free labor market to recon-cile discrepancies between particular labor supplies and particular labor demand." Yet in recent years the Gross National Product has grown as much as 6 per cent per annum, and few new jobs have been forthcoming for those needing them most – the displaced, the young, the unskilled. The industries in which displacement had been occurring were mature ones – autos, steel, food processing, apparel – and it seemed unlikely that they would expand their sales sufficiently under the new technology to replace the jobs that had been dispensed with. Automation had accelerated productivity in these industries just enough to keep pace with normal market growth while getting along with fewer workers. In fact, as Bert Hickman suggested, the structural problem seemed to reveal itself as a mismatching of specific demands with specific capacities. If that were the case, then an increase in general demand through fiscal measures might not be totally effective, as existing specialized forms of capital would hinder any quick adjustment of demand and capacity. That is, the problem stemming from changing technology could very well be one of "structural" unemploy-ment of capital.[4]

Despite the grudging recognition the Council of Economic Advisers sometimes gave to structural distor-tions stemming from technology, its position generally was that added investment and greater consumer demand would do more than anything else to ease the burden placed on those who had to find new sources of income.[5] The Council also insisted, citing the imperatives of national defense, that the encouragement of innovation – which meant automation as well as ordinary industrial change – was a direct responsi-bility of government. Research and development – for which government paid two-thirds of the $16 billion spent

271

in 1962–1963 and which had gone mostly for aircraft, missiles, electronics, chemicals, and machinery—had therefore to be continued. But what of those, like the hand-loom weavers of yore and the coal miners of today, who were unable to deal with the aftermath of automation? Did the government then have a responsibility?

From the point of view of the state—which wants unlimited technology—many of the measures now used to mitigate the effects of automation, measures like profit sharing, cost-savings sharing, and early retirement, are not really "practicable" in that they "cannot provide complete worker protection without unduly slowing the pace of technical advance," as the C.E.A. so bluntly put it. It seems therefore that ways must be found to help victims of material advancement, not because they are people, but because they are potential Luddites. Such curious views were embedded also in the Joint Economic Committee report of 1955 and were reflected in President Kennedy's attempt to create a Commission on Automation in 1963.[6] Such a commission was finally established in 1964 after heroic efforts by Hubert Humphrey, then a Senator, Senator Joseph Clark of Pennsylvania, and Senator Jacob Javits of New York. It was not empaneled, however, until late January 1965 and did not start its deliberations until March. The distinguished tripartite roster was expected to issue a definitive report by the end of the year. The Commission's three subcommittees were studying the printing and machine-tool industries; a manpower-demand projection for 1980 was being prepared; labor's stand on shorter hours was being reviewed; how education might help people adapt to automation was being examined; and the whole Commission was investigating what new adjustment techniques were needed. None of these efforts was either striking or new.

There are some who urge that precedent for government action was provided by the Employment Act of 1946. But this statute does not even offer a rough blueprint. Failing to define what "full employment" goals ought to be in an economy that undergoes continual change, the Act, which directs the Council of Economic Advisers merely to study conditions and to write a report, remains what it was intended to be—a superb example of legislative rhetoric. If one looks at the debates in Congress preceding its passage, one finds much talk on fiscal and monetary policy and how the Federal Reserve System might stimulate investment by manipulating interest rates and member-bank reserves and by buying and selling securities on the open market. Unfortunately, the Federal Reserve System is still a quasi-independent agency, and it has not always pursued policies that would benefit the rest of us. The Employment Act, therefore, is of little help in an age of automation.[7]

THE PRESSURES on government to do something, however, continued, and they finally boiled over in 1961 into the first major piece of legislation to deal with structural unemployment — the Area Redevelopment Act, authorizing the spending of $375 million to stimulate economic activity in depressed areas. One supposes that the model for such a statute might have been the Tennessee Valley Authority, which, since its inception in the 1930s, has developed resources, built dams, helped towns and counties, and strengthened local institutions.[8] But that, of course, was by no means the case. The models rather appear to have been the more modest state development programs, like those in Pennsylvania and New Hampshire.[9] Most of A. R. A.'s money was earmarked for long-term loans and some of it for grants to local communities. As the measure was not intended to deal specifically with the effects of automation, only a modest sum — not to exceed $4.5 million — was allocated for teaching the unemployed new skills.

As might have been expected, the program moved slowly. By the first quarter of 1962 only $4.3 million had been approved for eighteen industrial projects. A drumfire of criticism developed, mainly because critics saw the objectives of the Act being perverted by political pressures. Aid to recreational areas was challenged, and A.R.A. officials were careful to avoid business-expansion loans in order not to draw protests from competing businessmen. By the end of 1963, more than $200 million had been commited, presumably enough to create 20,000 new jobs in areas long afflicted by joblessness. Additional funds were, however, refused by Congress in 1963; moneys to help

273

communities build roads, sewers, and other public facilities had been exhausted, and the A.R.A. threatened to expire by mid-1965. The Great Society, however, made gestures to revive it, although Congress was not overly enthusiastic. Congress finally voted continuation, albeit in a somewhat different form. Yet any extension would have to eliminate the original Act's basic defect. For, although the idea behind A.R.A. was to plant seed capital in depressed areas to attract new ventures, the very restriction of loans to companies that were poor risks in the first place made it unlikely that much good could be done. Within the context of the present social and economic order, a depressed area seemed to need the kind of lift that could be generated by successful firms; marginal companies stagger no matter how much financial blood is pumped into them. The consequence was that any number of A.R.A.-supported firms collapsed before too long.[10]

The bill's origins lay in the 1955 investigation of the Senate Labor Committee into the causes of high unemployment in depressed areas. The Joint Economic Committee then conducted its own hearings. Soon Senator Paul Douglas started his several efforts to get a bill passed, only to have each of them vetoed by President Eisenhower. During the 1960 presidential campaign, John F. Kennedy promised to urge similar legislation on the Congress. The first piece of legislation he signed in May 1961 was the Area Redevelopment Act. Senator Douglas, its leading proponent on the Hill, thought of helping just a few of the hardest hit localities as demonstration projects: He wanted to show what could be done for areas devastated by time and technology.[11] But as the A.R.A. bill went through one session of Congress after another; through committee and subcommittee hearings; through drafts, redrafts, and rewrites, a pork-barrel sentiment developed. In response to pressures from mayors and governors all over the country, the A.R.A. geographic responsibility was widened and its possible effectiveness thereby diluted. Agricultural areas were added to the original list in order to obtain votes on the Hill; the result was the inclusion of more and more "depressed" areas. As Sar A. Levitan has argued, the program, considering its limited size, ought to have focused on declining areas—communities that were losing population and whose social capital (homes, schools, churches, businesses) was being left to waste away. After all, we were supposed to be helping regions where income was low, where 30 per cent of the homes were substandard, and from which 11 per cent of the population had fled in the decade of the 1950s. Instead, by the time all the baker's dozens of Congressmen and state and local officials got through there were enough growing towns in the program to convert it into a travesty.[12] Of course, unemployment in a town whose population is on the upswing is just as serious as unemployment in a town whose young people are running off to other places. But A.R.A. was not designed to cope with both situations: Its objective was supposed to be to encourage new industries—new to the communities—to move into *depressed* areas to provide jobs.

A.R.A. itself estimated that its various projects would provide some 70,000 jobs. Unfortunately, there is no way of verifying the official guess: The projection of the job-creating impact of A.R.A. undertakings based on the expectations of applicants could very well be rooted in overenthusiasm. W. H. Miernyk did find that two-thirds of those employed in A.R.A. projects in some thirty establishments were not working when they applied for work and that an additional 11 per cent were engaged only part time. On this basis, it might be fair to conclude that A.R.A. projects did some good.

Yet even if A.R.A. had stuck to the objective of drawing in new industries, it is doubtful that the program as conceived would have worked properly. A.R.A. assumed that bolstering existing social capital and social overhead would make a sick town with decrepit shells of abandoned factories attractive enough to draw in a new auto-assembly plant or an automated abattoir. This "trickle down" theory may have seemed plausible on paper, but, in the event, it proved difficult to convince a Ford or an Armour to invest in a town on the downgrade. In short, contemporary politics and economics had alike shown themselves inadequate to cope with the needs engendered by the new technology.

The A.R.A. was replaced in August 1965 by the Economic Development Act, which provided annual outlays of $760 million in depressed-area aid, almost twice the level of the total assistance under A.R.A. A tie-in was established with the War on Poverty by authorization of $500 million in annual grants for public works to provide jobs that would benefit the long-term unemployed and members of low-income families. The presumption was that public works would be established on which unskilled labor might be utilized—clearing streams, building fire trails, reforestation, and the like. Whether or not such projects would in the long run establish stable and diversified local economies was questionable.

One might think that the huge volume of defense contracts could be employed to help depressed areas. Some efforts were made in 1952 by the Office of Defense Mobilization to channel contracts to surplus-labor areas, but contracts had to go in any case to the lowest bidders. In 1962, 0.5 per cent of total military procurement went to the so-called "depressed areas."[13] The fact of the matter is that the Department of Defense cannot by law give awards to businesses in poorer areas if lower costs can be arranged elsewhere. The statute, of course, is based on normal accounting procedures. From a social standpoint, however, unemployment surely ought to be included in any calculus of costs, as it is in West Germany and Britain, where efforts are made to locate new plants in areas that need jobs; in Sweden, similarly, investment-tax credits are utilized to locate factories where they can be most helpful. Unfortunately, such ideas are much too suggestive of economic planning to be fully acceptable to American policy-makers; even Senator Douglas did not appear overly enthusiastic about the limited planning provisions urged by some proponents of the Area Redevelopment Act.[14]

What can happen when a town suddenly becomes "depressed" is illustrated by the case of South Bend, Indiana. Although the situation there did not stem from automation per se, South Bend's experience is nevertheless instructive. It will be recalled that Studebaker suddenly closed its plant just before Christmas 1963, selecting that moment, it was rumored, to avoid paying for three holidays. To counteract community reaction, the company promised to contribute $70,000—less than one-fifth of its savings on holiday pay—toward a retraining program. Fortunately, it seemed that a dismal future would be dispelled by the Administration in Washington; the President immediately ordered the Agriculture, Commerce, Labor, and Defense Departments to do something for South Bend. Surplus foods and new industry were to be moved into the community. One year later, of 3,900 older workers who had passed through Project ABLE (Ability Based on Long Experience), the counseling center set up by the National Council on Aging, 900 were still looking for work, 680 had retired, 123 were planning to retire, 140 were ill, 122 were being retrained, 90 had moved, and about 50 had died in the meantime. The unemployment rate for ex-Studebaker workers was estimated to be more than 30 per cent. The men were urged to apply at a Ford plant 200 miles away or to look for work in Michigan City. Job retraining had reached some 500 workers in a year's time, and the six companies that had bought the old Studebaker facilities could not make up the loss in work: Within a year, jobs in South Bend dropped by 7,000, with a decline in man-hours worked of 28 per cent.[15] Although South Bend has few signs of indigence, with retail sales holding up and with the building of new motels and warehouses, not much has been done or can be done for the ex-Studebaker workers.

Obviously, a good deal more would be necessary to help communities hit by sudden plant shutdowns or industrial obsolescence. In March 1965, President Johnson offered a revised program of aid to depressed areas, stressing regional development rather than assistance to particular cities or counties. He suggested substantial increases in the outlays made available to A.R.A. and through the accelerated public works-program, but the effort was nevertheless to be based on local initiative. Firms would be helped to pay the interest on loans borrowed from private sources, grants and loans were to be made to regional public agencies and industries to develop "growth centers" to create jobs in less prosperous areas, and working-capital loans would be guaranteed by the Federal government up to 90 per cent of their total amounts. But the request for aid would have to come from localities: Johnson was not prepared to offend local pride by calling them "depressed." Yet one wonders how effective the program will be, for to be eligible for assistance a locality has to show an unemployment rate twice the national average for one year out of two; 1.75 times the national rate for two years out of three; or 1.5 times the national rate for two years out of four. This requirement implies that eligibility will depend on an official unemployment rate of about 7.5 to 10 per cent of the work force. In 1962 the redevelopment areas had an unemployment rate of 9.4 per cent, compared to the national figure of 5.6 per cent, a ratio of about 1.7 to 1. There could thus be a four-year wait before aid would be granted under the President's new scheme. About one-third of the nation's counties, with one-sixth of the total population, would be eligible for assistance under the proposal.[16]

NOWHERE IN THE NATION had technology wrought more havoc than in the hills of Appalachia. As early as the 1870s attempts were made to bring out the area's bituminous wealth. Coal corporations organized by northern speculators bought acres of mountains for pennies to capture that wealth. The veins of coal ran deep, and a burgeoning economy needed it all. The exploitation of coal brought railroads and company towns, where the lives of the miners were scrutinized from birth to death with no less care than if they had been living in a twentieth-century totalitarian state. Periodically, the towns would turn sick as depression hit the economy: The coal barons would leave, but their return was assured with the next boom. As the native mountaineer was uninterested in mining or unbending to a boss, immigrants from Poland, Czechoslovakia, and Italy were brought in to supplement the existing supply of labor. Then came the Great Depression, and King Coal lay prostrate in a cloud of bituminous dust, never to recover his preeminence in the hills and valleys. Technology, with an assist from John L. Lewis, completed the destruction of accustomed ways and turned Appalachia into an economic wasteland.[17]

If ever a region could be called "depressed" it was Appalachia: Not until 1965 was a direct attempt made to deal with its problems, when in March of that year President Johnson signed a bill to provide $1.1 billion in aid to the eleven states of the area. Of course, efforts to focus attention on Appalachia had been made as far back as 1963, when President Kennedy held an all-day meeting at the White House to discuss the problem. About 76 per cent of the new bill's funds were to be spent over a six-year period on highways and local access roads. The remainder was to be distributed over two years for health centers, soil conservation, land reclamation, water-resource development, vocational schools, sewage-treatment plants, hospitals, and airports. It was evidently assumed that Appalachia's distress was caused by its physical isolation and that roads would open the area to the rest of the nation. As far as jobs were concerned, it was likely that not more than 20 per cent of the total man hours provided by road building and other projects would go to unskilled labor. And, as many of the inhabitants lacked construction skills, workers would probably have to be imported from other regions. If the building up of tourism was an objective, the generation of such jobs would have to await the completion of the roads, a goal that was some years away. As is generally true of such legislation federal funds in most instances would require some state or local matching—in an area where state and local governments were as poor as the inhabitants. In any case, effective area redevelopment might have called for a reversal of the proportions, as the central problem of Appalachia arises from the decay of its entire social-overhead inheritance. Individual states' rights are to be protected through representation by governors on the Appalachian Regional Commission. It was hoped that correcting the deficiencies of physical and human resources would draw in venture capital, but curiously the Administration seemed bent mainly on improving recreational and educational facilities. Not only is another uncoordinated effort in the offing, but once more officials want to siphon most of the funds into "growth centers." And, of course, final success will depend on the willingness of the eleven governors to make the commission system function effectively.

The first mountain dirt was turned at Isom, Kentucky, and Salem, West Virginia, in July 1965 to start construction of the 2,350 miles of "developmental" highways. According to observers, the onlookers seemed more enthralled with the huge yellow earth-moving machinery than with the remote benefits that might be brought to their communities in the future. One can anticipate that the Federal government and the states will wrangle over the highways planned for the region. They may accept proposals based on a "systems analysis," prepared under a $130,000 contract by a private consulting firm that stuffed masses of data into econometric models in order to decide which depressed spots need the roads or hospitals. The greater likelihood is that the governors will insist on locations that will return the most in the currency of state politics. More hopeful is the possibility that the "Appalachia" program will be extended to the cut-over regions of the Upper Great Lakes, New England, and the Ozarks. In early 1965 several legislators proposed not only grants and developmental loans for these areas but an indefinite extension of the expiring A.R.A. as well—this time concentrating on places with genuine economic potential and "a readily available supply of labor at advantageous wage rates and without anti-management attitude." Included in the advantages were low local and state taxes, low land and construction costs, and low power rates.

Some of the programs, however, may founder on local pride: Communities resent being labeled "depressed." An old man in a tar-paper shack in Marlinton, West Virginia, wants the government to "leave us alone," but the little town is quiet except for the men in the pool hall: No one is on the streets, and the stores are empty. Although many inhabitants of these small towns, picturesque but isolated from the traffic on the turnpikes, agree with the old man, others have begun to sense that they cannot survive without something like the $1.1 billion Appalachia bill. Yet they need more than the statute will provide: They need water systems, sewage plants, public works—projects once sponsored by the accelerated public-works program and now to be replaced by the new legislation. The road-building program may help; at least the people will be able to move in and out quickly and to overcome the barriers of narrow, winding goat paths. They may now get motels and restaurants and supermarkets, as well as billboards to replace the tobacco signs painted on the sides of decrepit barns. As the young people flee from Appalachia, tourists may substitute for them—once the roads are in.[18]

AMONG THE THINGS the experience of A.R.A. and similar programs revealed was an urgent need for a viable manpower policy. It was a need that arose, not only from persistent high unemployment rates and from the monthly influx of thousands of teen-agers into the labor market, but also from the dislocations created by automation. As we have seen, the employment situation is complicated and confusing: Disentangling in statistically precise ways the variety of elements involved can be an exacerbating task. Although some unemployment could be attributed to lagging demand, computer technology and obsolescense of older methods of making goods destroyed numerous skills while creating other, more esoteric occupations—which themselves required fewer bodies to fill them. It was doubtful that the heat emanating from a warmed-up fiscal policy would melt the icebergs of hard-core unemployment; only a war could achieve that. But what of the other schemes that were adopted—vocational education, retraining, and programs to improve labor mobility? How have they been faring?

To begin with labor mobility, there are some 1,900 public employment-service offices in the nation, operated jointly, as it were, by the Department of Labor, through the United States Employment Service, and the states. The Federal government provides technical assistance and funds and sets the procedures and methods, whereas the states actually operate the offices. The purpose is to facilitate the employment of all workers and to help employers fill empty slots. The effectiveness of the offices, however, varies from state to state, for administrators have been apt to think of the unemployment-insurance program in which they are involved as primary and of placement, counseling, and information as secondary and not very urgent responsibilities. In 1963 it took the chiding of President Kennedy and the continual prodding of the Labor Department to get the local offices to do more placement work. But for all the chiding and prodding and for all the appropriations—$172 million in 1964, of which $164 million went to the states to operate the local offices—"new hires" through state employment offices still run around a mere 15 per cent of the total number of new jobs acquired.

Perhaps the local offices can do better, despite the informal nature of the job market. For the fact is that the major sources of information about new jobs are friends, relatives, and the diligent pursuit of rumors: They account for about 60 per cent of new job leads. The more formal modes of searching for jobs, including "call-backs," come from applications at plant gates, newspaper ads, and both private and public employment agencies. Yet during World War II, when the job market had to be structured, the U.S.E.S. did yeoman service, recruiting thousands for wartime training and achieving more than twelve million placements in 1944, more than twice the level of 1940. But it was federalized then; perhaps it ought to be again. At any rate, federalization would help to establish uniform standards and staff salaries. Under the present arrangement, U.S.E.S. offices remain parochial in their outlooks and have but limited impact on the job market. They rely on personal contacts by individual solicitors and are generally held in low esteem by employers, who are more likely than not to call them the "unemployment offices." More chiding, more prodding, more pressure must be exerted to get the U.S.E.S. off the dead center where it has been stalled for so long.[19]

In 1962, the U.S.E.S. installed an "early warning system" to identify in advance groups of workers who might be threatened by technological displacement or mass layoffs. This system was an excellent idea, except that not all employers were willing to tell what they were planning far enough ahead for it to do much good: After all, to announce a layoff months in advance might have a harmful effect on a corporation's stock prices or might reveal plans to a rival. For the first two years of the "early warning system" reports on 250,000 workers who were permanently laid off were sent to Washington by the local offices: Only 40 per cent had been warned in advance. It may very well be that legislative sanctions will be necessary to reinforce a voluntary "early warning" system. At the very least, employers should be persuaded to register all job vacancies. Legislative action might start rather modestly by offering firms an adjustment in unemployment-insurance rates in return for registering contemplated openings at the U.S.E.S. But all such efforts have run afoul of the private employment-agency lobby of the National Employment Association, which has fought to reserve the cream of the job market for its members, leaving the more difficult to place to the government.[20]

It is sometimes argued that the unemployed could find jobs if they would only move elsewhere. But one fact is that those out of work are fairly mobile: In one study about 11 per cent of those who were unemployed at the time (March 1962) had moved to another county by the following year, compared to only 6 per cent of the employed. True, the mobile unemployed fared better than the immobile unemployed: Seventy-two per cent of the former were working by March 1963, in contrast to 55 per cent of the latter. But the migrants were younger men able to shop around for jobs. Marriage, the fear of losing seniority rights, and ties with family and community seemed to be powerful restraints against shifts elsewhere. Actually, little is known about the factors in labor mobility or how to facilitate the movement of the unemployed workers. Perhaps more will be learned from the demonstration projects authorized under the 1963 Manpower Development and Training Act amendment which set up a $4 million experimental relocation program for 1,500 jobless workers and their families. Additional outlays of $10 million for a two-year program were subsequently provided. The cost of moving to another area, plus "tie-over" allowances are part of the scheme, and the job search will be facilitated through the U.S.E.S. Defense workers are thus to be moved out of Long Island, former iron-ore miners in Minnesota shifted elsewhere, and a few ex-Studebaker workers helped to find jobs in another locality. Of course, they can always be encouraged to go into the service trades—cooking and clerking—where the pay is frequently low, about $1 an hour. In the meantime, researchers will learn whether or not home ownership inhibits mobility and something of the effect that inward migration has on a receiving community.[21]

BUT MOBILITY alone cannot work unless those with proper skills are directed to such openings as may exist. The key term, of course, is "proper skills," and here an effective training program is essential. By now, there seems little doubt that some members of the unemployed lack the skills that would qualify them to fill whatever jobs are available. In Washington, D.C., for example, there were in early 1964 several hundred empty jobs in the printing trades with no one around to do the work—and no program in operation to train unemployed individuals for these posts. As for the young, two-thirds of the new entrants into the labor force have no specific training of any kind: Even possession of high school diplomas does not necessarily qualify them for jobs. What is being done to provide all these people with the skills they need if they are ever to obtain work?

Unfortunately, the effort to educate and train youngsters does not begin to meet the need. The entire educational system is out of balance, for it is geared to the 20 or 30 per cent of students who go to college. Most are pushed out of the educational apparatus, or they drift out: Thirty-five per cent of students are lost in high school; 45 per cent of high-school students are lost in the sense that they wind up in dead-end jobs; 40 per cent of those entering college drop out. They join the ranks of unemployed youth or enter low-skilled, low-paying jobs. Yet ours is a society in which a job and an income are vital to a young person. As Paul Goodman says, money in the pocket of a youngster does much for his self-esteem; but although a job is an entree into adulthood, a dead-end post is defeat.[22]

The fact is that job training and adult education show no sensible pattern. The task is undertaken by different organizations, public and private, each going its own way without much regard for what the others are doing. Ideally, the programs ought to relate to some objective, like income maintenance, but this end is far from having been realized.[23] Of course, there has been a Federal program for vocational education in existence since 1917, when the Smith-Hughes Act first provided for sharing costs with the states. This program has provided about $7 million annually, to which additional sums have been added from time to time by other pieces of legislation—the George-Reed Act in 1929, the

George-Ellzey Act in 1934, the National Defense program of World War II, and the George-Dean and George-Barden Acts. Yet all these measures have added up to a meagre program at best: Only a fraction of full-time high-school students are enrolled in the vocational phases of the activities sponsored by these laws.[24] And in 1963, more than 60 per cent of that fraction was enrolled in home economics and agriculture courses: The rest was in trades, retailing-wholesaling, technical, and nursing courses — hardly a meaningful distribution for the future needs of an age of automation. The fact is that today there is no way of knowing whether or not a particular kind of training will carry one for as much as a decade. Hence the urgency of continuing education.[25]

Perhaps the new Vocational Education Act of 1963 will improve the situation: Funds have been allotted for construction of facilities, teacher training, and research. Together with the money made available under the Smith-Hughes and George-Barden Acts, the total sum available for vocational education will reach $235 million by the middle of 1966, whereas enrollment, it is hoped, will be increased to seven million by 1968. Also, it may be that cookery and farming will no longer dominate the program.

Some training was provided for unemployed people under the A.R.A. in 1961, but it was little more than a pilot program. Not until a year later was a more hopeful start made,[26] when the Manpower Development and Training Act was passed after much legislative travail. Few will question the worthiness of M.D.T.A. objectives: Yet there are some who say that the "hard-core" unemployed cannot be retrained because they have low IQs or because they prefer unemployment checks and relief payments or because they want training other than that provided under M.D.T.A. The difficulty of drawing hard-core unemployed into training programs stems, however, more from inadequate allowances, the ways in which the program may underline the participants' sense of inadequacy, and the plain fact that jobs are not available when the courses are completed.[27] People with ostensibly low IQ's are perfectly capable of being retrained, as was reported in *New Society* (October 31, 1963). A group of sixteen workers with an average IQ of ninety-five was put through an electronics course: Eleven completed the training successfully. Many employees refused the training because they recognized their own limitations—a lack of knowledge of algebra and basic electricity. The fundamental problem was poor educational background rather than low intelligence.

Given the "educability" of most people, the M.D.T.A. program makes sense. The projects are conducted all over the country without regard to the economic status of individual areas. The objective is to select unemployed individuals for training and to provide facilities, instruction, and subsistence allowances. In 1962–1963 these allowances averaged $35 a week. During that period, the Manpower Administration reports, there were 71,400 trainees in the various programs, and by September 1963 there were about 18,000 graduates, 70 per cent of whom had obtained jobs. Unfortunately, the programs in the beginning were highly selective: In order to show results quickly, administrators took the "cream of the crop" and chose only those who could be easily trained and easily placed. Even as a temporary policy, utilized to get a program under way, "creaming" is a dubious affair.[28] The sorts of jobs for which training was provided were the relatively simple ones—welding, small-appliance repairs, nursing, machine operation. The poorly educated and older worker was all but ignored as officials concentrated on high admission standards and younger people. They argued that "training is a salvage operation to help individuals without a marketable skill, not a real solution to unemployment" and that "the unemployed couldn't fill the jobs where most openings are if you trained them 100 years."[29] Still, as a result of the rather sharp criticisms of its initial efforts, the M.D.T.A. was revised in 1963 to reduce eligibility requirements and to provide for "multi-occupational training," through which the three Rs might be taught. In addition, some allowance was made for "manpower research" to forecast the effects of the new technology on employment, occupations, and skill requirements.

Nevertheless, a much larger program is needed if more than the present $\frac{3}{8}$ of 1 per cent of the labor force is to be reached. If the Swedish experience is any criterion, the training effort ought to be expanded to at least 1 per cent of the work force, or about two and a half times the first year's level. This higher percentage implies the inclusion of about 900,000 people in M.D.T.A. and similar training programs by 1975. The goal is not an impossible one if better allowances, moving expenses, and the like are provided. The average expenditure per trainee should reach about $2,200, or almost double the 1962–1963 level—a $2 billion annual outlay. If half of those in a 1 per cent program were unskilled or semiliterate, then more than 400,000 people would be receiving basic education—clearly a tremendous contribution. The question is how to reach these people, a problem underscored by the Norfolk, Virginia, experience in 1963. Quite patently, one needs to assure trainees adequate allowances and jobs afterward if frustration is to be overcome. In Norfolk it took an anonymous contribution of $29,000 for larger allowances to keep the program going: Participants had exhausted their credit with shopkeepers and landlords and the training program threatened to collapse after only seven months. Even worse, many of those out of work or who had never had jobs had lost contact with or were deeply distrustful of public agencies. Clearly, more strenuous efforts were necessary to reach these people.[30]

Despite the hopes for a good start in the training programs, officials finally had to acknowledge the deficiencies. With training predicated on expectations of job placement—expectations that were more pious hopes than reasonable forecasts—most of the trainees were selected from the "prime" age group of twenty-two to forty-four years, and they had to be at least high-school graduates with some work history. Only 10 per cent were more than forty-five years old, in sharp contrast to the 40 per cent of the long-term unemployed who were in the older age brackets. The outcome was that 60 per cent of the trainees already had twelve years of education; on the other hand more than 60 per cent of the hard-core jobless had failed to finish high-school.[31] Clearly, this program was "creaming." Said one state training coordinator who craved success, "We're not going to be caught dead training people who are inadequate."

The first twenty-nine months of M.D.T.A. saw 6,700 projects established with 320,000 trainees in them. But

Congress had hoped for 400,000 *trained* people in the first three years. During the 1963–1964 fiscal year, the Laboi Department reported 285,000 "approved" trainees in M.D.T.A. programs, of whom 185,000 were enrolled at the end of the reporting period. Those who completed their courses totaled 88,000. Although the placement record for those who were "graduated" was 73 per cent, the fact remains that completions were only 47 per cent of those actually enrolled in training courses. Clearly, something was awry. M.D.T.A. programs were simply not reaching the uneducated as they were intended to do. Although 27 per cent of the unemployed have less than eight years of schooling, only 15 per cent of M.D.T.A. trainees are at that level. Completions in 1964 decreased, compared with 1963, while the ratio of dropouts rose from 24 per cent to 30 per cent. Officials attributed this rise to improved economic conditions, a contention that may have a measure of truth in it as the increase in dropout rates was higher for men than for women. Yet bureaucratic hesitancy, inadequate allowances, poor job prospects, run-of-the-mill courses, and notable lack of enthusiasm from both unions and management also may have been elements in a confused situation.[32]

One of the groups most seriously affected by changing technology is the older workers, yet, as we have seen, the early retraining efforts all but ignored them. Even when they remain with a plant they are apt to be shifted to new jobs with loss of status, income, or both, especially when skills are limited.[33] And if he is displaced, the man over forty discovers that, although he may be too young to retire, he is indeed too old to work. The need to retrain such a man is barely accepted by a society that has declared him redundant. Yet there is ample evidence that he can be conscientious, responsible and loyal. His retraining may take somewhat longer than that for a younger man, but the investment may be worthwhile, as was demonstrated by a firm in Birmingham, England, which successfully retrained a group of fifteen men between the ages of forty and fifty.[34] In fact, it may be hazardous to predict success solely on the basis of age. The major factor appears to be education, or the lack of it, although frequently this lack may be counterbalanced by experience.[35]

288

Some community groups have, in exasperation, simply initiated their own training efforts without waiting for the corporation or government to extend their largesse. In Detroit, the Trade Union Leadership Council taught new skills to about 600 people over a two-year period, providing by far the best training course for Negroes in that city. The Council started in an old hardware store, which members converted into a school. At first, emphasis was placed on secretarial and clerical skills, expanding later to business English, remedial reading, sewing, and electrical work. The teachers were all unpaid volunteers, and all applicants were welcome—there was no "creaming."

In Philadelphia, an old police station ready to be razed was turned into an Opportunities Industrialization Center, with machinery and equipment for training technicians. Contributions of more than $500,000—from foundations and the Negro community itself—helped the O.I.C. to set up courses in electronics and how to wait on tables. Even one employed at a menial, low-paying job could register for a course to improve his skills. Within nine months almost 300 people were "in training," and more than fifty had been graduated. O.I.C. has been much more successful than has the M.D.T.A. program in the same city, perhaps because the community itself has a stake in what it does.[36] Similarly, a U.A.W. training program to teach white-collar skills under M.D.T.A. sponsorship has had a fair measure of success. In all such instances, the objective has been to develop skills that will be needed in the future. An experimental project in Washington, D.C., revealed that many people of average intelligence and limited education can learn the skills required for certain jobs in electronic data processing. It turns out that department stores and banks do not need engineers and scientists to do routine programming and that people without college education can handle the bulk of their data-processing work.[37]

Yet all these training efforts barely make a dent in the hard-core unemployment so characteristic among younger people, Negroes, and older workers. For the fact is that our emerging technology has little use for occupations that require no skills and no education. Furthermore, the fourteen-to-twenty-four-year-old group will probably reach twenty million by 1970; although the ratio of school dropouts may decline, it will not be enough to cut appreciably into the more than seven million youngsters who will have left school in the next five years. And the job-training effort, focused as it is on immediate blue-collar placement, offers only a stop-gap solution. Furthermore, those in charge of training programs often do not know enough about the people who are in need of training. The programs are in the main "short-run," and they consequently produce little or no positive effects on long-range employment possibilities: They are not geared to an economy undergoing rapid change.[38] As remedial measures they may be noteworthy, but they do little to maintain income over the long run or to create as many jobs as might be achieved through public works and cultivation of the neglected public sector.[39]

TO SUPPLEMENT job-creating techniques, society must provide income maintenance for those unable to adjust quickly. This help implies adequate social-security benefits, unemployment insurance, decent public welfare, and even outright income subsidies. Although these measures mean transferring income to those unable to support themselves, a practice that has long been in existence in Western nations,[40] in the main such redistribution is not from the middle or upper classes but rather from wage earners at work to the unemployed: Ours is a society in which workers support their own welfare programs.[41] More than three-fourths of social-insurance taxes are paid by those with incomes under $5,000 a year. Somehow this curious situation is justified by the argument that the indigent would anyway have to be supported by their own families and friends. In 1958, Old-Age, Survivors', and Disability transfers totaling about $4.5 billion went from those with incomes over $3,000 a year to those with incomes under $3,000. The effect on consumption standards could not have been very marked, as the marginal propensity to consume in all probability was not very different for the two groups. Furthermore, it is said, the lower-income groups may have borrowed, or dissaved, in order to maintain previous consumption standards. The multiplying effects of enhanced consuming power from income transfers may, however, have counter-balanced these impacts. Obviously, without O.A.S.D.I, the aged would have spent a good deal less than they did on clothing or personal services. And as far as retirement incomes encourage older people to move to Florida, where they may join with other senior citizens, geographic mobility is thereby enhanced.

Total O.A.S.D.I. payments in 1960 approximated $11 billion; they are expected to reach $18 billion by 1970. Coverage is extended to about 90 per cent of the population, and some two-thirds of those over sixty-five receive benefits. No doubt the availability of such transfer income has cut the participation of the aged in the labor force, although doubtless other factors are involved as well.[42] But it can by no means be asserted that such benefits are adequate in such an affluent society as ours. A retired couple in the 1960s might have received about $127 a month in O.A.S.D.I. benefits, but the requirements for a modest, adequate budget were perhaps twice that sum. The fact is that among the retired, 64 per cent of whom are social-security beneficiaries, over one-fourth of the couples, one-third of unrelated males, and half the unrelated females do not have enough income for subsistence living.[43] When the social-security system was established in 1935, the maximum annual earnings that could be credited for contributions were $3,000; the maximum up to 1965 was $4,800 (increased to $6,600 in that year), although the comparable figure today would be closer to $10,000. Benefits declined from 21 per cent of average monthly earnings in manufacturing in 1940 to 19 per cent in 1960[44] The number of aged receiving maximum O.A.S.D.I. benefits is pitifully small: In 1960 fewer than 10 per cent of beneficiaries were receiving $116 a month or more. The average was $74 a month, and almost 60 per cent were paid between $45 and $105 a month. Supplementary assistance frequently must be supplied by states and local communities, for otherwise starvation itself might be added to the annals of the poor in America.

At long last some changes were made in 1965. In addition to a health-insurance program for the aged of rather modest proportions — the famed Medicare plan — an increase in O.A.S.D.I. benefits of 7 per cent was provided. The definitions of disability and retirement were made more liberal, coverage was extended to self-employed physicians, and the contribution-and-benefit base was raised to $6,600. It is now possible for retirement benefits to rise to $168 a month for a single worker, with an ultimate family maximum of $368 a month. The proposed advance in benefits is still penurious, however: At the average level now paid it represents about $5 a month. To achieve a "modestly adequate" budget, most of the retired would need an increase of at least three times that amount. Furthermore, the contribution rates will rise to almost 5 per cent by 1973. If there were private pension supplements, the whole system would indeed begin to be a sensible one.

Another "income maintenance" program of great significance for the age of automation is unemployment insurance. Presumably this benefit helps to offset wage losses; it is supposedly a built-in stabilizer against economic recession. The payments, however, vary sharply from state to state. The duration of benefits also varies — from twenty-three weeks in Arkansas and Mississippi to forty-two weeks in California and Wyoming. Furthermore, all sorts of eligibility requirements, most of them intended to limit the program, restrict the extent of benefits. Exhaustion of benefits before finding a job is not uncommon: In the 1961 recession about 2.5 million unemployed used up their U.I. benefits completely and were still out of work. In addition, a 1962 Labor Department study indicated that fully 60 per cent of the unemployed in its "survey week" were not receiving U.I. benefits. The payments are generally less than half of the wage losses, with the heaviest impact falling on Negroes, older people, and those displaced by machines. The consequence has been that average weekly U.I. benefits fell from 42 per cent of earnings in 1939 to 35 per cent in 1962.[45] Clearly, benefits under unemployment insurance ought to be at least half actual earnings, if not more; duration ought to be extended to a minimum of a year; and coverage should be applied to all workers. About fifteen million workers are not protected by unemployment insurance, many in small firms with three or fewer employees. The costs of improvements are well within the limits of a 3 per cent payroll tax. An affluent society can easily afford to be generous, if not for humane reasons, then to ensure its affluence. The cost would not be excessive: It is estimated that a growing prosperous economy could readily sustain a $4.5 billion U.I. program by 1975. Income maintenance by our standards comes rather cheaply.[46]

But ancient habits continue to limit genuine possibilities. An archaic ethic that insists that he who does not work shall not eat; a congressional structure virtually unchanged since Colonial days; a federalism that fails to come to grips with the complexities of regional economies; an apathetic response from the affluent; and our persistence in riding off in all directions at once—all these elements raise almost insuperable barriers to the formulation of a reasonable program to deal with automation and its consequences. Meanwhile, the technology of our age—fostered by the state, which at the same time has responded with pathetic inadequacy to the problems it has created—continues to spread with undiminished force.

AN INTERESTING RESPONSE to the problem of displacement has been the idea of a guaranteed annual income. According to Robert Theobald, its contemporary progenitor, the notion can be traced as far back as Aquinas.[47] Theobald says he got the idea from Thomas Jefferson's belief that freedom and ownership of land were intimately related. Transposed to modern conditions, argues Theobald, this theory means "an absolute right to a share in the production of machine systems." In any case, the first clear statement of a guaranteed income may be found in Edward Bellamy's utopian novel *Looking Backward,* and it was later given some currency by Bertrand Russell in his *In Praise of Idleness*.

The most recent pronouncement was that issued by the Ad Hoc Committee on the Triple Revolution, a group of educators, publicists, and economists who, in March 1964, urged among other things the adoption of a guaranteed income as a way of meeting the impact of the new technology.[48] Fearing that automation—or cybernation, as some prefer to call it—was breaking the traditional link between

293

jobs and incomes, it prescribed a striking solution: Society, said the committee, should undertake an unqualified commitment to provide everyone with an adequate income as a *matter of right* without any necessary expectation that work would be demanded to earn such income.

The reaction was little short of amazing. One might have thought that the notion would be dismissed and forgotten as another wild idea from a group of harebrained professors and assorted radicals. Although official Washington did not respond (the committee had sent its report to the White House), hundreds of newspaper editorials across the land raged against this audacious attack on the ingrained Puritan ethic of our time. A major debate developed, which is still going on.

If some economists are right in contending that present unemployment is really hard core, afflicting mainly Negroes and youth, the technologically displaced, and the unretired aged, then the guaranteed-income plan may very well be the sole method for absorbing these groups into the larger society. The cost of bringing them up to a $3,000 a year level would be around $11 or $12 billion a year, or substantially less than 2 per cent of the GNP.

This idea is, of course, a limited application of the Theobald proposal: Probably the idea has the greatest relevance for these groups. If someone preferred to remain poor—a young artist or writer attempting to develop his skills—why not allow him to test his powers rather than exhaust himself in a dead-end job? And if someone wanted to seek more than the guaranteed minimum, there would be nothing in the arrangement to prevent him from doing so. Rubber workers in Akron working a short week also engage in moonlighting.

The feasibility of the Ad Hoc Committee's suggestion, which was so harshly rejected by academic economists and editorial writers alike, has been supported more recently by an income-subsidy plan for the poor. This plan is nothing but the guaranteed income in reverse. The irony is that the income subsidy, or negative income tax, was developed by academicians: It is therefore presumably more respectable. Under this plan, the government would subsidize all families whose incomes fell below a predetermined poverty line, however that might be defined. All families would thus be assured of at least a minimum income.

The negative income tax was broached in 1962 by Milton Friedman, a conservative economist who was one of Barry Goldwater's advisers in the 1964 Presidential campaign.[49] Professor Friedman was mainly concerned with abolishing social security, such categorical assistance as aid to dependent children, public housing, and the like. For him the negative income tax was a good device to get the Federal government out of the economic arena.

It is one of history's minor ironies that his notion, applied in a limited manner, offers a radical solution for some of our more pressing problems — those stemming from poverty and technology. Supporters of the Ad Hoc Committee statement do not find the Friedman idea unwelcome.

In any case, the negative income tax has received a fair measure of attention in recent months. According to reports, even the President may not be averse to it. The proposal has been considered by the Treasury and the Council of Economic Advisers (CEA), and it is now advocated by Prof. James Tobin of Yale, a former member of the CEA. For the fact is that tax cuts of the sort promulgated in 1964 do not help the poor, for they generally pay no taxes at all. In effect, the subsidy would be akin to a refund payment, except that nothing would have been paid to the government in the first instance.[50]

This scheme, of course, poses some neat administrative questions, for it would be up to the beneficiary to apply for his subsidy. Most of those lacking previous contact with the Internal Revenue Service would not have the foggiest notion of how to get their "negative refunds." An extensive effort by the government would be required in order to make all the payments. As the "refunds" might replace some present forms of transfer payments, it is conceivable that injury to some individuals could ensue.

Robert Lampman, in a study made for the Office of Economic Opportunity,[51] suggests one subsidy scale that ranges from $1,500 (half the poverty threshold) for a family earning nothing to a zero subsidy when the family income is $3,000. For example, with an earned income of $500 a year, there would be a gap of $2,500 between the actual income

295

and the poverty standard of $3,000. In such a situation Lampman suggests a "negative tax" rate of 45 per cent, giving a subsidy of $1,125 for a total income of $1,625. If the family's earnings were $2,000 — leaving a poverty gap of $1,000 — a negative tax rate of 25 per cent would add additional income of $250.

Of course, the subsidy rates are arbitrary and would be decided upon by legislative consensus. In any case, an incentive would be given, for, with actual earnings, the family is brought closer and closer to the cutoff line. In short, the scheme would provide additional income to fill the gap between actual earnings and some defined minimum income level.

Tobin's scheme is more involved: A subsidy would be given for each member of a household and then reduced by one-third of any additional income earned in the family until the family's income reached the nonpoverty level. As he explains it: "A family with no other income at all would receive a basic allowance scaled to the number of persons in the family. For a concrete example, take the basic allowance to be $400 a year per person ... a family's allowance would be reduced by a certain fraction of every dollar of other income it received ... [Let us] take this fraction to be one-third. This means that the ... total income including allowances will be increased by two-thirds of whatever it earns."

For a family of four the original allowance would be $1,600. Suppose there are actual earnings of $900; the subsidy would then be cut by $300, increasing the total income to $2,200. This net would continue to increase with earnings until some previously established poverty line was reached. In both plans, the incentive to earn more is encouraged, for the family keeps the larger part of any actual earnings.

The proposals are quite flexible: The key is in the share of new earnings used to offset the subsidy. Such a share could be one-third as in the Tobin plan or a variable one as in Lampman's suggestion. It all depends on what policy makers want to do.

The full substitution of the subsidy for present public-assistance programs would cost about $12 billion. The interesting thing about these plans, however, is their cautious-ness. The Lampman scheme would fill only about half the income gap, whereas Tobin would introduce his proposal in easy stages, using the Federal government's surplus gener-ated by continuing economic growth.

In either case, the guaranteed income would be given as a matter of right. Individuals would receive their pay-ments in periodic installments based on declarations of in-come, with final settlements made at the end of the tax year on April 15. Although the "negative tax" would be reduced by every dollar of earned income, there would be an in-centive to earn, as total income under the scheme would increase faster than the reduction in the subsidy. Existing forms of income maintenance like old-age insurance would not be disturbed, but the benefits under the latter would have to be increased in order to establish a measure of equity.

It is indeed an interesting irony that the Ad Hoc Committee's proposal for a guaranteed annual income, excoriated only two years ago as an exercise in gloom and doom, should now be seriously considered as a way of meeting critical social problems. And why not? There are some thirty million Americans for whom the connection between income and work has been severed. The guaran-teed annual income would offer them a measure of hope, much more promising than the degrading forms of cate-gorical aid developed over the last half-century.

The threat of unemployment and lack of income as a goad to achievement does not seem to work; it is evident that the Ad Hoc Committee proposals are worth a try, whatever shape they may be given. The choice between leisure and work would become real, in contrast to the pre-sent involuntary free time, which must then somehow be filled even though there is no income with which to do so. With a guaranteed income some people might discover real joy in doing things without the pressure of need: They would indeed have genuine leisure. Such an arrangement might very well make leisure activities respectable.

The more one reflects on the profound changes taking place in our society, the more one feels that guaranteed in-comes and negative taxes represent a sensible approach to solving some of the problems generated by these changes. A society that is in process of recreating Disraeli's Two Nations can ill afford to reject measures that promise to correct the ensuing imbalances.

Scientists, engineers, and archons

9

The computer revolution provides a striking illustration of the technicist ethos. The latter may be described as a combination of practices and attitudes which suggests that the world and its inhabitants are little more than a mechanical contrivance. Originating in the seventeenth century with the Cartesian upheaval in philosophy, the technicist ethos suggests that the world can be mastered by "thought," as all the attributes of the universe are reducible to space and mathematics. Such a belief provides the ultimate basis for the advance of technique. Nature is viewed as a self-contained mathematical machine comprising motions in space and time, whereas man as a sentient being is removed from the center of philosophic and scientific inquiry. To certain philosophers and scientists, the implications are self-evident — in a cosmos of geometry, behavior is completely mechanical and the brain but a complicated adding machine. Cartesian coordinates describe the world in which man's perceptions shape the material of his existence. Consequently, man turns to science in his search for a reality independent of himself, and it is to be subjected to his control because he possesses the faculty of reason. Physical things are weighed and measured and accuracy becomes as essential to science as it is to commerce. In the seventeenth century the clock, bookkeeping, and the scale were the characteristic instruments, and even society itself was to be measured by the "political arithmetic" of Sir William Petty.[1]

When Newton converted the world into a set of formulas, an ineradicable link of quantitative empiricism was established between science and technicism. The search for truth was to be directed not along "metaphysical lines" but rather through "positive" channels. Scientific observations were advanced by taxonomy and organization, and verification became the sole criterion for evaluating theory in both the physical and social sciences. Later on, theory was transformed into a set of statements about the operations that an investigator might carry out in his pursuit of the truth. In the event, science was to impose a strange and unaccustomed finality on both society and history.[2] For the incontrovertible fact was that the Cartesian space-time continuum became a dogma that excluded psychological experience and the involuted relationship of man to his environment. Those aspects of life that could be counted and manipulated were valued most highly, whereas the imaginative or emotional was not so much overlooked as ignored.[3] For the technicist, who is able to concentrate only on what he sees, the universe is a gigantic machine, and in the end man too becomes a machine — operated by the laws of nature. Conceptual thinking is rejected, for no statement makes sense if it can not be tested in the physical world, or perhaps by the manner in which statements are employed (a notion that comes fairly close to the pragmatism of John Dewey). Description is superior to prescription, for, as the latter is subject to debate, it can be only a social statement involving consensus, therefore not verifiable in any sensible scientific way. That knowledge is built communally, always drawing on social judgment, is of no import to the technicist.[4]

For his intellectual armament, the modern technicist has drawn on the work of such philosophers as Bertrand Russell and Ludwig Wittgenstein. Logical atomism and logical positivism have enabled the technicist to describe nature by weaving together small fundamental units of fact, each of which presumably can be verified separately. Furthermore, science is essentially an account of operations

—analysis in terms of "doings and happenings," to use Percy Bridgman's phrase—which discards concepts and is limited to examining possible alternatives for measuring phenomena. The creative process thus tiptoed out of the mechanical world of the technicist and left it to the IBM card. The tools of the technicist do not contribute to values and concepts. The latter, therefore, must be imposed upon him, but to escape responsibility he contends that recourse to values is unscientific, for values are not measurable, not verifiable.[5]

IT IS EASY to adopt technicist views, and, given the startling success and strength of modern technology, it is extraordinarily difficult to put them aside. The promise of technology can create a taste for such success and eventually for the power it brings, but all this power may be just as corrupting as it is in politics. Technology requires abstractions: They become tools for controlling nature and means toward practical objectives. Yet seldom are the objectives, or the means, measured by standards external to the system itself, for there is no metatechnic that can be brought to bear on such criteria. Technicist thought is singularly unidimensional, abstracting from everything else and reducing complexities to simple equations that predict with incontrovertible finality. Digital calculations lead to inexorable, inescapable conclusions. The abstractions of the technicist thus enter human life and, by a constant interpenetration with technology, impel humans to act through machines.

> Science manipulates things and gives up living in them. It makes its own limited model of things; operating upon these indices or variables to effect whatever transformations are permitted by their definition, it comes face to face with the real world only at rare intervals. Science is and always has been that admirably active, ingenious and bold way of thinking whose fundamental bias is to treat everything as though it were an object-in-general. . . . Constructive scientific activities see themselves and represent themselves to be autonomous, and their thinking deliberately reduces itself to a set of data-collecting techniques which it has invented. To think is thus to test out,

to operate, to perform—on the condition that this activity is regulated by an experimental control that admits only the most "worked-out" phenomena, more likely *produced* by the apparatus than recorded by it. From this state of affairs arise all sorts of vagabond endeavors.[6]

The rationalism of the technicist makes natural law a matter of faith: It is the only nonrational element in the technicist ethos. Such beliefs have become internalized habits of thought, enshrined as institutions and frequently providing vehicles for the exploration of the irrelevant. Economics, as Friedrich Juenger has said, is thus not a question of equity but of allocation, whereas politics has been conceived as a technical ordering of mass behavior rather than as an investigation of moral judgment.[7] This approach has a flavor of abstract disinterestedness, which in the last analysis suppresses personality in all its uniqueness. The consequence is a loss of balance and a growth of helplessness "directly proportional to human control over nature."[8] We are all resigned, each of us, to reduction to IBM numbers; we are all buried under a pile of digits in which technicism can flourish.

The technicist insists that events move from cause to effect. Behavior follows motivation in mechanical fashion; the human machine repeats itself endlessly. All that science can do is to describe action and reaction; it cannot ask why. It can merely say how, generally in some complicated mathematical manner that in no way alters the motion or direction of human response. It was a long time before these notions were overthrown in physics by such ideas as uncertainty, complementarity, probability, and purposive behavior. But in the social sciences technicism persists, as witness the activity of B. F. Skinner and the attempts of simulators and computer experts to replicate human behavior. To move so easily from pigeons and machines to men is now possible because the sense of the human has been attenuated and there is an avoidance of existence. When the technicist asserts that he will either control society or step out of it, it is the former that is the more likely contingency. For the technicist has on his side an implicit faith in the virtues of technology sustained by its enormous achievements over the last 200 years. Yet these achievements were secured by sacrificing quality for quantity, reducing attributes to measurement, and substituting sentimentality for humanism. The originality of nature is disposed of for all time.

Clearly, a pact now exists between the technicist and the machine. As a consequence, the more perfect and the more useful the latter, the more is man himself diminished. As far back as 1925 Paul Valéry questioned modern man's habit of continually constructing devices to relieve mind of its labors.[9] He asked, with no little reason if we are to judge by subsequent developments, if technicism was not decreasing the capacity to achieve a human style and if it did not enhance our sense of impatience with the world about us and with ourselves. As a consequence, the parasitic association of men and machines has even affected the entire apparatus of administration—the state, the corporation, education, the church, medicine.[10] Personal relationships within the organization demand the elimination of rivalry, says the technicist. Information must flow through feedbacks: There must be data communicators, transmitters of directives, receivers of orders, mechanisms to pass on information to the environment. An organization is a social analogue to the computer. Not only must the productive process be rationalized and centrally directed, but the humans themselves must also be converted into carefully regulated units of a rigidly defined hierarchy. The organizational collective now stands supreme, the perfect paradigm for the domicile of an emmet.[11]

THERE WAS a time when science manifested an independence of the state and of industry, even of its own hierarchy and its own dogmas. But during World War II science had to assume greater responsibility: It became answerable to all these elements and to public opinion as well. The struggle was an uneven one—if indeed it may be said that science did struggle—and nowhere was the surrender more evident than in the case of the computer specialist. Perhaps this surrender was in the nature of the case, for the technology with which computer specialists were concerned involved at first the needs of the state and then the needs of the business archon. At times there was a problem of bringing archon, engineer, and scientist together, if only because the technical language of science tended to create a "communication gap." The layman had to accept what the scientist was talking about virtually on faith, yet it was a faith with a high payoff. "Algorithms," "binary codes," "nanosecond," "inverters," "address," and "subroutines" may not have meant much to an industrialist, but as long as the new language helped to enhance production and to cut costs it was all worthwhile.

The scientist began to assume the aspect of a shaman, a superior being, and even congressmen were perturbed because they could not understand the new science and technology.[12] Suddenly there arose the problem of controlling the scientist: It was not merely a matter of knowing what he was up to but also of directing his research into channels that would offer even higher payoffs. At first engineers and programmers ran things quite their own way, designing projects and cutting across departmental lines with abandon. But in time the corporate chieftains learned more about computer technology: They began to exercise more stringent controls, and gradually the criteria of the budget governed scientist and salesman alike.

There are moments when the scientist expresses a sense of disturbance over the social consequences of his activity. The reaction of atomic researchers after Hiroshima and Nagasaki is a case in point.[13] And some computer specialists and cyberneticians—Norbert Wiener, Richard Bellman, Alice Hilton, and others—have wondered what sort of society we shall evolve when most of the population will have more time available than it will know how to fill. Or, as Dr. Robert Emrich told the Columbia University School of Engineering in November 1964: "Working as I do to bring about the realization of some of the benefits of the computer revolution, I feel like a man guiding a plow drawn by a tiger. As long as the tiger moves forward I am pleased at the progress being made. But what happens when the tiger turns around and fixes his eyes on me?"[14] Yet all these reservations have done little to lessen the drive toward the technicist society. The computer man does not even bear

the burden of that peculiar anti-intellectualism that sometimes engulfs his fellow scientists, for he, more than the
others, performs a meaningful corporate function. He does
not experience any sense of conflict with the requirements
of the state, nor is his place in the institutional hierarchy as
uncertain. He does not even have to worry about international ties: If some computer Rutherford were to deny
hospitality to his Kapitza, no one would be disturbed. The
computer man's loyalty is unquestioned: He serves the
state, the archon, the society of which he is a part.

And why not? Among the vast army of neutral scientists, unwilling or unable to examine dispassionately the
premises of their work, he is the most neutral of all. In the
words of L. T. Rader of Sperry Rand, it is no business of
the scientist to ask himself what the social consequences of
his discoveries might be—paralleling, in a sense, the economic creed that absolves the businessman of the direct consequences of his drive for profit. The infatuation with the
technicist ethos had become so deeply rooted that his pride
in the whole panoply of production miracles should be hardly surprising. Man behaves as he is born, and today he is
born into a technological milieu that has pushed the boundaries of possibility far beyond what they were two centuries
ago. The technicist, at least in this country, sees rich resources, an ever growing population, and an unquenched
pioneer spirit, and he is exhilarated by the prospect that
economic and technical conquest offers. It is not too onerous for him to affiliate voluntarily with the dominant groups
of such a society.[15]

Meanwhile, the creation of material goods and the
artificiality of their disposition take primacy of place. The
scientist, and along with him the engineer, designs factories
and machines, manipulates raw materials, and coordinates
activities with but a single commitment—to his own skill
as a technician. There are no other values with which he is,
or ought to be, concerned, unless they be those of the
market place. He moves easily from one company to the
next, for there is no substantial difference between them: All
are imbued with the technicist ethos. Whatever task is to be
done will be done, regardless of consequences, for "technique carries its own ethic with it and the use of technics is

not to be judged by a system of ethics outside it."[16] Yet the shape and purposes of technology are established by others; all too many scientists, particularly in the field of automation, do not care too much about what is done with their discoveries and inventions, as long as they themselves remain neutral. As C. P. Snow has said, they become soldiers working for someone else. And in their neutrality they have accepted the standards and criteria set down by those who have engaged them: They cannot escape the technological ethic, for indeed they helped to mold it.

The justification for this frame of mind is specialization and expertise. The expert is essential to the modern world, yet he suffers all too frequently from an inability to grasp the total condition under which he labors. He is often isolated and frequently disinterested in most of the human events that occur outside the closed circle of his own endeavors. He remains at arm's length from humanity, a member of a "guild of neutral artificers." Lacking humility, a quality that expertise is unlikely to provide, he cannot see in other fields what is obvious to other experts. Hence the collapse of communication and the increasing tendency to dismiss as inadmissable that which does not stem from one's own conception of the truth. As Robert Hutchins once remarked tartly: "A scientist has a limited education. He labors on the topic of his dissertation, wins the Nobel prize by the time he is 35, and suddenly has nothing to do. He has no general ideas ... He has no alternative but to spend the rest of his life making a nuisance of himself."[17] This observation may be too harsh, but the peculiar rigidity of the expert does confuse technical results with social analysis.

Such confusion occasions an addiction to the *forms* of science and to the assumption that only its methods will yield an ultimate wisdom. There is engendered the seductive belief that science, and only science, can solve all human problems. To paraphrase Bernard Shaw, it is presumed that science, like work, is play and that play is life. Although this phrase would be a noteworthy slogan for certain visionaries, in the technicist era it merely serves to mask fundamental realities. For in the context of practicality, which provides the backdrop against which scientist, engineer, and archon function, there is little stage room for the expressions of a Pericles or a Shakespeare. So basic is the stress on control and manipulation of the material environment that, despite all cautions, the genuine complexities of existence are disregarded. "Judgments of worth are no part of the texture of physical science," says Whitehead, "but they are part of the motive of its production." Somewhere between Copernicus and Einstein something went awry, for contemporary motives appear to have little in common with the ancient belief that science and technology are adventurous pursuits. As Norbert Wiener pointedly remarked, there are aspects of "automatization" that exceed the limits of scientific curiosity. No one questions the legitimacy of building automatic devices, either theoretically or actually, as an exercise in human intelligence, but the pursuit of gadgetry for its own sake, said Wiener, frequently reflects a search for power and an impatience with the plasticity of human nature.

It is thus doubtful that the good of understanding for its own sake offers our society a chance of formulating a new criterion of self-examination: The separation between values and facts devoid of values has become too wide to permit any negotiation between them. Today the scientist and engineer do what is necessary, what is expected of them. They assume no responsibility beyond the immediate discovery. This perspective even more self-deceivingly creates its own defense and justification: It was not surprising, for example, that a high NASA official could tell a conference of adult-education specialists in 1963 that it would not do much good to transfer a billion or two dollars from space research to the War on Poverty because Congress did not really care. Scientific neutrality had become a vested interest reflecting a new morality.[18]

Yet it may be argued that the commitment of the scientist does reflect some set of values, and the same is true of the computer specialist. But when they speak of "value-free" science, they relegate values to a hidden area of the mind, together with other unstated and unformed suppositions. An implicit belief in cause and effect still survives because it suggests the possibility of control: It is quite evident in computer lore where uncertainty is apt to be frowned upon because it is not conducive to control. The technicist is uncomfortable with the demand that ends and means require explication. But, because the computer bears down more heavily on "behavioral" science than it does on others, it would seem desirable to think of values and consequences.[19] This pressure may call for a measure of the kind of moral courage displayed by Norbert Wiener when he refused to work on any project that would contribute to war. Indubitably, such a question is as much inherent in computer technology as it is in nuclear technology.

But so involved is the technicist with what he does that he cannot pause to consider the effects of his work on others. As one writer put it, there is a hand-washing indifference to consequences. There is a deep concern with status as a professional, for such an image accords with the prejudices of the society: It lends a certain gentility to the manipulation of tapes and the act of pressing buttons, and it arouses the esteem of one's colleagues. It was not surprising that one study should reveal professionals and technicians to be more interested in climbing the bureaucratic ladder than in monetary rewards![20] How curious this attitude is when one recalls that the basis for an empirical view of knowledge was prepared by humanists in German universities. On the other hand, in England and in the United States, technology and science have been advocated on grounds of utility, with the result that specialists have been produced who are always under pressure to be practical and to deliver the goods.[21]

Such a commitment has created a serious deficiency in comprehending society. Even at those institutions where scientists- and technicians-in-training are required to take humanities courses, they do it grudgingly, as a necessary evil curiously fostered by the authorities. The poet Robert Graves once spent two weeks on the M.I.T. campus, where his reactions were hardly flattering to his hosts. Technologists, he observed, are kept by politicians and industrialists like silkworms in perforated cigar boxes, supplied fresh mulberry leaves, and left to spin silk.[22] The universities have responded so well and so readily to the demands of technology that they "run the risk of self-disintegration through too facile an adaptation to tomorrow's world."[23]

And it is doubtful that an uneasy obeisance to the humanities will provide a sufficient countervailance.

THE SCIENTIST and engineer are justly proud of their titles, which suggest attachment to a broad area of thought and action. The engineer thinks logically and rationally—or so he believes—and in a technological society engineers and scientists are precisely the ones to solve problems quickly, even nonscientific ones. There is no particular commitment to a given task: It need be only interesting, challenging, and necessary for an industrial society. Any company is a prospective employer whom one can serve either as specialist or as manager: The line between technician and manager is easily erased. Furthermore, success does mean an opportunity to rise into upper suburbia.[24] Yet many a technician's aspirations cannot be fulfilled so handsomely. Caught between the engineer-scientist and the industrial archon, the technician is more involved in the direct process of production, engaged in drafting, product design, installation, and inspection. Somewhat like a middle manager, he may be only several notches above a skilled craftsman. The sociologist often detects in him a "sense of deprivation": The technicist ethos may bring little satisfaction.[25]

With the advent of automation the question is who survives—the scientist-engineer or the corporate officer? The likelihood, of course, is that it will be the latter, at least if current trends are a harbinger of the future. In recent years the rate of growth in the employment of scientists and engineers did slow down: In 1959–1960 it was 6.4 per cent; in 1960–1961 it dipped to 6.1 per cent; and in the next year it dropped precipitately to 4 per cent. The decline for technicians was even more drastic—from 8.1 per cent in 1959–1960 to 2.9 per cent in 1961–1962.[26] For the first time in more than a decade, engineers were seeking jobs. It was not until the escalation of Vietnam that the situation was corrected.

Such a situation may make it easier for the businessman to manage the technician and scientist. In the corporate view, they ought not to be any different from other employees: The sport shirt and the beard are temporary

309

aberrations generously borne because of the exigencies of fulfilling a government contract. Yet there is no reason why the uniformity of corporate life should not apply to all. Although the scientist presumably searches for knowledge and does not respect the balance sheet, in the last analysis he can do only what the businessman is willing to pay for, and the latter is apt to stress "product possibilities." In computer research, however, even mild conflict of this sort is unlikely: Service to the corporation is direct and unmistakable. Scientific work and the needs of business are congruent. The business oligarch is not faced with resistance to traditional lines of authority, and he finds it easier to apply such devices as status seeking and a new laboratory as means of controlling the scientist-engineer. Research—that which the scientist does—becomes an institution replete with all the requisite formalities, including conferences, team effort, and collectivization. The scientist is easily converted into the image of the corporation; the virtuosi who cannot pay attention to the "improvement" of products must either change or get out. Creativity and individuality are deplored, as these attributes make a man less amenable to standardization and discipline. The logic of the corporation demands service to its collective ends.[27]

Bureaucratization makes the corporate official quite optimistic about the situation: Through it he can manage the scientist and the engineer. Furthermore, he often coopts to his ranks those scientists for whom administration has its own rewards. As the writer overheard one scientist say to another, "I'm about as big as I want to be, but I would like to grow another half-dozen men." The notion is then fostered that research can be subjected to standard management concepts, for if nonhuman nature is objective then human affairs can be objective also. The absorption of recruits illustrates the corporate technique for controlling science: A new man is assured that he will engage in basic research, and he is then "resocialized," so that in the end he accepts the dictum that he is not really free to pursue his own wishes. Of course, basic research is an attraction, but once the scientist enters the corporation, the corporation runs him: He must accept its goals, for in effect the corporation wants no geniuses.[28] The victory of the businessman appears complete once the scientist becomes a "laboratory managerialist" with a vision of spending as much money as he needs. As Norbert Wiener said, he becomes a gadgeteer anxious to see wheels go round. In the absence of philosophy, the managerial ideology is a sufficient substitute. "The degradation of the position of the scientist as an independent worker and thinker to that of a morally irresponsible stooge in a science factory has proceeded . . . rapidly and devastatingly . . ."[29]

Although science is an important force to be harnessed, its practitioners are assigned to specific rungs in the corporate status ladder. Eventually, scientific assignments are carried out by a subservient intelligentsia. Trained intellect is employed by the month or the year, for, as a group, the scientific intellectuals are "forced into compliance with the demands of the ruling powers, which can afford the luxury of a private army of picked scientists."[30] Like the labor power of Marx's proletariat, brain power is made into a commodity and an instrument for centralized organization utterly indifferent to the nature and purpose of its tasks. Instead of being a discipline, science is subjected to discipline, serving good and evil, the just and the unjust, the archon and the state. By its absorption into technology, there is engendered the neutrality of technicism in which the sole standards are utility, efficiency, rationality, and productivity. A few, like Wiener, may resist, but they are rare.

In the absence of restraint or planning, technicism breeds upon itself. The application of technical ideas requires an appropriate organization in which the participants are disciplined into cooperation. At first there was the discipline of the clock and then the discipline of the army. There was thus instilled in man, as part of the technicist ethos, a regard for sequence, command, and obedience. This discipline necessarily included specialism, an ability to focus on parts of a task without concern for those elements handled by others. Participants in the organization — and in the industrial process — were located in the line of command and were told what they must do as specialists. At no time were they able to grasp the character of the whole, for control could be forged only at the top by those whose view was unimpeded. In the exercise of his power, the businessman was required — by virtue of the technology he directed — to assign tasks to be done in particular ways by particular people. The needs of technics dictated the actions of everyone in the organizations, including the creation of new modes of production that might dispense with humans once committed to the operation.[31]

IT WAS ALL like Chinese handcuffs: The tighter the control, the more integrated the organizational system, the more further control was required. That is what the corporate oligarch likes about the computer: It has enabled him to reverse the trend toward decentralization, into which he had anyway backed somewhat unwillingly. Now top management can bypass intermediate staff people, for information comes out of the machine so quickly that the president knows a given situation before his divisional chiefs are aware of it. As *Fortune* once conceded, "Whenever a decentralized company has used the computer to automate operations and particularly when it has installed management information systems, it has willy-nilly found itself behaving more like a centralized company."[32] Although those below the corporate oligarch may object, there is no doubt that the "discreet monitoring of their activities by computer systems makes them more sensitive to the company's goals." At Westinghouse, for example, such "monitoring" led to a reduction of the white-collar work force by some 4,000 people, including not a few middle managers. The reasons are fairly evident: When markets are monopolistic and prices are administered by management fiat, the enormous savings made possible by the computer require more and more centralized control over production, inventories, and sales. Said one economist: ". . . the introduction of formalized decision procedures incorporating such tools as linear programming and dynamic programming has tended to centralize the decision-making process [through computers] . . . In practice the solutions are invariably obtained by centralized computations using algorithms like the simplex method and not by the *tâtonnement* of a market."[33] That is to say, the machine is superior to the market in determining resource allocation.

The integrated data-processing systems made possible by the computer reduce record keeping and the flow of information affecting decision making to manageable proportions. At a corporate board meeting, the chairman may soon be able to flip a switch and have an overhead screen light up with the company's profit-and-loss statement, calculated as of that morning's breakfast. The new technology provides instant reports on the latest developments in every phase of the business and thus offers management more direct control over activities that may be far-flung indeed. So tight can the control system become that even people once involved in processing information may be eliminated: The Sperry Rand PACC technique (Product Administration and Contract Control) now has nine people handling data that once kept 200 employees busy. An oil company executive told Ida Hoos: "We were moving in the direction of decentralization, but now we are definitely recentralizing . . . no matter how far spread out the branches are . . . you need no record keeping department. Modern bookkeeping tools make reintegration possible."[34]

In 1963 the U.S. Steel Corporation "reintegrated" seven of its divisions into its central operations to reduce costs and "enhance performance." District sales offices were reduced from fifty-three to twenty-eight and the reduction in salaried employees was estimated at more than 2,000. The production department was to become "more closely knit and compact" to enable plant superintendents "to act promptly in any situation." Research and engineering operations were also consolidated. The objective was to enable the company to react to market conditions in virtual "real time." None of these changes would have been possible without the integrated data-processing system of the computer. Said *Business Week*, reporting on U.S. Steel's new corporate look: "No specific job changes [were] announced, but it's plain that they will take place — literally by the hundreds. It's less plain, but equally inevitable, that there'll be a huge loss of jobs . . . the management fall-out . . . will involve dismissal and demotion as well as end many established paths for career growth . . ."[35]

Yet business leaders are unyielding in their demands

313

for more automation, more cybernation. They may recognize that the generation on which the initial impact falls may react in stunned silence, but they are confident that the glories of technology will be welcomed by succeeding ones. They are confident too that the harshness of the immediate adjustment will be forgotten in the future, as the pain of displacement suffered by worker and middle management is assuaged by a greater variety and quality of goods made available to the consumer. Therefore, despite all the disruptions, despite the idleness to which large groups of the populace are relegated, despite the creation of a class of people with no viable relation to society's affluent sector, the pace of automation must be accelerated. Bromides rather than analysis are employed to rationalize the incessant drive to apply technique to all facets of human existence.[36]

Among the methods of the corporate official in achieving his objective is one called "systems analysis." A system in this sense implies that all the inputs and outputs of a company are *automatically* coordinated. For example, a customer's order means a certain assignment of labor and materials and consonant adjustments in inventories and available work force. As the market projection is now made by the computer, all the manager has to do is to read the tape and decide what action to take. Furthermore, if the machine is of the problem-solving variety and is properly programmed, it may indeed suggest what action the manager ought to undertake. In effect, a "system" permits management to integrate related departmental activities — it can break up little empires in the organization; it extracts policy decisions from what is properly routine work; and it mechanizes manual operations. And, as we have indicated earlier, the executive may be able to converse directly with the machine through visual-display devices that make it possible to present problems to the machine and to obtain direct answers without having to rely on programmers.

According to the systems analysts, the natural goal for the organization is a single unified way of handling information. First, the general requirements of an integrated approach are outlined, enabling critical areas of data to be identified. For example, if the transmission of information must employ ordinary communication links like telephone lines, certain problems of competing uses must be solved. Decisions on hardware cost and availability have to be reached. Finally, the organization has to install the system, at which point "people problems," as one computer expert put it, suddenly become urgent. The program must be sold at various management levels and to the work force, even if the workers are to be fed the legendary bitter pills of Murti-Bing (Stanislaw Witkiewicz, a Polish writer, told in a 1932 novel of the Mongolian philosopher Murti-Bing, who invented a pill that made men serene and happy; the pill enabled the Sino-Mongolian army to conquer the West). Starting with routine administration and personnel, the systems man proceeds to engineering design, product scheduling, and preparation of the input-data method. This process provides the executive with an integrated technique of control and monitoring.

An illustration is the system installed by the Hotpoint division of General Electric. Employing magnetic tapes alone, fourteen main subsystems are integrated through thirty-eight interrelated input tapes. The subsystems handle customers' orders, invoices, carloading directives, and the like. The staff comprises six systems managers, with five programmers and four systems – design experts assigned to each. In manufacturing and engineering, the "total system" – complete automation – was only 20 per cent short of completion by mid-1964, yet the whole operation paid for itself by producing useful information the company could not otherwise obtain. This subsystem handles production schedules, procurement, payroll, and standard costing. Furthermore, it keeps track of parts and the appliance models to which they have to be attached. For those appliances the assembly of which stems from decisions in the shop (rather than being predetermined in the front office), the computer calculates the optimum ratios of work load to the number of workers on the line. By this sort of line balancing, labor utilization has increased from 85 per cent of available time to 93 per cent.

Does this method pay? According to one report, the Electronic Specialty Company of Los Angeles was converted within nine years from a floundering firm with only a few items on its production line into an $85 million company with a full line of related products by the use of systems analysis. Other companies have evidently had similar experiences, with the result that "systems" based on computers are now all the rage. Although 19 per cent of capital spending by industry in 1963 went for automation and systems, in some industries the ratio was even higher — 26 per cent in automobiles, 30 per cent in electrical machinery, and 33 per cent in glass, stone, and clay. Despite the fact that the experts do not agree on how close industry can come to the total-systems idea, it seems worth while to try, particularly when complete monitoring of business activities — automatic control of inventories, production, shipments, payroll, and anything else that can be reduced to mathematical equations — is made more and more feasible. An apocryphal tale is told of one ambitious president who installed such a system, even teaching the computer to simulate his thinking and was then promptly fired by the board of directors because he was no longer needed. The reality is that the machine can do more things than we are ready to believe. The new "systems" appear essential in view of the huge scope of operations of many companies, the diversified products produced, the geographic dispersion of plants and offices: Only computer-based management systems, it is said, will permit management to bring order out of threatening chaos. In the meantime, the "people problem" remains.[37]

ALTHOUGH SOME COMPANIES are rather lax, from a "management science" point of view, in their use of computer technology, in that middle managers are allowed to apply the machines as they see fit, in most instances the ultimate objective is control through a single programming staff. The intent is to exert a central discipline on policy production and procedures, particularly over outlays for direct labor and materials costs. Not surprisingly, the effort to centralize via the computer often generates opposition within the organization, especially from middle managers. Computer programming for control purposes requires a precise statement of function: Loose verbal formulations that were once used are no longer satisfactory. But when the systems man asks a departmental manager to state what it is that he does, there frequently is resentment, for the detailed questioning is apt to be interpreted as a search for weakness. What was once an accepted easy adjustment is converted into strains and challenges. The middle manager fears that coordination and integration will curtail his prerogatives. Furthermore, he knows that a computer places him in a glass cage: One reel of tape contains as much information as does a standard file cabinet, whereas several tapes provide all the operating data for a whole division. But these tapes are not under the control of the middle manager; they are stored elsewhere and can tell top management what goes on without the department head knowing anything about it. In effect, the middle manager has been bypassed. As one such department chief exclaimed, "My data could be picked up, read, misunderstood and I could be fired without ever knowing why!"[38]

Nevertheless, the top manager is determined to take back the reins of power he had to surrender under the rule of decentralization, and the computer is helping him to do just that. In company after company, headquarters specialists have been installed to assist top management regain control: Technical-information officers, information-retrieval specialists, and product-engineering coordinators digest masses of detailed information flowing out of the computer to keep the archon advised in language that he can understand. In essence, then, the computer removes control of operations from the middle stratum and hands it over to a small corps of specialists responsible only to the top, where planning now takes place. Meanwhile, the men in the middle are pushed down. For the fact is that the alteration in middle-management jobs is taking place more rapidly than is the conversion of the skilled machinist into a machine tender. The supervisor and the department head become sergeants rather than company commanders.[39] No less an authority than Herbert A. Simon has asserted that by 1985 it will be technically feasible to replace many if not all human functions in organizations with machines.[40] The only question to be answered is whether or not, as a matter of economics, it would pay to dispose of all the people all at once. In any case, the decision-making process acquires a new transparency through monitoring by the computer and provides for just the sort of *Gleichschaltung* desired by the archon.

In recent years the number of middle-management jobs relative to output has declined. Indicative is the fact that between 1950 and 1960 the average annual increase in white-collar positions was 2.8 per cent; in 1963 it was 1 per cent. T. L. Whisler, who has studied the impact of automation on management more closely perhaps than has anyone else, reports a cutback in one company of managerial posts as a result of computer installations of almost 30 per cent.[41] The computer is upsetting functions, displacing managers, and wiping out jobs, said *Fortune*, and consequently it generates fear and resistance even among the highly skilled white-collar men. Yet corporate officials appear reluctant to talk about this phenomenon, as they are reluctant to talk about displacement in the factory. When the Ford Motor Company took over Philco, it reorganized and rationalized the latter's production lines and cut back the number of employees from 27,000 to 20,000, also eliminating many executives who had thought themselves secure. The tightening of the executive lines stems from the new philosophy of centralization engendered by the computer. This process has been going on now for several years in many an American corporation. The result is a lesser need for middle-management skills. Certainly, an important function of the intermediate posts has been to provide training grounds for movement up the corporate ladder. But, when jobs can be combined or handed over entirely to the computer, there is not much opportunity for management apprenticeships. Remarked one engineering consultant, "The National Science Foundation says we'll need 700,000 more engineers in the Sixties, but I'll wager that a fifth of these will be unemployed or out of engineering by 1970, three out of five will be disgusted with their lot because they're not being used fruitfully—leaving only one-fifth actually functioning satisfactorily as true engineers." Added another consultant: "[With] computerized applications . . . we will not need as many people in management

318

positions ... Bitter as will be the resistance and fierce the rationalization, the process of elimination of management positions is necessary and will proceed inevitably."[42]

Even the buyer in a department store is threatened by the computer. In late 1964 a management consultant told the National Retail Merchants Association that by 1970 buyers would make no merchandise-control decisions: In fact, there would be no merchandising middle management at all, as the machine would control inventory, assign sales-clerks, process credit applications, plan advertising campaigns, and handle accounts receivable and payable. The computer would provide data on sales performances, undertake customer "walk-out" studies, and "peek" into every selling area of the store to evaluate what employees were doing. Customers would be rated on marital status, education, place of residence, and type of work. And, said the specialist, all of this work would be under a "vice-president for management services" reporting to the top man and possessed of a "rare combination of [knowledge] of retail practices as well as computer systems."[43]

This unconcern with the fate of the middle manager is sometimes justified by saying that more featherbedding goes on in certain management circles than labor ever enjoyed. Because automation leaves little or no genuine decision-making power in the hands of middle-echelon executives, it becomes relatively easy to cut away redundant staff. The one who gains the power is the one who oversees the computer operation, often the controller. It is he who generally becomes aware of the potentials of the machine; it is he who attends manufacturers' briefing sessions; it is he who begins to speak of floating decimals and binary digits; and it is he who is ready to use the machine for payroll and accounting records. Sometimes a controller is not fully aware of the way an integrated system can provide almost instant control over operations: In such a case the development of computer operations lags because the controller's imagination fails or perhaps because he lacks the authority to install at least the beginnings of a computer system. But the exhortations of manufacturers' representatives and trade-journal writers have created an atmosphere in which these deficiencies can readily be eradicated.[44]

319

To achieve the ultimate objective of control, future systems will no doubt be based on direct visual and voice communications with the machine, that is, there will not even be a need for programmers. Module equipment will provide flexibility, and self-correcting programs and heuristic techniques will permit solutions to be derived for the most difficult problems. It seems evident that the sort of control systems envisaged by these developments, which will employ information retrieval, direct document reading, simulation, and the like, will require a new corporate structure with management skills converted into mere reactions to a total information-processing system. The traditional operations of market analysis, production, sales, and finance will be linked by unbreakable reels of tape.[45]

IN THE MEANTIME, the controller, or whoever it is that plays godfather to the machine, must call upon allies to computerize the organization. Electronics engineers, mathematicians, and technicians — all high priests of mystery with their own traditions to foster — have been recruited to assist the archons; immediately they have started to carve out their own empires. Conflict has often been the consequence, for top management is clearly set on establishing its own control. In recent years, this control has been made easier to achieve, for, once a program is firmly set, anyone with average intelligence, aptitude for logical thought, and in most cases no more than a high school diploma can be trained to operate the computer. Of an average of about fifteen men working on a large installation, no more than three earn more than $7,000 a year, and at most one or two are the "systems" specialists. It is the latter, of course, who give top management the tools for integrated control. Although "old-timers" often express resentment at "change for the sake of changing," the fact remains that the future will see a new generation of computer specialists achieving their goal of total integration — an objective implicit in the science they have learned and the philosophy they voice.[46]

What sort of men are these systems specialists? Fostered by computer manufacturers to facilitate the permanent placement of equipment in industry, they are generally young, ranging in age from the mid-Twenties to mid-Thirties. They are well educated, with masters' degrees in accounting, statistics, civil engineering, and even library science; a fair number of Ph. D. degrees in chemistry, physics, and mathematics may also be found among them. Logical aptitude is the major requirement for their work. As the early accounting-machine operators have moved up in the last decade or so to controllers' posts or out to sales managers' jobs, the new information specialists have begun to occupy the data-processing posts left vacant or opened by advancing technology. They now "systemize" accounting, engage in "operations research," develop technical reports, and have the machine produce parts catalogues, directories, and customer listings. They are thoroughly committed to the computer, displaying a professional passion for the machine.

Yet they are hardly organization men of the sort so brilliantly sketched by William Whyte, Jr.[47] Too many are nonconformists, "other-directed," somewhat like the adventurous entrepreneurs of a bygone era, and just as gauche. Replied one scientist when asked about a book he was writing, "I've sent down eleven chapters to the Technical Information Division for Englishing." Yet their knowledge of hardware and software is baffling to others, and they may be treated with the deference accorded to outside consultants. The systems men want to get things done: They therefore find the most difficult problems to be the inner politics and conflicts of the organization. Furthermore, their closeness to the archon is apt to generate hostility and resentment, but assured of top management's support they design their own projects, ignore time-honored rules of the corporation, and cut across departmental lines — all to achieve a total integrated system. And they are more than likely to tell a personnel manager worried about displacement that it's "all none of your business." When social scientists ask about the impact of the changes they have initiated, the systems men reply that "everyone is thrilled with the challenge of automation." All the maxims of conventional wisdom are employed to justify what it is they do: Automation causes no job losses; it reduces costs; it has not really affected the work force; it upgrades workers, and, besides, all problems will be adjusted — in the long run.

Despite the sometimes serious hassles with others in the organization, the systems men invariably win out, simply because they have the support of the manager. They may not know much about measured-day work or cost accounting and may be more interested in variables, optimums, closed loops, and other recondite problems, but their efforts all enhances control from the top. For, as we have argued, systems techniques shift the center of gravity in the corporation from middle management to the front office. The work that the former used to do is given over to the machine, which now processes information at a pace fast enough to supply facts on events simultaneously with the events themselves, that is, in "real time." In the last analysis, control of the corporate organization is centralized through the computer in the hands of less than 0.5 per cent of the population — the managerial group that constitutes the class of the archon.[48]

And this centralization arises from the way in which we have allowed our technology to dominate us and to "reshape man in the image of the apparently flawless machine." As Charles Malik has said:

> A world of perfect technicians is the aim, not a world of human beings, let alone of beings divine. A dreary and boring world where there is nothing beyond man and his mastery over nature, including his mastery of other technicians through his scientific management of them. Perfect hierarchy, perfect organization, total efficiency; but no spirit, no freedom, no joy, no humor, and therefore no man.[49]

FOUR

Portent and Implication

Conventional wisdoms   10

That the machine does in fact displace workers had been directly experienced during the Industrial Revolution by hand-loom weaver and Luddite. Yet economists have persisted in consoling workers with the optimistic notion that in the long run new techniques will increase output sufficiently to create jobs for the displaced. Unfortunately, they have failed to add that the process may take decades. Furthermore, many of those subjected to the indignities of job loss may be in industries only tangentially related to those in which innovation is causing upheaval, and they will suffer too. That is, the effects are frequently indirect, showing up as ripples on the edge of a lake into whose center a heavy stone has been tossed.

The main argument of the optimists, who see no real difficulties, no genuine hardships stemming from technical change, has been based on the ineffable harmonies of Say's Law, a creation of Jean-Baptiste Say, a French disciple of Adam Smith. Say argued in 1803 that production expands indefinitely and thus creates its own effective demand. First, improved productivity reduces costs; therefore, under conditions of a competitive market, lower prices will necessarily ensue. Even if a consumer does not respond to reduced prices for particular commodities because his demand is inelastic — as could be the case with certain necessities — the additional real income will then be available for purchasing other goods. Furthermore, if some prices are "sticky" and do not fall, then the higher profits garnered by capitalists will impel them either to consume more on their own behalf or to expand investment. The requisite demand is thus bound to be created as a result of the unimpeded circular flow of income.[1]

Over the years, proponents of this comfortable doctrine have pointed to the increase in the employed work force as an incontrovertible demonstration of the propostion that the production of goods itself generates demand for goods: Furthermore, to increase the quantity of any one good implies an increase, however small or large, in the demand for all other goods. There have been a number of variations in the theme: If the quantity demanded were to increase proportionately to the fall in costs stemming from improved technique, then the same number of workers as were previously employed would still be required to produce the additional output; and if demand were to respond more than in proportion to cost changes, more workers would be employed. But what if demand were inelastic? Would not unemployment result? Here the conventional wisdom comes to the rescue, for, it has been argued, invested savings would supply jobs. As Paul Douglas stated the case in 1930, "At the same time that men are being squeezed out of [one] business, purchasing power formerly expended upon the products of this industry is transferred to other industries and builds up added opportunities for work there."[2] Even more miraculously, the creation of jobs in such other industries would exactly balance the losses suffered elsewhere in the economy. "For every man laid off, a new job has been created somewhere."

This argument represented the classical view of how adjustments to technological change occur, a view for which the eighteenth and nineteenth centuries, with their penchant for pushing aside troublesome questions, had expressed unbounded enthusiasm. James Steuart, the last of the mercantilists, found nothing but great "utility in the augmenting of machinery": Besides, unlike the worker, the machine did not consume food. And if distress was momentarily caused by the machine, then the state would step in.[3] Adam Smith's views, on the other hand, were broad enough to accommodate any interpretation of technical change: Growth was limited only by the division of labor and the extent of the market. His theory of technological change or capital accumulation, was rather loose so that his scattered remarks were sufficient for Say to build his gloriously optimistic "law." Nevertheless, the problem persisted, as both Sismondi and Malthus acknowledged. The latter had argued that the introduction of new machines could have a harmful effect on employment, simply because purchasing power might be inadequate. Sismondi in turn rebelled at the notion that every supply created its own demand. Applying what today would be labeled "period analysis," he asserted that goods made "yesterday" had to be exchanged for income generated "yesterday" in a transaction taking place "today." Revenue, however, consisted of profit ready to be spent "today" plus wages paid for "yesterday." If the capitalist consumed too much "yesterday," his control of the economic process would enable him to recapture some revenue by depressing wages, thus leading to an impairment of capital and a break in the flow of income. Now, continued Sismondi, such overconsumption could be caused by innovation as well as by any other cause. (The consequent identification of overconsumption and overinvestment did not seem to trouble Sismondi.) Furthermore, there was no inherent reason why a technological change should bring about price reductions, for the capitalist was always in the driver's seat. The possibility of a shrinkage in purchasing power was ever present: And if there were no new capital available for expansion, then labor displacement was bound to occur. Substantially the same argument was advanced by Malthus, who saw no guarantee in the way the economy functioned that markets in fact would be extended, unless consumption increased or more capital entered the investment stream.[4]

David Ricardo, England's great nineteenth-century economist, at first opposed the Malthus-Sismondi formulation, on the ground that something would be produced as long as capital and machinery were available: Essentially, he failed to recognize Malthus's attempt to account for responses to technical change in terms of demand elasticity.

Ricardo's admirers, especially John McCulloch, were already proclaiming that machinery reduced neither wages nor employment. Great therefore was McCulloch's dismay when Ricardo added his famous chapter on machinery to his *Principles of Political Economy* conceding that the "substitution of machinery for human labour is often injurious to the interests of the class of labourers."[5] Influenced by the pamphleteer John Barton, the Ricardian restatement revolved about the question raised by Sismondi — could capital accumulation be used for investment rather than for additions to the wage fund, as was implied earlier? If, in effect, circulating capital was convertible into fixed capital, then a diminution of the former would result in unemployment, particularly in those sectors in which it was a major component. A sudden introduction of innovation would be quite disrupting, thought Ricardo. The significant point was that the new "theory," hesitant and tentative, represented a shift from the rather smug view that the worker had no one but himself to blame for his difficulties (he was so excessively procreative) to one which asserted that failure could be located in the economic system itself. Although Ricardo made no strenuous effort to develop his thoughts on machinery, they were disconcerting enough to give much pain to his disciples.

The best they could do was to reiterate Say's Law. The rout was almost completed by Marx, in whose grand system technology appeared as a fundamental disruptive force. (At the same time, John Stuart Mill was saying, "The demand for commodities is not a demand for labor.") Accumulation, said Marx, involved changes in the organic composition of capital or an increase in the ratio of constant capital to labor input. Disturbances were inevitable because constant capital in the producers' goods sector rose faster than the output of consumers' goods. The assumption here was that changes in "organic composition" stemmed only from labor-saving equipment; had Marx accepted capital-saving as a real possibility, he might have acknowledged other sorts of technological effects.

Orthodox theory was then rescued by the marginalists, who restated the concept of equilibrium in a way that seemed difficult to refute. While supply continued to create its own demand, more intensive accumulation of capital would overcome breaks that threatened the income cycle. In fact, when unemployment did occur, said the new theory, it was simply because wages were inflexible, a condition resulting from labor-union resistance or other institutional barriers. When a new technique entailed alterations in the production function — the relationship of inputs to outputs — it necessarily established new marginal productivities. If the unemployed would accept jobs at low enough wages, they could effectively inhibit mechanization by the simple expedient of outbidding the machine. So comforting was this theory that it found its way quite readily into neo-classical doctrine. Under conditions of perfect competition the easy adjustment of wage rates to shifts in demand would assure everyone of a job regardless of the dynamism of technology or the gyrations of the business cycle. These notions became the object of Keynes's scorn, and he demolished them, presumably for all time, with a powerful demonstration that low-level equilibrium could exist together with high unemployment.[6]

CONVENTIONAL WISDOM now seeks to convince us that the present is analogous to the past. England's Industrial Revolution did indeed foreshadow a long upward spiral, and there evidently was some unskilled work for the displaced to move into — usually at lower wages. But even then unemployment was not absent; the troubled times of the 1830s and 1840s brought virtual starvation to many workers. The attitude of the nineteenth-century industrial archon was extraordinarily callous. The machine was frequently described as a weapon to subdue the worker by promising to displace him unless he accepted the terms offered by the businessman. The loom and the lathe were to be used as instruments for discipline, as was advocated by Andrew Ure, England's "philosopher" of the factory, who visualized manufacturing as an "automaton" that would undermine the position of the "cunning workman."[7]

Today's technology imposes equally severe burdens — on young people without skills, on Negroes, on those displaced by the machine. Despite these difficult problems, most economists continue to assert that "automation is not an industrial revolution . . . it is a completely normal evolution in which progress is being made in all fields of industry by the application of advanced . . . techniques."[8] Furthermore, it is argued, there are certain limits to automation.

With its major motivation the desire to reduce labor costs, automation frequently brings about unexpected savings. John Diebold cites the case of a chemical company which estimated that, for every dollar of labor savings, it also saved three dollars by operating more efficiently and with less waste through automation.[9] Some have argued that the high costs of the new technology inhibit any thrust toward rapid development. But the initial cost of automating a plant is not so great as generally supposed. Whereas the price of making a plant fully automatic varies from one industry to the next, the average for all industries, according to Wassily Leontief, is only about 6 per cent of total plant cost, hardly an insuperable barrier. Automation does not require the relatively heavy investment that was necessary for industrialization in the nineteenth and twentieth centuries and can therefore proceed at a fairly rapid rate, as indeed it has.[10] Where automation has developed slowly, as in steel and textiles, the reason may be attributed to the cautious and conservative attitudes of management. Nevertheless, once the Europeans and the smaller American firms had demonstrated the technical and economic feasibility of continuous casting, oxygen furnaces, and computer-controlled processes, the others hastened their pace. The conservatism of the American corporate oligarch was dissipated once the Germans, Swedes, and Japanese had demonstrated that their methods were superior.

To these forces conventionality is blind. Technology indeed moves quickly. James Bright has said that, even in 1958 when he reviewed the advances made in thirteen factories whose methods he had studied but three years earlier, he was startled to discover the older technology overtaken and surpassed. By 1960 it was evident that a "technological ferment was burgeoning. The growth of the computer [had] exceeded all but the wildest expectations. The numerically controlled machine tool [for example] was far more useful than most of us had believed."[11]

There had been no lack of bromides. Automation it is said, helps fill the cupboards, gives us new foods, provides home conveniences, and gives lots of time for "do-it-your-self" around the house — assuming one really knows how.[12] The more sophisticated optimist will argue that the effects of automation on employment are nothing new, that these problems can be solved if the correct policies are utilized, and that as we achieve the latter automation will prove to be a blessing. Although automation may destroy certain jobs, says Gardner Ackley, Chairman of the Council of Economic Advisers, we must consider the job-creating ability of the economy as a whole.[13] The proof of this argument lies in our history: A technological society has always offered more work, better income, superior goods, and greater leisure time. Yet, by Ackley's own admission, we would have needed several million new jobs during 1964 and 1965 to bring the unemployment rate down to 4 per cent of the work force, which could have been done only under the high pressure of "defense" expenditures. In the absence of the latter, the official rate of unemployment hovered about the 5 per cent mark; the unofficial figure may have been closer to 9 per cent. This sort of analysis, popular in certain government and academic circles, declares that we are merely traversing a few rough shoals in technological growth and that we shall soon break through to smoother waters. The way new industries have developed in the past, we are told, gives assurance that we can rely on history to get the unemployed back to work. Those who do not have jobs — *rentiers* and the poor — are social mutations anyway. As W. H. Ferry remarked, this argument is attractive to those who believe that the atom bomb is just a big hand grenade.[14] They fail to recognize that "the moment of truth on automation is coming — a lot sooner than most people realize. The shattering fact is that the United States is still almost totally unprepared . . ."[15]

A good many writers on automation would prefer to agree with E. W. Leaver, an electronics specialist, for whom the notion that automation causes unemployment is a total myth. The problem, says Leaver, is that there are not enough "job generators" and too many "job users," the latter being the kind of worker "who either cannot or will not decide what he is to do in the economy. He looks to someone else to do this for him. He is looking for a job." The reason we have too few "job generators" is based on the philosophy of the times: Too much emphasis on security, automatically supplied by government; too much socialistic propaganda; too much bureaucracy; too many taxes that stifle enterprise. Our standard of living depends on higher productivity, and that is what automation can supply.[16] Robert Solo of Princeton University has argued that automation does not result in job displacement, for it has been developing rather slowly.[17] (But Robert Solow, an M.I.T. economist, has demonstrated that technical progress proceeds at an exponential rate: As long as net capital formation takes place there will be rapid improvements in technique that will markedly affect the level of output.[18]) In fact, says Solo, "No general statistical evidence has been adduced in support of the alleged importance of automation as a component of technological progress in industry . . ." Its effect, he continues, is essentially minor, and there is no instance in which computer-based methods in production are of more than trivial significance. It is rather difficult to deal with such statements, deeply rooted as they are in ignorance of current technology. How trivial the computer is in production is revealed in the petrochemical industry, in the new steel plants, in machine-tool operations, and in the materials-handling devices linked to sensory apparatuses, to say nothing of data processing.

NEVERTHELESS, the counterattack continued. In January 1965 defenders of the traditional view launched an all-out assault on those who insist on calling attention to the dark side of automation. Within a few days of one another, *Look*, *Fortune*, and *The New York Times Magazine* issued glowing stories on the blessings of the new technology, minimizing at the same time the ominous government and private reports that dared to suggest otherwise. Aside from the curious phenomenon of simultaneous publication and the striking similarity in their tones, one could only react with dismay at the distortion of fact, the fundamental ignorance of the new technology, the strings of *non sequiturs*, the

332

primitive use of *ad hominem* argument, and the simplistic and archaic conceptions of the economic forces involved.

Of the first of these extraordinary pieces, by T. G. Harris in *Look* (January 12, 1965), the less said the better. To Mr. Harris, the worker was winning his battle against machines by sheer guts and education. The second, entitled "The Real News About Automation," was by Charles Silberman, a *Fortune* editor. It began with a naïve exhibition of statistical manipulation and offered with all the excitement due a great discovery a statistic that could very well end all statistics: As the employment of manufacturing production workers, Silberman said, had increased by one million from 1961 to 1964, any assertion that automation destroys jobs was a case of false gloom. He then used his new-found number to clobber Donald Michael of the Institute for Policy Studies, the Ad Hoc Committee on the Triple Revolution, Alice Mary Hilton of the Institute for Cybercultural Research, and John I. Snyder, all of whom had been urging that, given the nature of our social system, automation spells trouble.

Well, what about Silberman's numbers? Among the statistician's bag of tricks is the selective use of a base year: He can prove almost anything he wants by choosing the appropriate one. Silberman's choice of 1961, which was a low point or "trough" in the employment series, served his purpose quite well, as any upward movement is apt to look good when one is starting at the bottom. Movements from one year to another, however, generally require comparisons between peaks and peaks or between troughs and troughs: At least this is the method employed by the highly regarded and quite careful National Bureau of Economic Research. One simply does not set a peak against a trough or vice versa when evaluating trends in employment data: To do so is to commit a statistical howler of no small proportions. (Technically, the trough-to-peak, which measures the bottom-to-top spread, indicates the length of one-half a business cycle.)

If the base were shifted back to 1959 it would be clear that industries that were adopting the new technology, including the computer, had continued to suffer declining employment — steel pipes and tubes, primary aluminum, primary nonferrous smelting, various kinds of machinery, typewriters, and sewing machines were all good examples. Nor did Silberman mention other areas in which employment had continued to drop, for example, motor vehicles, food processing, and petroleum refining, all major users of the new technology.

Of course, total employment had increased, but there was also a virtual explosion in the work force and in the population. This phenomenon was job-creating, after a fashion: Together with the larger consumer market that it supplied, the vast growth in output, almost 50 per cent in real dollars, provided the necessary fillip. If there had been no job gain at all we should be in a perilous condition, indeed. But it had not been sufficient, for most of the job advance came in those soft-goods lines that had not yet been caught up in the new technology and in service and government occupations — beauty shops, hospitals, teaching.

Curiously, Silberman evidently had not read his own magazine. For years, this fountainhead of business wisdom had published articles on computers, microminiaturization, artificial intelligence, data processing, systems analysis, and other exotic features of the new technology, which were fairly accurate. But they had been written by other editors (who recently put all the pieces together in a new book for quick access). Without this background, it was easy for Silberman to minimize the application of automated controls in such industries as oil refining, chemicals, and paper. For example, he cited the fact that there were only 300 process-control computers in the United States. (Industry sources, cited by *Business Week*, said 400, but no matter.) Ready as they were for automation, said Silberman, these industries never took the next step. He did not say, however, that in 1955 there had been only a handful of process-control operations in existence or that it was expected that another 100 to 125 would be installed by 1965 or that by 1970 manufacturers expect to have completed 4,000 of them. Are we then really a long way from the completely automatic factory? We do not have too far to go to 1970.

But the force of the new technology compelled even Silberman to concede that *in time* computers would control much of American production. He simply did not think machines would displace people. Although this view makes the businessman something of a philanthropist, officials in the United Steelworkers' Union have looked with marked trepidation on what these technical developments would do to the work force in that industry. A recent report on the displacement of factory clerks by computers prepared by the Wisconsin State Employment Service had this much to say: "The number of new jobs and positions created by computerization was insignificant in proportion to the number of positions eliminated by the computer." (An ironic note: Immediately following Silberman's article, *Fortune* published another captioned, "The New Glow in Steel Technology," replete with pictures of a new bar mill, a vacuum-degassing unit, and a reversing mill with an automatic monitoring system that controls plate thickness, width, length, slab temperature, and roll force and drastically reduces labor requirements.)

And so we come finally to Silberman's contention that there are no fully automated processes for any major product in any industry. If by this "straw man" he meant that there are still no automated installations in which absolutely *no* humans are to be found, he is right. But that is hardly the point. Even in a completely automatic power plant there are one or two men around reading dials, and a petrochemical factory will still have several hundred workers to climb ladders and tap on tubes and do data logging. Yet even these men can be eliminated, for the computer is fully capable of recording the data, whereas the ladder climbing is a form of industrial exercise intended to keep maintenance men busy. Interestingly enough, Silberman cited Texaco's Port Arthur refinery, which employs several thousand men, to support his argument that humans are still necessary. Of course, he did not tell his readers that most of the displacement had occurred several years prior to the time he was writing about. Furthermore, when the Oil and Chemical Union struck the plant a few years ago, production went on unimpeded with all the data logging and dial watching done by supervisors.

Much more devious was Peter Drucker's article "Automation Is Not the Villain" in *The New York Times Magazine* (January 10, 1965). One of the nation's shrewdest managerial apologists, Drucker once hailed automation as a harbinger of paradise. A decade ago he predicted that the new technology would lead to the greatest advance in upgrading that labor would ever experience. Routine jobs, he asserted then, would become a thing of the past, and only technical, maintenance, and professional occupations would constitute the work force of the future. Yet the facts now show Drucker to have been a poor prophet. For, as James Bright of Harvard University has demonstrated, many of the maintenance and technical jobs are transitory. After an automated installation has jelled, there is little need for highly skilled personnel: Even now high-school graduates and dropouts are being trained to put reels of tape into computers. There is nothing else for them to know, as the machine does all the work. The prospect for high labor skills in the future is not nearly so bright as was once anticipated. With increasing automaticity, control over machines is exercised by machines, measurement is done electronically, and computers can do the data logging. The outcome appears to be a relatively small gain in employment for highly skilled workers, a market apt to be quickly saturated anyway, counterbalanced by unemployment of the unskilled, who if lucky can drift into the odds and ends of the service trades.

But all these facts meant nothing to Drucker, for in his *Times* article he placed exclusive blame for unemployment squarely on the shoulders of the unemployed. Referring to teen-age unemployment, which at fifteen per cent was enormous, he said the teen-ager had priced himself out of the market. And what of Negro youth? asked Drucker. They simply live in the wrong places: Negroes live in the city slums, whereas the job opportunities are in the suburbs. Besides, he continued, women are taking all the jobs that used to go to teen-agers. Obviously, the kids of America are lazy. Look what happens when they come of age and enter adulthood: The jobless rate suddenly drops. Indeed it does, if only because employers are more likely to select twenty-one-year olds than seventeen-year olds.

One need not go into Drucker's use of employment statistics: It was the same mishmash into which Silberman had dipped: illegitimate use of base years; putting supervisory and production workers into the same bin; assorted *non sequiturs* (after talking about man-hours, Drucker dragged in take-home pay by the heels); straw men of more flimsy nature than Silberman's; and citations from the usual anonymous professionals in the Labor Department. On this last point, said Drucker, "... the most experienced and most respected labor economists in the country, the professionals in the U.S. Department of Labor, are convinced that we are today liquidating jobs at a lower rate than at most times in the past." Again, "Labor Department economists believe that we create new jobs at a somewhat higher rate than we did in past periods ..." Now, although labor specialists may not share completely Drucker's sudden enthusiasm for the bureaucrat, they do have high regard for their colleagues in the Labor Department. Seldom have they heard, at least in this writer's fairly long experience, anything quite as nonsensical from a Department spokesman. A few phone calls could not turn up a hint of who might have said or written what Drucker said he did. Were these citations the normal "not-to-be-attributed-to-me" items, or were they simply imaginary?

IT IS INTERESTING to note that Daniel Bell—whose writings on work and technology have been up to now quite sound—has fallen in with the camp of the complacents (*The New York Review of Books*, August 26, 1965, and November 25, 1965). He quotes approvingly Silberman's arguments that automation is no problem as there presently exists no major industry that is fully automated. That industry sources expect process-control installations to number 4,000 by 1970 may be illustrative only—Bell calls it argument by "for example"—but it does suggest the magnitude and direction of the trend. And to deny, as Bell does, that discrete production can be converted into a continuous flow and thus subjected to computer control simply reveals a lack of knowledge or understanding or both of what is now occurring in the factory. All Bell can do is to repeat arguments heard at Automation Commission sessions—that the new technology is only more of the same kind of change we have had since the Industrial Revolution; that its pace is not accelerating; and that we need a higher level of aggregate demand to ease whatever strains it causes. Now, few economists will deny the last proposition, but some have been concerned that high aggregate demand often is not available in peacetime. Consequently, they understandably cast about for alternative methods of alleviating unemployment. That Bell now apparently rejects the irony of a solution dependent on war production suggests another kind of conventional wisdom.

In an effort to demonstrate that automation is not really "biting in," Bell resorts to a Department of Labor report that purportedly analyzed the effects of the computer in thirty-six different industries. In his interpretation of the "data" it appears that the computer's applicability is limited. When one looks, however, at IBM, Rand, RCA, and all the others in the business of selling computers for data processing and process control, one wonders what Bell means. Curiously, in both his original article and his subsequent response to his correspondents, Bell refused to identify the report on which he had relied. Donald Michael, one of those who responded to Bell in *The New York Review of Books*, inquired at the Department of Labor, and the respondents there could not say which report Bell was referring to. If it is indeed the study I have in mind, then Bell can be charged with an artfulness that he had never revealed before. The report I believe he cited had nothing to do with the *specific* application of the computer in the thirty-six industries reviewed but only with probable technological trends in the broadest sense of the term. But a more important consideration is that the authors of the report have privately conceded its extreme unreliability. The document had been quickly prepared at the request of a presidential committee that was holding hasty one-day briefing sessions a few years ago, and the compilers had to rush to meet a deadline without any really intensive check of their data.

Central to Bell's argument is the contention that technology manifests no accelerated development. It is a knotty problem. The point is that once again economic analysis is insufficient; one must resort to other bits of information like the study of innovations, diffusion, and the like. The

338

Automation Commission thought that it was worthwhile to investigate these aspects, but Bell, a member of the Commission, has simply ignored the reports submitted to that group. To quote from an early Commission draft, ". . . The time between the initial technical discovery and recognition of its commercial potential had declined from about 30 years before the first World War to 16 years between the wars and 9 years for the post World War II period." Surely this decline suggests strongly an acceleration in technical change.

It seems to be an article of faith in the establishment these days that the easiest way to assuage the concern of those who wonder what the new technology — automation or cybernation or whatever one wishes to call it — will do to our society is to offer some simple numbers. They are the productivity figures, said to be *the* measure of technological change. Like some economists, Bell largely rests his case on these numbers because the data show only relatively modest growth over the long haul. But Bell seems unaware of the conceptual morass that passes for productivity measurement. The extrapolation to the entire economy of the indexes for a handful of the more than 400 industries that constitute the manufacturing sector alone is hardly a foolproof measure of what goes on in the "total private" economy. For almost one-third of production workers there are no data for physical quantities, making any index pure guesswork. And in the service sectors — like retailing, which employs more than eight million people — there are no official productivity indexes at all. Yet Bell takes at face value and as gospel truth all the gabble about "modest productivity growth in the private domestic economy." To be sure, economists use the numbers, but they know they must handle them gingerly: Only when they are ready to propagandize for the establishment does caution suddenly disappear. In any case, it is clear from the evidence that the pace of productivity increase for the total private economy was higher in the postwar period than in the previous four decades — 3 per cent a year from 1947 to 1963, compared with about 2 per cent a year from 1909 to 1947. "For example may be no proof," as Bell quips, but one looks with wonder and awe at the auto industry's output in 1964 — almost eight million vehicles produced with one-sixth fewer workers than were used for a similar output in 1955.

Nor does Bell see clearly the relationships that hold between Gross National Product, productivity, and employment despite the apparent ease with which he describes these terms. The issue is really not so difficult if one expresses unemployment$^{(U)}$ as the difference between the total labor force$^{(L)}$ and those employed.$^{(E)}$ Stated this way, the equation appears rather banal. It is necessary, however, to "decompose" the last element into a more subtle expression—employment equals the Gross National Product divided by the product of productivity$^{(P)}$ and available man-hours per year$^{(H)}$.

$$U = L - \frac{GNP}{P \times H} \tag{1}$$

The objective of policy would then be to increase the value of the last expression in order to reduce the gap between it and the total labor force. There are *three* elements involved—changes in GNP, productivity, and man-hours. Standard neo-Keynesianism focuses mainly on GNP and depreciates any other policy.

There is no necessary correlation between advances in GNP and productivity, as Bell seems to believe. Given the effect on capital-output ratios that the new technology appears to be exerting, it is entirely possible for productivity to increase with less than a proportionate change in output. When it does, assuming no alteration in hours, labor displacement can be the only consequence. The situation is worsened during a downturn in economic activity, even a slight one, for technological achievement is irreversible. There is no turning back to simpler modes of production; if productivity is enhanced while output remains intact, jobs will tend to drop. Such indeed has been the situation in manufacturing: Productivity in that sector has been rising faster than output. For every unit increase in the latter, we obtain less employment than we did in earlier times, a phenomenon noted by the Labor Department's productivity expert, Leon Greenberg, in October 1965.

But Bell looks magisterially at the data and concludes

that the rise in productivity in the private economy has been quite modest. The implication is that there has been no cause for concern in the recent past: Aggregate demand will sop up any unemployment. And, of course, it appears that such is the case at the moment, given the sort of business we now have in Asia. But suppose peace should really break out? Are we so cocksure about the kind of fiscal policies we can make politically palatable by relying solely on neo-Keynesian devices? Even Bell's modest percentages have a compound effect. As the Automation Commission acknowledged, a 1 per cent rate of increase doubles productivity in seventy-two years; a 2 per cent rate in thirty-six years; and a 3 per cent rate in twenty-three years. And what if the rate of increase in productivity rises faster than 3 per cent, as it has in manufacturing in the last five years?

As if to evade the consequences of simple arithmetic, Bell and other writers, among them Robert Solow of M.I.T., offer the disingenuous argument that agriculture accounts for most of the recent gains anyway. But to say that is to insist that the tail wags the dog. Agriculture, which has enjoyed a productivity gain in recent years of about 6 per cent per annum, has provided about 4 per cent of GNP. Now, the total annual gain in GNP due to productivity advances approximates $18 billion. We are then asked to believe that agriculture's less than $2 billion productivity advance explains the $18 billion figure! There would have had to be a rise in productivity in agriculture of 15 to 20 per cent before one could assert with confidence that the pace for the entire private economy was affected markedly by agriculture's 6 per cent rise. But the artfulness goes further: Productivity in manufacturing, say Bell and Solow, is really only 2.5 per cent per annum, although the Automation Commission, of which both were members, admits that it is really 3 per cent and that for production and maintenance workers in the last five years the pace has stepped up to 3.4 per cent a year. Those points are not quibbles, for a jump from 3 per cent to 3.4 per cent represents a change of one-seventh and one from 2.5 to 3 a change of one-fifth.

What is important is acceleration in the rate of growth of productivity. Gardner Ackley recently commented that in the last few years "... labor productivity increased solidly at a rate above the postwar average." The data suggest he is right. In the language of calculus, one must look for the second derivative as he moves up the curve, at changes in the rate of change. Even if one relies solely on productivity data, a questionable business at best, the analysis should provide more refined calculations than Bell and Solow have hitherto offered.

Casting about for further ammunition in his arsenal, Bell then calls attention to Herbert A. Simon's book, *The Shape of Automation* (1965), in which Simon resorts to some simple formulations drawn from international-trade theory to prove that technological innovation is severely limited in its power to spread. In describing Simon's position Bell says: "Technically, the decision to use any new technology depends on its comparative price – of labor and capital. The market price, which determines relative use, will be proportional to the marginal productivity of each factor. In other words the structure of employment will shift in proportion to the man-machine productivity ratios." It is, of course, interesting to note this flirtation with archaic classical economic doctrine, but in any case the statement is a mishmash. First, the formulation is derived from the theory of a perfectly competitive market in static equilibrium under conditions of full employment and has little relevance to our monopolistic economy. In such a competitive market entrepreneurs cannot affect price but can merely respond to it, so that cost as well as relative price is an element in "relative use." Second, the model is timeless, allowing for no adjustment; technological change, if it has anything, has a time dimension, which is also a factor in "relative use." What Bell and Simon refer to, of course, is the principle of comparative advantage that was employed by Ricardo, Mill, and other classicists to explain the flow of trade among nations. The "law" assumed, however, in addition to equilibrium and full-employment conditions, fixed proportions between capital and labor; as a basis for analyzing the spread of technology within one country this model has little relevance. A further assumption is constancy in cost; in other words, no advantages can accrue from mass production. Indeed, if resource use and other factor endowments were as fixed as the theory says, one would be hard put to explain the diffusion of technology at all. Recognition of these difficulties in classical trade theory generated a rather furious debate over the years, one that has pretty well undermined the simple textbook version on which Bell relies.

Indeed, the relevant theory for an analysis of the economic feasibility of automation would be one based on a straightforward benefit-cost study. As the mathematicians are wont to say, this approach is much more elegant and direct. The underlying assumption is that any technological innovation must yield a present gain or benefit in excess of its cost. As there are elements of futurity in investment (returns will flow to the firm over a number of years), a compound-interest component enters into the businessman's deliberations. Therefore the present value of a computer or other automation device has to be related to expected future returns and to rates of compound interest. This argument sounds quite technical, but it underscores the palpable fact that a decision to employ a piece of equipment depends on the length of life of the machine, its initial and maintenance costs, the rate of interest, and the net returns for the duration of its use. Considering the fact that the computer is a general-purpose machine, the rationality of these calculations can be applied to a simultaneous replacement of bookkeepers and clerks.

In short, it is important to have some grasp of what the modern computer can do and will do. Its capacity is now so large and its speed so great that, even though it may be *less* efficient in handling a clerk's work than in handling a bookkeeper's, it will still do the work of both because it is faster than both. The law of comparative advantage, as interpreted by Bell and Simon, suggests that the computer would do only the bookkeeper's work. But the limitation of factor endowment, which seems so reasonable a restraint in the simple model of international trade, does not hold for the new technology. In the long run, as Norbert Wiener once said, the only competition for the machine is a virtually costless human slave. Furthermore, one ought to add some noneconomic elements to the Bell-Simon law of comparative advantage. As a sociologist, one might have expected Bell to pay attention to another law—"Keeping up with Jones."

Portent and Implication

As we have shown earlier, too many companies have installed the new equipment because IBM salesmen told them rivals had just put in computers.

Simon also wishes to prove that, whatever the character of the technological change, labor as a whole is bound to benefit to the detriment of capital. He begins with an equation in which the total product is distributed between capital and labor. That is, wages and the cost of capital equal output, which Simon sets at unity in order to study shifts in the proportions. As each of these terms comprises an input coefficient and a rate, we may state the equation as

$$WL + RC = 1 \qquad (2)$$

According to this formula, the wage rate times the labor input, plus the rate of interest times the capital input, equals the total product. So far, so good, although we must caution that this statement describes only the *distribution* of the product; it says nothing about the *level* of output. Now, argues Simon, because the rate of interest is constant, any gains stemming from technological advance can benefit only labor; if the technical change is capital saving, the proportions shift in labor's favor. If the change is labor saving, then the wage rate rises.

Of course, the rate of interest is hardly stable, as witness recent Federal Reserve Board action. Yet what of the wage rate? Simon "proves" that wages will rise (here he commits a serious error by confusing wage earnings and wage rates) through a simple algebraic transformation. The first equation is transposed into

$$W = \frac{1 - RC}{L} \qquad (3)$$

This equation demonstrates that, whatever the nature of the technical change, W, the wage rate, will increase. If automation reduces the labor coefficient, that is, the quantity of labor input, then by inspection W must rise. Good — but what happens to the incomes to those thus separated from the economic process? The rate may rise, but that does not mean that the earnings of the entire group will rise also. If the worker is unattached he has no income. Although the change means a larger value of the fraction on the right side of the equation, L is also smaller by virtue of the technical change. More important, if the displaced worker does succeed in obtaining work "in the next best alternative", his marginal productivity will fall and so will his real wage.

Had Simon formulated his model to allow for output levels, other interesting possibilities might have emerged. Suppose the original formula is recast as

$$WL + RC = Y \qquad (4)$$

and that Y represents the level of output. Now, from Equation (1), it can be shown that output is a function of the labor coefficient, productivity, and hours worked, that is, $Y = L(PH)$. Substituting the latter in Simon's formulas, we wind up with

$$W = \frac{L(PH) - RC}{L} \qquad (5)$$

A technical change of the labor-saving variety thus alters both numerator and denominator: Output may be reduced as well as labor (of course, productivity takes care of that contingency) so that the wage rate may not be so happily enhanced as Simon anticipates. Generally, it would require a more than proportionate increase in productivity to counterbalance the depressive effect of labor cutbacks on the wage rate itself. Of course, that too has happened, but technical shifts of considerable magnitude can cut into wage *income*.

ANOTHER ARGUMENT against the impact of automation is that it reduces prices. Surely that must be an advantage of the new technology, at least, television sets cost less than they did five or six years ago, as do washing machines, vacuum cleaners, radios, and refrigerators. It has been said that price reductions are necessary if automated factories are to operate full time, as they must to be economically practicable.[19] Yet the implications that automation "restores" flexibility of prices is unwarranted, for those industries in which automated methods are becoming predominant have shown little downward price movement in recent years — chemicals and steel are cases in point. Furthermore, consumer durable prices respond to pressures other than the methods of making the products—for example, discount merchandising and fluctuations in the prices of raw materials.

The indexes of wholesale prices for such items as industrial chemicals, iron and steel, metal-working machinery, and automobiles exhibited rather remarkable stability from 1957 to 1966, suggesting that the cost savings from automation were absorbed by higher profits. In 1958 the profits per sales dollar of American manufacturers were 4.1 per cent, in 1961 4.3 per cent, and in 1962 4.5 per cent. Some prices for "automated" goods have gone up—gasoline and fuel wholesale prices increased about 25 per cent between 1957 and 1964, and certain types of machinery went up 16 per cent during the same period.[20] Patently, automation has done little to alter the oligopolistic behavior of the major industries in America.

Finally, conventional wisdom tells us that automation is no problem because it is just more of the same; it represents progress and should be welcomed; it helps us meet the challenge of foreign competition; natural economic forces will carry through the necessary adjustments less painfully than we expect; new industries will provide ample jobs for those displaced or just entering the labor force; we should rejoice in the opportunity for the leisure that automation affords; the market is infinitely expandable, which alone will create the necessary additional demand; the income pie will become larger, so that everyone will enjoy a larger slice; automation will develop slowly because it requires long-range planning, massive investment, and skilled personnel that we do not yet have; a developing labor shortage means that we must have more and more automation; over-all employment has been increasing; such unemployment as we now have must have been caused by factors prior to the advent of the new methods; management's conscience will not allow hardships to develop; such difficulties as do arise are a small price to pay for progress; and automation is the only way to beat the Russians.[21]

They are rather straightforward rationalizations, and most of them founder on the hard bedrock of empirical fact. But there are also other arguments, the egregious quality of which is perhaps best typified by the statements of

Yale Brozen, an economics professor at The University of Chicago. Brozen concedes that automation causes displacement but argues that ". . . it does not create unemployment in the sense that a larger number are unemployed than would have been if no automation had occurred."[22] Though it is difficult to discern what Brozen means, he seems to be asserting that automation is a way of solving unemployment; it might be described as the job-creating argument with a reverse twist. In thirty-one cases of automation studied by R. A. Beaumont and R. B. Helfgott, however, employment declined in twenty, remained the same in four, and increased somewhat in seven. The average drop in two-thirds of the instances in which employment declined ranged from 20 to 25 per cent. In one situation, direct production workers dropped from 78 per cent of the work force to 52 per cent, whereas maintenance and technical employees increased from 22 to 48 per cent. Nevertheless, the *total number* of employed declined almost 30 per cent![23] One searches in vain for evidence of universal job increases stemming from automation: Surely if they were there, businessmen would be delighted to present the data to a troubled public. IBM was supposed to have made a study showing substantial employment increases owing to automation, but the report presumably is confidential,[24] although one is hard put to understand why.

Brozen goes even further: The real blessings of automation have been inhibited by the increases in real wages. He points to a study of conditions in Michigan in which it had been argued that a 1 per cent increase in relative wages led to a 2 per cent decline in employment. These results, of course, arose from the inordinate power of the unions,[25] inevitably resulting in a substitution of capital for labor. Unfortunately, the elasticity of substitution in the study cited by Brozen was defined as the ratio of labor input to value added. As this ratio is the reciprocal of only one possible measure of productivity—value added divided by labor input—the relationship was bound to be negative. The ratio of labor input to value added conceivably might have been used as an index of labor requirements, however, and, if it fell, it would merely demonstrate the point that Brozen wishes to deny—technical change does reduce the number of workers. But the problem was more complicated than any statistical measure could reveal, for as Daniel Fusfeld demonstrated, the economic situation in Michigan was conditioned by other factors—the decentralization of auto assembly, a sharp drop in defense contracts, and the self-reinforcing nature of the automation process itself.[26] The conventional mythology of automation is equally self-reinforcing as one observes the argument passed from economist to economist, eventually to find its way into the culture of the day. Thus "... the plight of a major portion of [the] unemployed can be laid directly on the doorsteps of all the misguided forces in the country which have contributed to the diversion of the productivity gains into unjustified wage increases for the employed."[27]

One can deal with such a farrago only by a review of the facts. Although output per man-hour in the private sector of the economy rose by almost 25 per cent between 1956 and 1963, real income, in terms of hourly compensation for employees, increased by about 18 per cent. Furthermore, the gap between the two series has been growing over the years. And business outlays for new plant and equipment went up 22 per cent from 1956 to 1963 and by 1964 promised to be 35 per cent higher than in the base year.[28] Real wages for factory workers increased by about 3 per cent per annum between 1947 and 1956; in more recent years the average annual increase was 1.6 per cent. It is rather difficult to see, therefore, how wages have been drawing off the benefits of greater productivity, especially when payroll costs per unit of output were 7 per cent less in 1963 than in 1958.

A PROPER ANALYSIS would acknowledge that increases in real wages, given our rules of the economic game, are occasioned by the competition of growing industries for resources. Such an effect was observed almost three-quarters of a century ago by Knut Wicksell, the famous Swedish economist, who had remarked that expansion must take into account increased real wages. For, as long as earnings are sustained by growth or shifts to new techniques, there should be no objection by entrepreneurs to improved standards.[29] In fact, most discussions of this question—the relation of real wages to capital accumulation—assume perfect competition and a homogeneous production function: Under conditions of monopolistic or imperfect competition, the relationship poses even less of a problem. Provision necessarily must be made for a larger amount of "subsistence" goods, that is, for real wages, unless the entire added accumulation is to be applied exclusively to capital purposes. Indeed, this situation cannot arise in an economy in which decisions on savings and investments are made by different people. Investment without any absorption can occur only when the saver and investor are identical—as in a command economy with strict central planning.[30]

The historical process has been such that real wages must rise as the economy shifts to new techniques. Otherwise viability is impossible. In a severely restricted model, real-wage increases might limit depreciation reserves so that replacement costs would be inadequate but only in a model. In real life, such a contingency is of no consequence. United States Department of Commerce reports reveal that corporate profits, after taxes, in the first quarter of 1964 were more than $30 billion at annual rates—42 per cent higher than in 1961. Between 1953 and 1963 profits after taxes plus depreciation reserves (corporate cash flow), rose from $32.2 billion to $59.5 billion, a jump of 90 per cent. Evidently the modest rise in real wages in recent years has not exerted any inhibitory effects on capital accumulation. Furthermore, the excess cash flow from 1959 to 1963 exceeded actual investments in new plant and equipment by $8.7 billion.

One must also take into account the level of effective demand—a lesson driven home by John Maynard Keynes thirty years ago. In the context of sticky prices and wages (at low levels of equilibrium), it is possible, as Joan Robinson has said, that "... each entrepreneur individually gains from low real wages in terms of his own product, but all suffer from the limited market for commodities which a low real wage rate entails."[31] If prices and wages are flexible, a condition that ordinary theory deems desirable, and if population increases more rapidly than does investment, then all that will have been achieved is a pool of unemployed, whereas the real wage may at best remain unchanged. Maintaining the same rate of investment will not create more employment. When prices are sticky and wages flexible, the situation will be even worse, for both demand and investment will stagnate.[32] Of course, if investment were to grow and the real wage along with it, then the economy might achieve a state of nirvana, but the possibility of a bleaker prospect cannot be denied. The crux of the situation, consequently, is that real wages must move in consonance with productivity to provide enough demand to absorb the larger output from the investment of capital. What is more, if population keeps growing, then expansion of production must be even greater simply to absorb the additional bodies entering the labor force. And, to compound the difficulty, additional investment may not contribute much to maintaining the requisite balance because capital saving is now a significant feature of newly installed equipment. That is, surplus savings unmatched by investment or consumption can develop and upset the delicate balance of the equations. In essence, underconsumption, so long depreciated in standard economic theory, is an ever-present ghost at the banquet table.

Real wages must thus keep pace with productivity if a market for goods is to be maintained and capital accumulation is to continue to provide capacity for growth. It is essential if jobs are to be provided under conditions of innovation.[33] The economy might still exhibit manifestations of exhilaration, even when real wages are lagging, but the truth is that trouble would be in the making. It therefore seems evident, from the point of view of both theory and fact, that automation requires a high level of real wages rather than a low one. With the latter, conditions are bound to develop such that marketability of goods and capital accumulation would both grind to a halt.

Innovation is a dynamic, active process involving numerous complex noneconomic as well as economic considerations. But to the orthodox it is all quite passive and purely economic.[34] For example, Brozen cites the construction of U.S. Steel's Fairless works as an illustration of pure economic behavior, relating costs to output in a manner reminiscent of the curves in an elementary text-book. The advanced techniques in the new steel plant were said to have cost $100,000 per man, yielding 300 tons per man-year, whereas conventional methods would have provided only 160 tons per man-year. Naturally, these factors are important, but also meaningful was the desire of the company to move closer to its consumers, an action that involved the abandonment of the basing-point system for the F.O.B. mill-pricing method. Furthermore, de-pletion of old sources of raw materials required U.S. Steel to set up facilities at an eastern port to make it easier to obtain ore supplies from overseas at minimum cost. And it was to be expected that the latest technology would be employed in a new plant constructed afresh from the ground up.

This point emphasizes that the choice of technique is frequently a matter of responding to a number of prevailing parameters that affect the utilization of both capital and labor inputs. If an alteration in capital use impels the selec-tion of some alternative method in production, there is apt to be a shift in labor utilization as well, a point that Brozen does not always specify. Not only does the production function change in complicated ways, but also the decrease in production workers is never fully counterbalanced by increases in maintenance employees, who in any case are apt to be cut back after an automated installation begins to work efficiently and with dispatch. To these effects, one must add the tendency in a nonwar economy to create a stagnant pool of surplus labor. Historically, capital has been substituted for labor because of a relative scarcity of the latter. That, at least, was the experience of the nineteenth century in the United States. Theoretically, the availability of surplus labor ought to have exerted some restraining influences on such substitutions, for when labor competes for jobs, especially in a fluid labor market, the "capitalist" presumably has less motivation to mechanize. In effect, labor competed against machines. Given an advanced technology, however, such competition can occur only between machines and *usable* labor.

Meanwhile, the Wicksell effect, operating through the real wage, tends over the long run to absorb a portion of capital accumulation in that sector of the economy employing a usable work force. In order to maintain a predetermined ratio of profit to capital accumulation, it would be necessary for the "capitalist" to mechanize and automate even further, which in turn would make some of the skilled workers redundant. This all important ratio of profit to capital accumulation may be maintained by resorting to capital-saving investment: In fact, this course is often preferable as it makes the application of accumulation to investment more extensive, thus yielding an even greater volume of profit. But what it suggests is that the "coefficients" implicit in the production function are not invariable. They shift with alterations in the underlying technology and do affect the ratio of capital to labor. The crux of the problem seems to be that the surplus-labor pool that accumulates is less and less usable for the existing techniques and cannot really compete with machines. One cannot simply dip into the pool, for the relevant labor force must have certain skills and education.

For the more mechanized an industry, the more fixed the specific labor skills required per unit of capital or per unit of output. Furthermore, this consequence is apt to be accompanied by a decline in the transferability of skills. In effect, there is a tendency for all labor to be converted into fixed overhead, the utilization of which would depend only on capacity. Skill, as it was once defined, would not be utilized, and in the absence of use it would deteriorate, creating a continuing barrier between the displaced and the employed.[35] Conceivably the pool of unskilled would become stagnant, untapped by society because it would have no function—it would become a conglomeration of economically and socially useless persons.

AND WE MUST again stress that the process today is sustained by vast accumulations of capital and heavy expenditures for research and development, counterbalanced only by an artificial layer of effective demand arising from the exigencies of defense. At this point, optimistic economists offer the bromide that the trend to automation will slow down in the future because outlays for research and development in the 1960s will be only half the growth rate of the previous decade. There is no doubt of the latter, if the analysis is viewed solely in terms of percentages. The meaningful figures, however, seem to be the absolute dollar amounts: "R & D" expenditures by the Federal government may have been a mere three-fourths of a billion dollars in 1940; in 1962 they were more than $9 billion. At $16.4 billion total "R & D" outlays had more than tripled in 1962–1963, compared to a decade earlier.[36] Industry spending may easily have reached $15 billion by the mid-1960s, of which perhaps half has been supplied by government. It is unlikely that these sums will be inadequate to provide the scientific basis for further technological advance.

And to assume, as Brozen does, that it would take $2 trillion to automate American industry is to suggest that it cannot be done. Yet it is being done; the cost of computers is coming within reach of even small companies, and, with interchangeable programming, computer manufacturers are impelled to compete on price.[37] Furthermore, because much of the new equipment is capital saving, there should be little fear that trends in capital formation will be inadequate. In manufacturing, the average annual increase in capital from 1945 to 1956 was more than 6 per cent. About one-fifth of manufacturing concerns experienced annual increases of 3 to 5 per cent; one-fifth had gains of 7 to 9 per cent; and almost one-fourth showed advances of more than 9 per cent. From 1946 to 1955 the average annual net capital formation was about $8 billion a year. The net stock of capital has grown from about $2,100 per worker in the 1870s to about $6,400 in 1955, faster than the growth in population: There does not appear to have been a great dearth of accumulation.[38]

As we have observed several times earlier, one of the more consoling propositions is that productivity growth these days is neither remarkable nor unusual. A. J. Jaffee told the Senate Labor Committee in 1963 that only one worker in twenty is engaged in an industry that has enjoyed productivity expansion of 5 per cent or more.[39] He concluded that there was no reason to become hysterical over automation, as output per production worker was what it had always been. Aside from the patent fact that such industries—utilities, chemicals, telephones, coal—are precisely those with high degrees of automation, a more reasonable classification would include industries with higher than average productivity rates, those showing increases of 3 per cent or more. When this classification is used, one discovers that more than one-fourth of the work force is in industries generating high productivity. Furthermore in addition to the service sector, which is presumably low in productivity gains, employment projections indicate a palpable shift to the automated areas. Is, then, the work force becoming polarized, moving toward those very sectors in which the most serious problems arise? If Jaffee's figures appear inconclusive, one can draw more precise observations from Bureau of Labor Statistics sources, showing that output per production worker in coal, iron mining, railroads, utilities, petroleum refining, tire manufacturing, and aluminum increased markedly from 1957 to 1962.[40] The increases—even in terms of production workers rather than of man-hours—ranged from 35 per cent for railroads to almost 53 per cent for aluminum. At the same time, unit labor requirements dropped 29 per cent for petroleum and tire manufacturing and 34 per cent for coal and aluminum. In all the industries cited, the employment of production workers sagged—from 3 per cent in utilities to 16 per cent in aluminum to 46 per cent in coal.

Supporting these trends has been the decline in the capital-output ratio, indicating a tendency toward larger output per unit of capital. In transportation, communications, and utilities, the secular movement was from an average of about one to twelve ($1 of output for $12 of capital) in the 1880s, to one to 6.5 at the turn of the century, to one to 3.5 in the 1920s, and to one to 1.7 in 1950. The situation is similar in manufacturing, where the ratio dropped from 1929 to 1957 by almost one-third. Meanwhile the ratio of man-hours worked to output fell 45 per cent.[41] Perhaps these relationships changed as they did because much of the investment has been of the capital-saving variety. A recent illustration is a Carling's brewery, which utilized a new continuous process for making beer that was not only more productive but also required only three-fourths of the capital investment of a conventional plant.

Still business leaders will deny that technology and automation have any sort of displacement effect. Henry Ford II insists that those who blame automation for unemployment are speaking the "most dangerous sort of nonsense." Admitting that the unemployment rate may have been too high in recent years, Mr. Ford nevertheless argues that, with the jobless rate held at about 5 per cent over the last half-dozen years, new jobs were created faster than old ones were eliminated.[42] Others have argued that the average of four million or so people who were unemployed each month in recent years did not always include the same people. It is conceded, then, that in some years no fewer than fifteen million workers were unemployed at some time between January 1 and December 31, that is, fifteen million jobs ended temporarily or permanently during the year. Therefore, according to the striking conclusion, fifteen million new jobs began.[43] More striking is the fact that fifteen million people suffered joblessness. The arithmetic also omits that at the year's end there were still four million or so people out of work. Although this figure was reduced toward the end of 1965, one must search for political rather than for purely economic reasons.

Let us review some of the points that cast grave doubt on the standard view, for the fact is that recent economic exhilaration has obscured the major impacts of the new technology. Automation is an accelerating process: Those firms now automating their plants and installing process controls and advanced data-processing systems will force their competitors to follow suit or go under. Lack of a job, given the present work ethic, means lack of income, which is not merely a tragedy for the individual but, with relaxation of upward economic pressures from defense requirements, can become a major social catastrophe. Automation by itself has failed to create job opportunities for everyone, especially for the millions of new entrants into the labor force. And we still await the vast new industries that have been promised to take up the slack. (To repeat — war is always available.)

Clearly, there are some businessmen who avoid conventionality: They too are concerned with the future shape of our society. Clarence Randall has said, "Management

355

which takes the profit from automation must share the burdens which it begets." He has urged retraining as an expression of management's responsibility for preparing the displaced workers for other jobs. And he had even suggested that we might profitably imitate Sweden's system of building tax-free reserves, which might be used to cushion economic shocks and disturbances. The late John I. Snyder, who constructed and sold automation machinery, was upset because what he and others did destroyed, according to his calculation, 40,000 jobs a week. (This figure may be an overstatement: The Council of Economic Advisers estimate in 1963 was 28,000 jobs a week.) Mr. Snyder used to look to new industries and the new markets to solve the problem, especially in the service sector. (But if, as Robert Heilbroner has pointed out, automation invades this third area of employment, where will people go then?) Thomas Watson, whose IBM provides more computers to the world than do all other makers combined, tells the International Congress of Accountants that computers have an infinite capacity for mischief, likening the new technology to an "automated nosy neighbor."[44] Yet there are those who insist that all is well.

WHY THIS FAILURE of imagination and perception? Several factors appear to be responsible: the failure to grasp the clear-cut distinction between ordinary industrialization and automation (or cybernation), which has led many to assume that it is all of a single piece; the lack of a sufficiently rapid economic growth in the Eisenhower years, which intensified the effects of the new technology; and an inordinate infatuation with the impersonal mechanisms of standard Keynesianism, so indifferent to specifics, which has impelled many to accept the belief that monetary and fiscal policy is quite sufficient to correct all ills. This last view is especially prevalent among economists of a liberal persuasion. Aside from depreciating the urgency of technological displacement, they insist that demand is the crucial factor: When demand expands as fast as the output we *could* produce, then automation, they say, will indeed result in more jobs. Hence the need for a high level of effective demand. Of course, the $10 billion tax cut in 1964 did raise the Gross National Product by some $27 billion, yet the level of unemployment was not pushed below 5 per cent.

Let us state once and for all: A high degree of demand is a *sine qua non* for a viable economy and an essential base for solving the persistent problems of the time. It is a necessary but not a sufficient condition. We cannot assume that resources and manpower are readily available to fulfill the needs of rapid expansion. We cannot assume that obsolescent skills, geographic distortions in the distribution of the labor force, and inadequate data on labor market requirements are of little significance. Obviously, the so-called "structural" treatment implied by such questions would not be successful in a great depression such as we suffered in the 1930s. In that situation, the effective demand cure was required. Again, the cure worked in the decade of the Forties because we went to war. The most recent experience has been the enjoyment of a fast-moving economy, which nevertheless in normal times left behind large blocs of the populace. As we rushed down the highway, the road got rougher. To shift the image, bottlenecks tended to develop, and we discovered that the economy, even with its "normal" government programs, could not employ the untutored, the unskilled, the displaced. In 1950 the unemployment rate for those with elementary-school education or less was 7.6 per cent; in 1962 the rate was more than 8 per cent. The better educated had a substantially lower unemployment rate, and by the end of the twelve-year period it was but 1.4 per cent. As Charles Killingsworth has asked, could fiscal and monetary measures alone increase jobs for the uneducated six times faster than for the educated, given the nature of today's technology? That is the question that advocates of "tax cuts alone" must answer.[45]

Clearly, the problem is considerably more complicated than the proponents of automatic adjustment suggest. Is there some optimum rate of innovation that would cause neither disruption nor technical stagnation? What are the indirect impacts of automation, that is, how does automation in one sector of the economy spill over into others? How do geographic shifts stemming from automation affect people, industries, regional economies? Can demand keep pace with

357

output? Can output keep pace with population? Will capital accumulation be employed in ways that will ensure a balance between savings and investment, between capacity and demand? Or shall we have to break the traditional work nexus of our society by providing, as a matter of right, incomes equal to the "wages" of the machines that have displaced human beings in production?

These questions are the elements of the present debate. As Robert Heilbroner has said, they reveal the failure of economic and social theory to deal in meaningful ways with the problem of technology. For technology is central to contemporary existence, and traditional economic theory's incapacity or unwillingness to deal with the machine merely reveals its purveyors to be victims of whole generations of defunct economists. What we lack, says Heilbroner, "... is a conception of the technological process sufficiently broad to comprehend its long range and its short range impacts, alive to its secular re-arrangements of society as well as its mixed creative and disruptive effects..."[46] We ought to have a theory of technology in which monopolistic competition is the framework of corporate behavior; in which innovation is a guided and directed and government-supported process; in which technology so alters the organization of business as to raise critical questions of control; in which mass reaction and mass behavior are realities; in which affluence seldom spills over into the realm of public services; and in which a proper social response could make automation the blessing it has not yet become.

Time on our hands   11

Thorstein Veblen used to argue that work was an important instinct in human nature. By this he meant nothing more than a general proclivity, an urge to do what has to be done: Man worked because he was man.[1] The latter-day contention that work is onerous, said Veblen, really constituted a "conventional antipathy" stemming from barbaric traits superimposed on the natural instincts of workmanship, idle curiosity, and parental bent. Whatever irksomeness appeared in work stemmed from the indignities enforced by barbaric traits. The instincts, given free rein, could signify not only survival and welfare but also the advance of humanity. Unfortunately, pecuniary principles, inherent in the fabric of modern institutions, impeded their proper functioning, argued Veblen, so much so that it was doubtful that the common sense of workmanship could alter the situation before it degenerated into collapse. There were too many instances in history illustrating how imbecile institutions triumphed over life and culture to offer much faith that it would be otherwise in our time.[2]

THIS DYSPEPTIC VIEW of the course of man's history was not groundless. From a philosophic standpoint, work is that common element of civilization that unifies its politics, science, art, religion, economics, and language.[3] This is perhaps more evident in primitive societies, which are unfragmented and holistic and in which specific activities are related to one another in a system that "strives toward maximum equilibrium."[4] The primitive partakes in all aspects of his culture in a way that the inhabitant of modern technological civilization cannot. The primitive is a hunter, craftsman, and herder and is knowledgeable in the legends of his tribe. He is an engaged man in control of his technology. He governs the work he does and is related to his society in a totally unalienated manner. His is a natural milieu of work, which expresses without mediation of the machine the relation of man to nature, a relation that has now passed from the human scene. It would be utterly wrong to assert that primitive man responds to his environment as an automaton; this statement is merely a projection of present-day "civilized" routine. The primitive response is very human, and it stands in glaring contrast to the character of work today, a contrast that Veblen, among all early American social scientists, was perhaps the first to grasp.[5]

Work implies force in action. It is an expenditure of effort and energy seeking to overcome the resistance of recalcitrant materials. Moreover, the materials themselves will, in reciprocal fashion, affect the structure of work.[6] Significantly, work is done "in the interest of him who does it," an interest that is shaped by a particular area of the culture — politics, art, religion, economics — and is rooted in either tradition or convention. It is also presumed that work will conform to some standard of efficiency, that it aims for maximum achievement at minimum outlay of effort. At least, that is the modern convention; some modification may be imposed by the culture, as in the case of slavery in which "economic" principles were hardly controlling. The home weaving of thread on a spinning wheel was work in the sixteenth century; today, it would be a curious hobby devoid of economic content, unless, of course, there were a leisure-time industry in existence to supply wheel and antique spindles.

It is said that work is motivated by an urge to maintain oneself and one's family, but its meaning assuredly stems from more than this prescription, which originated in

Genesis. Work is the most important activity in which man engages, for it provides *the* standard for judging his worth. So pervasive is this concern that many seek to elevate themselves by borrowing dignity from titles, for example the press-relations man *né* press agent or the mortician *né* undertaker. This search for dignity suggests that financial incentives may not be the sole driving force in work; rather, an unquenchable urge exists in man's breast to make work meaningful.[7] The fundamental question for the individual worker must be the shape and form that his work assumes. When technology was less structured and more amenable to human control, the individual could mold his work directly, lending a pride of craft, even a joy in bending himself against resisting forces and compelling them to assume shapes undreamed of in a rude state of nature. Material was torn out of nature and converted into products of man. This situation, indeed, was his true social condition.[8]

Yet as the mode of work was increasingly directed and specified by advancing technology, it became less flexible, offering less freedom and maneuverability to the individual. And in dialectic fashion, the alterations in work required by technology were such that the ". . . structure of work must again account for the progressive narrowing of the scope of freedom in proportion to the specificity of the [technological] norm . . ." pursued.[9] The norms alluded to, in this quotation from Paul Schrecker's perceptive analysis, represent in a sense Veblen's state of the industrial arts; they have a marked bearing on the structure of work and lend to it a particular historic style. But the fundamental involvement was a complex of aboriginal needs and desires, each of which sought a given method for achieving fulfillment. The result was not only an activity that guaranteed survival but the creation as well of things that lent permanence to what man did.[10] Nevertheless, the various urges did not exhibit uniform development: Conflict could emerge, as when the satisfaction of an economic need might clash with an ethical principle. Thus, work could not satisfy simultaneously all the requirements of the human spirit, giving rise to tensions, as politics, science, art, religion, and technology contended for the central position in society.

In our own time, it appears that technology has won out.

Portent and Implication

As the offspring of science and economics, it ought to have mediated between the two fields. But the healthful norms that technology might have provided have been submerged and distorted. It has been rather the frenetic and consequently desiccating qualities that have prevailed. One can almost predict today that a sharp alteration in technology will enforce shifts in economics, then in politics, and on through the entire society, so pervasive has technology become. Furthermore, the imminence of social disaster appears most likely when such shifts are resisted and when the demands of archaic economic practices are superimposed upon technological imperatives. The evidence for such conditions may be drawn from the pages of history, mute witness to the repeated episodes of human anguish. The demands of politics, as well as of technology, today have tended to dominate all other urges, with the consequence that values have been distorted and those of power and pecuniary success allowed to dominate all else. The genuine scientific spirit has withered, accompanied by the decay of human perceptions and the heightening of frustration.

The effect on work is obvious. The emotional and psychological needs the energies of which could be discharged only through work were twisted beyond recognition. When a problem is assigned by a corporate oligarch to a scientist, the standards and sanctions can be only those implicit in the realm of economics; on the other hand, the scientist can function best when he is motivated by the norms of his own field. Yet working for the archon, he soon discovers that he must pervert *his* norms to satisfy the needs of those who employ him, a situation that issues in pseudowork, unsatisfying and alienated in the most profound sense. Work becomes a mechanical reaction of those pursuing the dictates of a single set of values; it loses its spontaneity and its creativeness and is converted into automatic behavior. Society becomes an anthill and, like a machine driven by perpetual motion, enters the realm of anonymous history. Meaning disappears as work takes on the character of a continuous process. When it does, those humans utilized by the process become mere automatons. And a civilization that distorts a human response in this manner is itself gross and distorted.[11] As Schrecker remarks, there are priests but no prophets who might urge alternative modes of development. Meanwhile, the priests are impervious to the pressing demands of the noneconomic and nontechnological urges. There are optimists, of course, who hope that viable work in the realms of the latter will soon advance, but at the present juncture of events this possibility seems dubious. Siegfried Giedion has said:

> We are confronted ... by an immense storehouse bursting with new discoveries, inventions, and potentialities, all promising a better life ... But the promises ... have not been kept. All we have to show so far is a rather disquieting inability to organize the world, or even to organize ourselves. Future generations will perhaps designate this period as one of mechanized barbarism, the most repulsive barbarism of all.[12]

The fact is that contemporary society lacks balance, a condition typified by the shape of work that has now upset the equilibrium between inner and outer reality.[13] Man, once *homo faber* and at the center of work, is now *animal laborans* and at the periphery of work. Historically, this change has seemed inevitable, stemming from the ways in which work has changed. And where such alterations were once imperceptible, allowing man to readjust and to keep control of change, they are now abrupt. But the penchant of historians to trace the aetiology of change back to the wheel and the spade converts a radical shift into a mere epiphenomenon, so that macroeconomic impacts are seen as the accumulation of small increments of history. Such an arbitrary procedure leads one to say, for example, that automation is simply more of the same. It leads to a depreciation of the cataclysmic, for technological leaps do not merely alter older forms of work: the latter are simply discarded and replaced by new forms.

Clearly, freedom—freedom to relate oneself to society and the environment—can be sustained best when work is part of an evolutionary process. Although work may then appear to be somewhat anonymous, it has a specific cumulative force moving in a meaningful direction. The newer revolutionary modes of work, however, assign particular functions to everyone or shove people aside if no functions can be assigned. This consequence stems from the very rigidity of work, and, set against the decline of freedom, the impact can be no less than revolutionary. For freedom implies an ability to function within the standards established by human needs and this in turn implies a capacity to choose alternatives. Under modern technology, however, there is no choice. Technology is unfree, for it imposes its requirements on all others and therefore abolishes freedom. What ensues is a "callous and rigid automatism," in which modes of work, despite their novelty, represent stultification. The human being can take part in only a limited range of activity — the economic and the technologic — and is thereby denied an opportunity to relate himself usefully to others. In fact, at one time work was an instrument of learning, a cultural device for the transmission of man's inheritance. Without work he could in no way give form to the world about him, for, lacking the stimulus that stemmed from nature's challenge, there was no means for acquiring the knowledge essential to survival. Work thus established an essential connection between man and nature.[14] But today work, such of it as remains, is simply converted into a general activity, the worthwhileness of which is measured by the involved indirectedness employed to satisfy cultural and biological needs. There is no sense of achievement in it: It consequently becomes a form of nonwork impeding the growth of personality and man's effort to offer viable contributions to his civilization. It does not help shape the world to man's understanding; it is rather a burden signifying toil and misery. At the end of one's daily hours of labor, one can but collapse into a chair and stare vacantly at the television screen. Under the best of conditions, the sense of workmanship is subordinated to other interests.[15]

YET WORK IS an essential attribute of existence. Eliminate work, or empty it of meaning, and grave difficulties are inevitable. As Freud said:

> Laying stress upon the importance of work has a greater effect than any other technique of living in the direction of binding the individual more closely to reality; in his work he is at least securely attached to a part of reality, the human community.

Work is no less important for the opportunity it and the human relations connected with it provide for a very considerable discharge of libidinal component impulses ... than because it is indispensable for subsistence and justifies existence in a society. The daily work of earning a livelihood affords particular satisfaction when it has been selected by free choice, i.e., when through sublimation it enables use to be made of existing inclinations, of instinctual impulses that have retained their strength ....

Yet there is failure, for

... as a path to happiness work is not valued very highly by men. They do not run after it as they do after other opportunities for gratification. The great majority work only when forced by necessity, and this natural human aversion to work gives rise to the most difficult social problems.[16]

Here is the tragedy of the human being, for it is only through work that he can exert his influence upon society. And, although he rejects the amorphous, distasteful shape it has assumed today, he must subject himself to the lashes of necessity via the cash nexus. All that remains is pecuniary reward, often of a pitiful nature, replacing the urge to undertake activity for its own sake. Humanity is thereby diminished.

Can only those who partake of "higher" forms of work express a sense of engagement? John A. Hobson, the English economist, once suggested a hierarchy of work in which satisfactions or utilities might be compared with the costs or pains incurred.[17] In his scale, art in its various forms represented the highest type of work because of its life-enhancing qualities. The utilities far outweighed the disutilities, for there was a total involvement and a total commitment to work in itself. But as one descended from the arts to other forms of work, more human costs emerged. One encountered repetitive and arid activity that generated feelings of dissociation. For example, administrative work could lead to an oppressive sense of burden, whereas the purely pecuniary pursuits engendered a certain moral callousness that could only intensify human costs. The laborer, said Hobson, who must tend a machine "presents the supreme example of imitative work, with a maximum of human costs and a minimum of human utility."[18] It is not merely the fatigue and the wear on the human constitution but the mindlessness of the work itself that contributes to the enormity of the situation. Hobson's analysis may appear simplistic, but it does underscore the elementary notion that work without achievement is a desolation. Surely that can be overcome only with a sense of craft; but the latter is no longer in evidence. We are now concerned rather with the manipulation of others.[19]

CRAFT, as an element in work, existed even among the Greeks, although Pericles's free citizen did not deem it an authentic way of life. Members of the polis sought rather lives of contemplation through which they might observe the perfection of nature and its superiority over man. And while the craftsman might indeed relate himself to the materials of nature, wrestle with them, and shape them to the needs of the community, he was not really free because he had to undertake an activity dependent on mortal want. Such a condition, said the free Greek, was a barrier to the fulfillment of civic tasks, a fulfillment that underpinned the ancient political ideal as expressed in the relationships existing among free men. The world of things created by craft offered a life toward which the classic Greek philosophers were antipathetic, even contemptuous. Work meant to be enslaved by necessity: The Greek had not yet discovered what modern man came to know with bitterness—that necessity and freedom are intimately related. The escape for the Greek was to become a slave owner and thus to gain victory over necessity. Even Hesiod's oft-quoted line, "Work is no disgrace," was merely an admonition that a modicum of prosperity was essential to freedom. For the Greek, work was to be excluded from the human condition.[20] Such was the view of the philosopher who gave Greek culture its flavor, even though the noise of the workshop and the market was not lacking. (The Corinthians charged that the Athenians failed to enjoy goods because they were always seeking more; for the latter the quiet of inaction was utterly disagreeable.[21])

The fact that work was done mainly in the household, in the privacy of the home as it were, may account for the

Greek attitude. On the other hand, contemplation of civic duty was essentially a public and political activity. In the polis men were equal, whereas in the household there was inequality.[22] A certain historical irony may be seen in this juxtaposition, for today work is public, and it has carried with it all the hierarchies of the Greek household. Individuality has been suppressed because patterns of work have become the touchstone of public existence, with the consequence that man as a political animal has been conditioned by the exigencies of inequality.

In any case, to the Greek work was an unworthy endeavor, and it was not until the medieval monk sought to rescue civilized man from chaos that it was redeemed. Work then became an honorable path to salvation. Although for some it represented punishment for man's fall from grace, the Benedictine precept, "Work, do not despair," did lend some dignity, since work, coupled with spiritual pursuits, became an instrument of salvation. The Franciscan friars were obligated to work, and by the time of St. Antoninus, who had done so much to adjust canonical doctrine to communal reality, work had become an activity worthy of man's effort. This view was strengthened appreciably during the Renaissance, when work was regarded as a matter of craft. The process itself had become important: The rationale of work was work.[23] For a brief moment in civilized life there came about a unification of the privacy of work and its public manifestations. It did not last for long. Reality seemed to be elsewhere—perhaps in the realm of the consumer rather than in that of the producer. If that was indeed the situation, then the older notion of productive and unproductive work—but work nevertheless—must be contrasted with the contemporary confrontation of work with nonwork, of occupation with idleness.

But this cleavage anticipates the nature of the transformation, for long before these developments came to the forefront of man's consciousness Martin Luther had prescribed work as a remedy for sinfulness. One served God through work; mere contemplation was not a sufficient condition for a genuine state of grace. The Reformation made work a fulfillment of religion and a commitment to faith. With Calvin the prescription became more intransigent: Work was the very will of God who had commanded His people to undertake unceasing effort in a methodical self-discipline the ultimate purpose of which was to bring to the blessed the greatest possible return on their investments.[24]

BY THE NINETEENTH CENTURY the idea of work had become universal. Everyone was convinced that it was good, even though it became more and more difficult to discern how it might provide the essential connection between man and existence. Perhaps more significantly, work became a secular activity, for, by turning his attention explicitly to material conditions rather than to the life hereafter, man shifted from spiritual contemplation to worldly transformation. Furthermore, the ideology of work became an instrument by which the burgeoning middle class could attempt to convince the workingman that for the sake of his soul he should subject himself to the crushing discipline of the factory. In the historic process of transferring his energy to a commodity the control of which rested in other hands, however, man really lost control of himself. Objects created by work passed into another realm, distinct from and basically hostile to work. It was the world of marketable goods, where man was opposed to himself in the most profound meaning of the term, for marketability was the antithesis of the free activity engendered by work. What was virtually a component of human nature became a mere instrumentality. Work was freed from tools, craft, and community and was metamorphosed into a commodity with a price tag attached to it. The significance of work was twisted; man became a laborer, without a sense of being or of engagement in the meaningful. As a laborer he engaged in uniform activity, mere expenditure of energy. Yet work was once a diverse phenomenon, gathering esteem by its very particularity and providing joy in the articles produced. There was human delight too in its structure and organization and in the comradeship gained from other workers.[25] There was a sense of dignity in work. Unfortunately, the elements of craft — spontaneity, exuberance, and freedom to perform — which made work, play, and culture virtually identical have now been irretrievably lost.[26]

Why is this consequence so inimical to the fundamental nature of man? Is it that the increasing division of labor implicit in modern work leads to a distortion of values rather than to their integration? Is it that anxiety over marketable goods displaces interest in man as maker? These elements indeed appear to be the conditioning factors in work today. For an intense application of the principles of division of labor can only issue in an automatic expenditure of energy devoid of creativity. The fragmentation that ensues severs work from all other human activities and empties even them of freedom. Work becomes labor, a discharge of shapeless and formless energy, in which the only concern is the job.[27] Furthermore, it is labor ultimately controlled by the contingencies of the market. Useful and specific products become generalized artifacts, a process accelerated by the development of money as an abstract medium of exchange and store of value. The consequence for work has been that specialization has replaced professionalization: The outlay of labor is unrelated to a product in which a craftsman might vent his personal prowess and skill. The only relationship is to a process.

When one examines the nature of this process, it is found to be oppressive, with rhythmless, chaotic noises and a collective shape that is the antithesis of genuine communality. Time flows pitilessly, subjecting everyone in its grasp to the impersonal movement of the clock. Eventually only nothingness remains, intensifying anxiety and monotony. As Simone Weil has said, when the whistle blows at the day's end, it reminds the worker that he has been all the while in an alien milieu. It is evident that the fundamental aboriginal drives that accompany man to his grave cannot be mechanized without cost and agony.[28] Despite the allegedly recent acquisition of a middle-class fascination with consumer commodities, the worker—if he is still a participant in the process—works with unbearable intensity. Yet he is hardly proud of what he does: He must borrow prestige from something other than work; and he either "moonlights" or puts in overtime to pay for those luxuries that he has been persuaded are really necessities.[29] Work—at least that part of it that is relegated to the factory—is mindless, filthy, insecure, and devoid of achievement, as

Harvey Swados reminds us. Those attached to the line work only for income, for that is the only incentive that now remains.

Yet the worker is human: He understandably resists being converted into an automaton. And so he tries to "beat the line." If he is paid piece rates, he works furiously during the early part of the day to meet the quota set for him, so that he can pace himself more leisurely later on. In essence, he attempts to set his own schedule despite the unceasing pressures exerted by foremen and time-and-motion experts. He tries to impose his will on the machine. But with the advent of automation even this mastery can no longer be achieved. The battle moves to other grounds — toilet facilities and coffee breaks become the primary issues in the never-ending quarrel over work. In the meantime, prestige and status do not inure in work itself but stem rather from labor unions or other associations or the commodities that are bought. The dignity that the medieval monk, for example, visualized in work has been lost forever. Modern technology "desocializes" the worker, tears him from his comrades, and isolates him. He works because he must.[30] As Lewis Mumford has said:

> Man gains through work the insight into nature he needs to transmute work into artifacts and symbols that have a use beyond ensuring his immediate animal survival ... The *role* of work is to make man a master of the conditions of life: hence its constant discipline is essential to his grasp of the real world. The *function* of work is to provide man with a living: not for the purpose of enlarging his capacities to consume but of liberating his capacities to create. The social *meaning* of work derives from the acts of creation it makes possible.[31]

Presumably, the ideal society, while emancipating man from labor, would create meaningful activity as a viable substitute. But achieving this ideal seems a bootless hope, for those severed even from the *process* of labor are merely cast into idleness. The choice is between the latter and holding a job, a meaningless act in terms of human function yet an essential mode of entry, because of income, into whatever else man might seek to do. Job holding, however, does not appear too closely related to such other activities.

The individual seldom has energy left at the end of his shift to participate in them: Exhaustion is apt to overtake him long before he can learn to write poetry. He becomes a fit subject for Orwell's *1984* – and this end too is inherent in the technology of the time. With automation the disintegration of work is accelerated. Industrial hierarchies, as we have already demonstrated, are vastly simplified, facilitating the centralization of control, and at the same time the lines of command are made more rigid. The machine now comes between man and the clock, attenuating still further the connection with work. Ultimately work disappears.[32]

It may be that men do seek happiness, as Freud has insisted, yet they suffer too, and this suffering is revealed not only in biological decay but also in destruction triggered by external forces, including the complex of relationships developed with others. As the latter include the world of work, it is necessary to search among these relationships so that we may perhaps uncover the roots of unease. And as we undertake this exploration, we need to keep in the forefront of our analysis the character of modern work – work in an automated society. Quite different qualities are now required: Whereas man once was present in work, today he is absent. Yet it is a curious sort of absence, for it is most efficient in subordinating man to the needs of contemporary industry. It makes man ill at ease, generating a tension from which he is forever attempting to escape. Either he indulges in fantasies ("I'll own my own business some day"), or he adjusts to the machine in fatalistic fashion, in which case he is caught up in the cogwheels of organizational bureaucracy. Unable to lag behind, because then he would hold up everyone else, which is unthinkable, he is close to the breaking point. Under the early modes of industrialism, man might react by simply stopping the machine or by throwing a wrench into the works. With automation this violent response is impossible.[33]

LET US GRANT that work today may be less fatiguing and occupies less time. Jacques Ellul insists, however, and he seems to be supported by Sebastian de Grazia, that man works more now than he did in the eighteenth century. The ever present *need* to work and its endless intensity make work more oppressive. Indeed, man may be working more today than did the ancient slave. But in addition man today must rationalize what he does and must make himself believe that it is really essential. Work becomes an omnipresent virtue of the Puritan, as well as the liberating myth of the totalitarian. Above all, work is also aimless and absurd, for it has been converted into labor with virtually no resemblance to meaningful effort. The corporate archon understands this phenomenon perhaps better than anyone else, as he is ever ready to utilize all the arcane arts of "human relations" and such devices as rest periods, dances, and Little League baseball to make his workers happy.[34] Yet it is doubtful that all these substitutes are really effective: Employees continue to be disturbed and resentful, enough to cause one exasperated executive to exclaim, "The biggest trouble with industry is that it is full of human beings."[35] But no doubt the computer is well on its way to solving this problem; if Frankenstein and his monster have been keeping house together, as Charles Frankel says, it will not be long before the latter puts his creator outside the door.

What we are compelled to witness, then, is an increasing sense of powerlessness stemming from an inability to control the machine. Increased rationalization, with its accompanying fragmenting of work, intensifies the meaninglessness of modern work, while a thoroughgoing separation of the worker from his product and the enhanced marketability of the latter create precisely that sort of isolation that has been described as alienation. As Marx observed in his early philosophical papers, the product stands in opposition to the worker, exercising a power derived from marketability that is quite its own. It is an objective power, which the worker is compelled to serve, and it is a servitude that has been vastly magnified under the new technology by virtue of greater rigidity and more intensive integration.[36]

It is at this point that we confront the phenomenon of alienation. If the word is now so fashionable it is because the condition is so universal. Employed by psychoanalysts, sociologists, theologians, philosophers, poets, and publicists, it is "a convenient label to stick on a general sense of loneliness, numbness and lack of identity which appears to afflict persons as differently situated as the assembly line worker and the advertising executive."[37] Doubtless the word originated in the transfer of goods from one person to another, but through the years it has taken on the connotation of loss and estrangement. It thus describes a psychological and emotional rending of subject and object. Relationships in the realm of work become impersonal, and it becomes difficult to locate the point of responsibility for human action. Things are done because technology demands they be done: The extreme example is the neutral executioner of the death camp.

Alienation is now a social syndrome. Yet some writers, evidently unaware of the nature of automated techniques, can assert that continuous-process production overcomes the alienated response. Robert Blauner's study is a case in point.[38] Unfortunately, Blauner's data are drawn from a 1947 opinion poll: They have no application to the present. Recent evidence suggests a more widespread sense of isolation in an automated plant than Blauner is ready to admit.[39] There may indeed be banks of dials to watch. But what is the satisfaction to be derived from recording their movements? If stoking coal is no decent work for humans, neither is tending a set of gauges. Or there are those who refuse to be exercised by alienation because it is an omnipresent phenomenon, appearing in different guises in different societies; it must therefore mean little more than ordinary frustration.[40] But surely there is a marked qualitative distinction between the dissatisfaction of a Roman pleb and those of a displaced miner today. And of those who continue to be occupied in the modern factory, one can only guess at the enormous hatred they express for their work. Said one worker: "The job gets sickening—day in and day out plugging in ignition wires. I get through with one motor, turn around and there's another motor staring me in the face. It's sickening." Even among engineers, white-collar employees, and better-paid blue-collar workers there is no great attachment to the work they do. If they do not feel alienated, neither are they fascinated by what they do.[41]

It is this sort of situation that causes man to lose touch with his environment. Yes, man has created many marvels

—machines, airplanes, microscopes, cameras, and computers —yet he is unable to handle the consequences of his achievements. He has been so routinized that the only mood that possesses him is complete dissociation. Work once provided certain norms that man could grasp and utilize because they were human norms: Those of the machine are "ahuman." It is therefore not enough to say that alienation has always been with us, for there were once whole categories of norms based on human needs that gave guidance to man. Some means of association was available; today that is no longer the case. There is no time for man, for he stands at the periphery of situations and consequently is unable to make the smallest commitment. He cannot exercise his reason to comprehend all of existence. And because there is no time, there is no present to allow communicating with the past or constructing the future. Man can thus have but a partial awareness of the world about him. In short, the very connectibility that assures viable relationships between individuals and their surroundings is severed. The outcome is a fear of contingency, a fear of the future, and nowhere is this fear underscored more sharply than in a society intent on automating everything in sight.[42]

Consequently, the individual becomes a member of a collective, rather than a participant in a community. There is no choice—at best an illusion of choice remains—for refusal to participate in the society implies complete withdrawal. Existence under advanced technology is despised, but it must be pursued even though the needs of the individual can in no way be fulfilled by the collective of which he has become a part. If private desires become overwhelming, the individual reverts to internal exile, descending to a condition of emotional vagrancy. As there is no meaning in society, why bother trying to alter it? Too many have become vagrants in this sense, avoiding change, serving all masters with easy adjustment, devoid of principle. To such people, everyone else is a fool. As Merleau-Ponty has said: "Alienation is not simply privation of what was our own by natural right; and to bring it to an end, it will not suffice to steal what has been stolen, to give us back our due. The situation is far more serious: there are no faces underneath the masks, historical man has never been human, and yet no man is alone."[43] Those who search for positive values in the present situation are merely disguising their anxieties. They pretend to have visited the River Styx and to have returned unchanged.

No self-identity is possible in the modern technological milieu, perhaps not even for the archon who controls it all. For it is evident that man ". . . was created for a living environment, but he dwells in a lunar world of stone, cement, asphalt, glass, cast iron, and steel . . . Cats and dogs disappear little by little from the city, going the way of the horse. Only rats and men populate a dead world. Man was created to have room to move about in, to gaze into far distances, to live in rooms which, even when they were tiny, opened out on fields . . ."[44] But man now lives in artificial cliffs or chaotic bedroom suburbs, which make it impossible to generate a genuine community.[45] The outcome has been a collapse of human form and the creation of "ahumanity." Communal relationships that once provided roots for man by satisfying his aboriginal needs and desires have been destroyed beyond redemption. It was through the community that man realized the necessary connections that allowed him to perceive all horizons and, furthermore, in a manner that defined self-awareness as involvement in and commitment to pre-existing conditions in which meaning had already been established.

It was precisely this sense of community that earlier technology began to destroy and that automation will end. The latter substitutes a complete collective, absorbing individuals and imposing a common objective on them all, even though they may manifest no common interests or origins.[46] The imperatives of the collective govern; the demands of efficiency and rationality acquire utmost priority. But the criteria of action in the collective do not stem from the aboriginal needs of man; they grow rather from the standardized requirements of the technicist ethos and are thus indifferent to man. Existence assumes an anonymous quality that clashes violently with human nature. As Ferdinand Tönnies has said, we have shifted from an association of people that exhibited organic roots to a formalized, contractual way of directing people for specific ends.[47] In an age of technology such ends can be only technological:

> The present forms of living as generated all over the globe by Western civilization are not a genuine style of life; they are *abstract standards* imposed by objectively tested experiences, by scientific and technological precepts, by industrial production and baseless, commercially devised fashions. What determines the conduct of people today is, in a rapidly diminishing degree, tastes and preferences, but more and more the inexorable factual and practical necessities of collective work and the collective facilities it produces.[48]

The strongest evidence of the sort of dissociation we speak of is to be found in literature, drama, and art. Indeed, if there is any hope for man, it is in the art he creates, which now cries out with pain as it calls attention to the spiritual darkness and emptiness we face. Existence has a Janus head, one face of which announces man's availability for self-destruction. The alternative is withdrawal from external contact to preserve the illusion of uniqueness in the individual. Yet the pervasiveness of modern technology makes self-awareness and genuine individuality virtual impossibilities. Man lives from moment to moment, and each contains its own crisis. He is always in the present, unable to achieve a mood of possibility in which conceivably the power to choose might arise. He is dominated by a whole collection of urgencies that stress material advances, the gathering of goods, and gains in productivity. "The overvaluation of productivity that is affecting our age has so thrived and its pan-technical glance has set up a senseless exclusiveness of its own that even genuinely creative men allow their organic skills to degenerate into an autonomous growth to satisfy the demand of the day..."[49] As Karl Jaspers says, the age of technology bears witness to a "catastrophic descent to a poverty of spirit, humanity, love and creative energy."[50] Everything has been sucked into technicism, leaving even the scientist and intellectual helpless outside their own spheres. The peak performance of the technicist, and the prime illustration of complete alienation in our time, is the neutron bomb, which can kill people but leave *things* untouched.

IT IS SOMETIMES said that leisure will enable man to regain his sense of self. Leisure is presumed to be one of the good things in life. It represents enjoyment and respite from work, and perhaps, as with the ancient Greeks, it will allow us to achieve understanding. We no longer disdain to use free time, for there is so much of it now. Such an attitude contrasts sharply with the Puritan ethic, which specified work itself as the highest good: Because leisure was reserved to those who could afford not to work, it was for a long time the object of marked disapproval. Yet today our technological society has engendered a cult of leisure, not, to be sure, as an aristocrat might enjoy it, but rather as a period of time in which masses of people are to draw pleasure from continuous rounds of frenetic activity. Sebastian de Grazia, who conceives of leisure as time for contemplation, argues that it is nonexistent. The average work week, he says, still approximates forty-seven hours. Add eight and a half hours for travel to and from the job, five hours for work around the house painting and repairing faucets and furnaces, and two hours a week for shopping and other chores, and there is little time left to sit under a tree and simply think.[51]

Such a problem could arise only because work and leisure had been split from each other. In primitive societies they were closely related and intertwined with significant ritual, so that work, leisure, and play were virtually indistinguishable. When primitive man had obtained all the food he needed and had satisfied other material needs, he turned naturally to leisure and play. In fact, the availability of leisure time made possible a collection of artifacts that were functionally related to his existence, and they always grew out of a variety of rituals and social gatherings. Only with the rise of a priestly class was leisure time arrogated to a single group, together with a fair proportion of the goods not absolutely essential for subsistence and survival.[52]

Leisure becomes a social problem when its purpose, the regeneration of the human being, is denied or debased. Regeneration can be realized only when leisure confronts work that is meaningful. Then the human spirit recoups its energies for another bout with nature. In a sense, leisure is earned through such a confrontation. But under modern technology free time can be used only as an escape from the oppressiveness of the industrial system. As we shall see, however, free time is itself "industrialized," and there is no genuine escape. Moreover, under automation, leisure's task is to fill empty time, something that modern man does poorly anyway. The irony is that work is employed to supply leisure with objects to make the latter ostensibly enjoyable, whereas leisure is frequently used to advance one's status in work, as on the golf course or in the upper reaches of the corporate milieu. But there is no organic relationship here: All that is visible is a mechanistic exploration of one realm by the other. Besides, the use of leisure as leverage in work is reserved to the upper classes in our society.

Meaningful leisure shares with work the function of transmitting the values of a culture, making them fruitful and in the process educating the individuals involved. Clearly wealth is not essential for fulfilling these purposes: During medieval times city inhabitants were able to create leisure activity around holidays and the dramatic spectacles stemming from ritual.[53] The values of a community were made meaningful for all. Obviously, leisure today might perform a similar function if it substituted the satisfactions and challenges for which work no longer suffices. But all leisure can supply is the consumption of goods and an escape from industrial routine. When work has no substance, leisure cannot realize its regenerative potential; it is essentially a utilitarian diversion, not a confrontation of work. The monotony of work penetrates time allocated to leisure, making the latter equally monotonous. Or one may attempt to use leisure as a realm from which to borrow prestige, for work is no longer capable of doing that. That is, leisure becomes a way out of work. But if work is nonexistent, empty, giving leisure the same characteristics devoid of sense, what is it that we depart from, and what is it that we enter?[54]

No doubt one must attend to a variety of cultural compulsions, even in leisure activity. No time, as Wilbert Moore says, is free from social constraints.[55] In this sense, leisure, like work, operates in a context of necessity. But what is necessary today severely limits the capacity of man to employ leisure as regeneration or to develop personality, as David Riesman hopes it may. Such gains would be extraordinary in an age when leisure is organized, administered, institutionalized, and commercialized. The various elements of leisure that have spontaneous character—play, for example—are eroded as the result of the imposition of an external form that often make them absurd. Furthermore, the individual is frequently thrust into leisure, such as it is, utterly unprepared. Psychiatrists are not unfamiliar with the new suburban phenomenon known as "week-end neurosis," in which a man literally goes to pieces each Friday at 5 p.m. What then would extensive free time mean for the untutored and the unimaginative, who are equally unprepared and who, under automation, will have time endless visited upon them? The painful discovery of their own self-limitations is apt to make them easy victims of leisure racketeers, those ready to peddle gadgets and nostrums suited to the emptiness of time. A more troublesome prospect, as disillusionment sets in, will be the avoidance of both work and leisure.

The loss may very well be immeasurable, for leisure, particularly in its play elements, performs a cultural function by inculcating a sense of rules, surely an important device for associating the individual to the group. When leisure involves games, it creates conditions of equality not found in ordinary work pursuits. Games provide an important regenerative element, for in leisure play the individual "avenges himself upon reality, but in a positive and creative way."[56] When leisure attains this active mode, relationships among individuals may be enhanced in a manner that modern work fails to provide. Leisure can thus express an educative function, in that it gives incentives to perfection. Unfortunately, such motives all too often are corrupted by professionalism in which the quality of pure play is leached out in order to convert leisure and play into a form of business. Then the confrontation of work and leisure is eliminated, and what was once leisure is enveloped by the same work attitudes that exist elsewhere in society. Then activities—sports, movies, television—are not leisure even for the spectators, who fill the stadiums, theaters, and living rooms simply to engage in expenditures of time. Hero

379

worship replaces the admiration of skill, as violence dominates the activity itself.

LEISURE OUGHT TO BE a serious activity; instead it has been corrupted by the technology of industrialism and converted into unfree engagement of time. Were it genuinely free activity, it would then generate seriousness, just as the play of children is serious.[57] Of course, a temporary illusion of freedom may exist, in which case the individual believes that he has achieved the sort of regeneration characteristic of true leisure. Actually, the general experience today is no more than a momentary relaxation to be followed quickly by a resurgence of that unidentifiable tension so common to our age. The leisure we possess is essentially passive, as we attempt to utilize recreational facilities in a manner in which sheer waiting consumes a growing proportion of the time available.[58]

The increase in nonworking time, often asserted to be leisure time, has been attributed to increased income, suburbia, and overweening concerns with consumption. Yet, as Harold Wilensky has demonstrated, such time is unevenly distributed. "A growing minority," says he, "works very long hours while increasing millions are reluctant victims of too much leisure."[59] It is patent, from the available data, that time not spent at the job has increased; at least that has been the case in the United States, where traditionally there have been fewer holidays and shorter breaks in the working day. Still, professionals, government officials, and corporate executives have not shared in the increased hours of free time. Their year-round tasks have required them to work on the average 400 hours more per year than do manual workers.[60] Furthermore, the professional tends to work an entire lifetime, whereas the executive leaves his post at a later retirement age than does the ordinary worker. The latter now works fewer hours per week than he did a century ago, and when he retires he joins the unemployed as a reluctant beneficiary of the new leisure. The sort of occupations that older men once filled — ticket takers, doormen, watchmen — are virtually extinct. The irony is that those whose productivity is the highest work to support the leisure of those who are compelled to enjoy it.

What is more, according to Wilensky, whenever free time is increased, it tends to be bunched rather than evenly distributed over the work cycle. It is not uncommon, for example, to close a plant in the needle trades to give all the workers simultaneous vacations. Long sabbaticals in the steel industry represent another form of bunching. No one asks whether or not a shorter work day might be psychologically superior to the compression of free time. As it is, everyone descends on the parks, hotels, and beaches at the same moment, desperately searching for a place to park or a spot of sand on which to place a luncheon basket. We may think we are in possession of leisure, but the harassing experiences accompanying its pursuit make it frighteningly illusory.[61]

Sustaining the illusion is the *business* of leisure, which aims to supply a consumer-oriented society with sports, autos, boats, liquor, dress, cosmetics, tours, and entertainment, all justified by a morality of fun. In fact, work is made completely subservient to leisure, for "leisure is the way to spend money, [while] work is the way to make it. When the two compete, leisure wins hands down."[62] But it is a leisure that has been forced into a commercial mold: The important thing is to sell leisure and even to make it look like work. One does not simply go bowling; one joins a league. One does not waltz for pleasure but to improve physical fitness. Or one becomes involved in spectatorship, busyness, and boredom.[63]

And so we Americans travel — 105 million of us each year undertake 377 million pleasure jaunts 100 miles or more from home. We spend $22 billion for plane fares, gasoline, hotels, and restaurants. Of course, not everyone partakes of this activity equally. Whereas half of those with family incomes of $4,000 or less per annum take one such 100-mile trip a year, more than 83 per cent of those earning $10,000 or more are able to do so. Slum dwellers do little traveling. In 1963 some 65 per cent of America's sixty-eight million autos were driven for a minimum of one 100-mile trip each away from home. Everything Madison Avenue can think of to get America on the road is done: Texas is the "Fun-tier" State, New York had its World's Fair, and California has its Disneyland. The leisure market extracts $23 billion for amusements, sports, travel, and reading for relaxation — and some $17 billion for alcohol, television, phonograph records, and dining out. Included in the 16 per cent of family income spent on leisure needs are expenditures for souvenirs, travel guides, night clubs, cameras, sunglasses, and fishing rods for vacation time. But few go on vacations where the car will not go.

About five times as much is spent on leisure in the United States as on medical care. The official $40 billion total — merely what is counted in the Gross National Product — does not include that part of transportation that goes for leisure activities, about $15 billion worth. Model kits cost us some $60 million a year, purchases of cameras and photographic supplies total $400 million, and gardening requires an outlay of $800 million. Even in the Great Depression of the 1930s, when some fifteen million people were unemployed, Americans spent $1.5 billion on sports, hobbies, and pets. To the government, leisure is an important source of revenue; in more than half the states it provides tax income. For an appropriate fee, the tourist visiting a state park is supplied with all the comforts of home: plumbing, hot and cold water, and a cocktail lounge. Imposts on playing cards, admissions, cameras, and phonograph records add to the public coffers. A large slice of the advertising business depends on convincing everyone to have fun. As Harvey Swados says, leisure is intertwined with the content and control of mass media, pointing to a central issue in our commercially oriented society.[64] Industry knows that it needs the consumption of the worker: Its determination to make life comfortable has become big business.

If leisure is to have more meaning than it now exhibits, we need public libraries that really function, museums, and centers for the arts. We do fairly well with museums, but what of symphonies and the plastic arts? Leisure, to be fruitful, requires a better urban environment than is now available and a countryside uncluttered by billboards. Leisure ought not to be subjected to the demands of increasing productivity. Can we learn to use what we have? Does the "enhancement of life" necessitate even more gadgetry? Such are some of the questions asked by leisure experts; their objectives are the training of intellect and the improvement of human skills and aesthetic sense. Unfortunately, most men, when asked what they would do with more free time have answered: "work around the house," "spend some time with the family," "go to the ball game." We do not know whether or not they can really accept such a regimen for long. Rubber workers on a short work week in Akron simply took second jobs; if they did not "moonlight," they played pool. But in that city the "living theatre is practically non-existent, there is no professional symphony and although the public library is good, one can search . . . in vain for a bookshop devoted to selling new books." In all the communities of America, only about 30,000 people are involved in symphony orchestras, and this figure includes professionals, whereas amateur theatricals provide leisure activity for about 40,000 to 50,000 people. In contrast, eighteen million Americans prefer to fish or watch prize fights. That seems to be the reality of leisure.[65]

The aims of the high priests of leisure seem unlikely to be met: The continued high-pressure consumption of goods that provide no regeneration for man is the more probable contingency. The technological society leads the worker to bouts of drink, gambling, stock-car races, and horror movies. All this activity is an escape from modern work, intended to help him forget the factory or the frustration that comes from no work at all. Time must be "killed," an expression that reveals, as few events can, man's final separation from a world he did not make. In fact, time, both in and out of the work place, is completely mechanical. Dragooned into leisure, man must conform to the dictates of a culture that is thoroughly pervaded by the technicist ethos. Everything is utterly rational; it is the protest, rather, that is irrational. In this atmosphere there can be no freedom.[66]

We have said that work was once a means for transmitting the values of a culture. Now that work has been emptied of meaning, debased, turned into drudgery, it cannot perform this function: The worker merely seeks to escape from the factory into something called "leisure." But, as we have argued, leisure too has been converted into a mirror image of modern work; it is equally meaningless and equally incapable of carrying the burden of culture. To paraphrase Harry Levin, man has become less a culture bearer and more a codifier of programs and a manipulator of electronics.[67] Modern man then faces a dilemma, one that was no doubt a long time reaching a condition of complete fission and which has now been hardened by the technology of the time.

Ice age of perfection 12

At the present juncture of events, few people seem concerned about the consequences of the new technology. The apparent affluence of the age has instilled in many an indifference to the character of the changes society is undergoing. The pursuit of the immediate has focused attention so forcibly on present pleasures that any effort to discuss probable trends is at once totally unpopular. Few observers can attempt the role of seer with impunity. A national opinion poll in May 1965 revealed that 90 per cent of American adults did not view automation as very much of a threat to their jobs. Half the respondents believed that automatic devices — computers and their ancillary equipment — helped to increase efficiency and reduce prices and costs. Here new mythology appeared to be in the making, despite considerable evidence to the contrary: Prices, for example, were continuing to drift upward, so that by the second half of 1965 they were almost 10 per cent above the level of the base years 1955–1957. The use of more productive equipment did not appear to have acted as a price stabilizer.[1]

Nor was the common belief that automation creates jobs sustained by *businessmen's* views. A Manpower Research Council survey, published in 1965, concluded that less than half of *its* respondents — men accustomed to gauging the state of future economic conditions—believed automation would increase jobs in the nation as a whole in the coming five-year period. The remainder—57 per cent—thought the number of jobs would decrease or remain about the same. For their own branches of industry, only 29 per cent of the respondents foresaw increases in jobs from automation; in their own companies' production areas the proportion dropped to 22 per cent; and in the office areas the expectations for increased jobs went down to 21 per cent. What these data suggest is that most executives hope that other industries and other firms will take up the slack. In this sense, business executives share the same mythology as does the rest of the populace.[2]

For the fact is that automation, once it becomes the major expression of Western technology, is bound to spread. Its effects and consequences can be overcome, given existing social and economic relationships, only by an incessant, ceaseless expansion in the economy. Most authorities concede that the rate of growth in Gross National Product would have to reach 6 or 7 per cent to outweigh the changes wrought by technology: This level has not yet been achieved. Automation—or cybernation as some writers prefer to call it—is patently upon us, and, although the future cannot be predicted, it already has been invented.

Recently two RAND Corporation experts asked eighty-two other experts what were the most likely inventions to be developed in the next fifty years. In the field of automation, these scientists predicted for the Seventies a tenfold increase in capital investment in process-control computers; the use of predictive computers to track aircraft; direct linkage from stores to banks to record credit and other transactions; widespread use of teaching machines; *displacement of 25 per cent of the work force in offices and services*; automated libraries; automatic translations with correct grammar; and automated rapid transit. In the following decade—the Eighties—they anticipated electronic prosthetic devices; robots for refuse collection and sewer inspection; and machines that would comprehend standard IQ tests and score higher than 150 on them. By the turn of the century automobiles would be controlled by adaptive autopilots and legislation passed by automated plebiscites.[3]

Nor is the assumption that an ample supply of cheap labor will restrain such rapid developments at all warranted. Nations like the Soviet Union, with more than adequate numbers of workers, are not inhibited in their drive to achieve industrial pre-eminence. Totalitarian in structure, they can afford to be more ruthless and more calculating than their neighbors in the West, and if automation means redundancy they could not care less. But in the West, there is a presumable concern with welfare. At any given time there is a complex of equipment and resources and a work force – an assortment of people able to engage in certain tasks. Some members are old, and some are young; there are those with highly developed skills, and those who are totally untrained. Similarly, the resources vary in quality, and the equipment assumes particular forms and shapes. The latter may be old or relatively new, capable of application to a variety of jobs or highly specialized in form. The economists' principle of efficiency demands that workers and equipment be matched so that maximum production may be achieved, for only in this manner can output per capita be increased. It is also hoped that capital accumulation will be sufficient to provide for gains in excess of capital retirements. Now, according to some variants of economic theory, the added or marginal output establishes the real wage for labor, whereas the average or per capita output determines the real income available for distribution. But if the former is low and the latter high, wages will represent a small share of total income, with most of the output going to entrepreneurs.[4]

A high rate of technical progress involving labor-saving devices simply intensifies the problem, for it increases output per head while enhancing the real wage rate only for the remaining attached work force. The absorption of displaced workers in the next best alternative requires a reduction in *their* real wages, and indeed this necessity may explain to some degree the lower level of wages for those compelled to shift into the service trades. The unequal distribution of income is intensified, a possibility that is just beginning to dawn both upon the prophets of the new technology and

387

upon the corporate archons. In theoretical terms, automation may very well enforce a rise in output per capita, as contrasted with changes in the marginal output of labor. It thus becomes increasingly difficult to meet the welfare objectives of the economic system exclusively through internal mechanisms. The welfare state must resort to *ad hoc* measures in order to maintain income levels.

YET AUTOMATION has been sprouting around the world – to use a business journal's apt phrase. Most nations have reacted in quite the same way as has the United States. Little has been done to prepare for the painful problems that promise to arise. New plants being built in Western Europe or in parts of the Far East utilize in most instances the newest technological devices, placing automation in these areas about where it was in the United States five to ten years ago. And there is a similar lag in thinking of what the impacts might be. True, there is some general awareness that certain jobs may shrink in number and that whole industries may become obsolescent. But little foresight, little planning, is in evidence. It is felt that the recent high rates of growth will more than adequately compensate for the effects of the new technology.

Yet rapid advances in automation will continue and indeed seem inevitable in Europe and elsewhere. In 1963 IBM shipped one of its 1620 computers to Kanpur on the banks of the Ganges River in India, where it was scheduled to become the nucleus for a computer center at a new technological institute. That same year an IBM 1401, a widely used medium-sized computer, was installed for the state-owned Nigerian Railway Corporation in Lagos, to keep track of freight cars and payroll. All too frequently simpler sorting devices would be sufficient to meet the needs of these nations, but IBM is convinced that its most advanced machines have a place even in the least advanced nations. All too often there may be trained programmers in an underdeveloped nation before there are ordinary skilled mechanics.

In Europe the O.E.C.D. nations set a common goal of a 50 per cent increase in production between 1962 and 1970.

Obviously, a steady rise in productivity will be necessary to help achieve this objective. Although Western Europe's approximately 3,000 computer units compare unfavorably with our 20,000 units, the rate of growth across the Atlantic has been phenomenal, more than matching the 300 per cent expansion of the United States between 1960 and 1962. For example, Denmark's computers increased in that short span from 55 to more than 200, and most of the O.E.C.D. countries experienced increases of 300 to 400 per cent. It has been estimated that by 1970 Europe will enjoy the benefits of more than 14,000 computers of all kinds.

Now, in some of the Western nations such expansion seems quite sensible, for they still suffer from tight labor markets, to which automation is the expected response. Furthermore, the new technology is seized upon by both government and management as the only effective means for suppressing an upward drift in wage rates, certainly more effective than direct controls. But what is one to say of the "underdeveloped" nations, with their critical problems of overpopulation and disguised unemployment? Is automation also the sole answer for them, as indeed was suggested by Gabriel Ardant, French Inspector-General of Finance? M. Ardant believes that the proper goal for underdeveloped nations is not to attain full employment, always possible by "make-work" schemes, but to achieve the most productive full employment. Accordingly, technology that saves labor should not be rejected, for otherwise manpower would be wasted, creating barriers to future improvements in work methods. The manufacture of goods earmarked for export, the construction industries, and certain consumer-goods industries in those nations ought therefore to be automated, argues M. Ardant.[5] In the meantime, what work is to be given to the mass of people?

In Western Europe, of course, these questions do not arise. When one man guides thousands of automatically run spinners in a Belgian textile mill, it is because automation is needed to remedy the labor shortage. And in Sweden the pressure of job vacancies spills over into such nonautomated areas as management, engineering, teaching, and the foreign service. Toward the end of 1963 Swedish labor-market officials estimated 180,000 job vacancies. As one employer in that country put it, the Swedes were too few for the size of their ambitions. With a work force of only 3.8 million the nation was competing vigorously with industrialized countries many times larger. One solution was to upgrade as many of the higher vacancies as possible leaving the bottom ones to be taken care of by automation.[6]

The West Germans have had a similar experience. For them automation has been thought a blessing, for, with a manpower shortage of enormous proportions, the economy has had to resort to the machine. It has been estimated that 1.5 million jobs per annum, equivalent to almost 10 per cent of the German work force, are being taken over each year by automated equipment. But then, there were no humans to do the work to start with. Despite the intense pace of automation, more than 800,000 foreign workers were recruited in 1963 to meet unfilled demand. The major concentration of automation is in mining, metal, and textiles, with banking providing the leadership in data processing. As in the United States, the petrochemical industry is completely automated. Lacking waiters and waitresses, rest stops along the autobahnen are equipped with machines to serve coffee and hot meals.

The importance of automation to the West German economy was stressed in a study of ten manufacturing concerns in which it was found that automated equipment made it possible for 14,000 employees to do the work of 29,000 men. So rapidly had total output of the firms expanded that without automation they would have required 138,000 men to match the new levels of production. Nevertheless, German economists anticipate that by the 1970s migrant foreign workers from Turkey, Italy, Greece, and Spain will number almost two million. But the latter are given unskilled jobs, those offering the least security against automation. In any case, the motivation for automation in Germany and other parts of Europe is not the same as here; these nations rationalize not to cut labor costs but to increase production despite labor shortages. They automate to eliminate jobs that cannot be filled for lack of manpower. Naturally, such a situation offers little to disturb the future. Neither the Bonn Government nor German industry feels it necessary to prepare plans for the time when automation will bear down on the unskilled and untutored. Nevertheless, the trade unions have expressed the usual concern: IG Metall—the metalworkers' union—has urged management to consult with the unions on automation plans and to provide severance pay, as well as other adjustments, for displaced workers. But management is not overly interested.[7]

Britain's first computer dates back to 1945. It was followed by 300 more within sixteen years, with almost as many more on order by 1961. At present rates of expansion, British experts anticipate 2,000 computers in operation by 1970. The British have become as accustomed to the new technology as have Americans and Germans. The Spencer Steel Works, opened in 1961, utilizes a cluster of small computers to take orders, dispatch finished products, and accept directions from computers at higher decision levels. The system has been described as the closest approach to complete automation yet achieved. British steelmakers use proportionately more process-control computers than do American firms. An automated reservation system is operated by BOAC, storing up to 64,000 items of information on bookings for twenty weeks ahead. Machines do industrial blending, select data for specific processing, route baggage, locate aircraft, and transmit documents. In short, they are applied to the same striking uses as in the United States.

The sharpest impact in British industry has been in the office. Although no large-scale displacement has yet appeared, it has been mainly because data-processing equipment has gone to public agencies where surplus staff can be handled through attrition, retirement, and some retraining. Nevertheless, a Trade Union Congress investigation in 1963 detected a growing fear among office workers—fear of losing jobs, fear of losing status, and fear of losing promotion prospects. Unable to visualize the economic consequences, the T.U.C. turned its attention to psychological effects: Its report pointed to a high incidence of nervous disorders in automated offices and to the problem of boredom and fatigue and insisted on the need for frequent rest periods. The unions, said T.U.C., are willing to cooperate in introducing new techniques without friction as long as they will be able to "protect the interests of their members and secure for them a share in the benefits of the techniques."[8] The British journal *New Society* commented on the T.U.C. report: "By 1970 ... the picture will have changed drastically. Instead of a large number of clerks doing moderately interesting and demanding jobs there will be a relatively few highly paid people directly associated with the work of the computer ... The filing clerk and key-punch operator ... might very well disappear."[9]

Although the British may be somewhat laggard in applying the new technology in all fields, the same is not true of the Eastern countries. The Poles have built a computer industry considered second only to that of Russia among the Soviet-bloc nations. Although the latter are still far behind the United States and Western Europe in most aspects of data processing, it was evident by 1965 that significant accomplishments had been made. Poland had designed and built forty computers through its own efforts, and its work in programming had been notable. Although the Poles lacked "hardware," a strong corps of mathematicians was able to develop sophisticated "software," including methods of automated programming not unlike the FORTRAN language employed in the United States. Modular compatible computers are among some of the equipment developed by the Poles. An illustration of Polish advances is the ZAM system, introduced in June 1965. It comprises a comprehensive range of computers suitable for time-sharing operations. The core memory has a capacity of more than 250,000 words. The tape readers are able to read 1,000 characters a second, and the line printers can work up to 1,200 lines a minute. The machines can be applied in all fields, including complex-process controls. And the central planners propose to foster the use of computers in both production and data processing.

THE FIRST NATION to establish a ministry for automation was the Soviet Union, which has not hesitated to utilize the new machines to the fullest in its effort to "catch up and surpass the West." Khrushchev made this demand at the Twenty-first Party Congress in 1959, and he proposed to use computers and automated equipment to attain his purposes. The Twenty-second Congress re-emphasized the goal, declaring that it was "imperative to organize the wider application of cybernetics, electronic computer machines, and control installations in production . . ." Perhaps in this way the shortages of skilled labor and the infuriating red tape could be overcome without undermining the institution of central planning. American observers did not think this objective was fanciful, for with the Soviet concentration on basic research in computer technology it was conceivable that the country might overtake the United States. Said *The Wall Street Journal*, "Important discoveries in automatic production might permit Russia's economy to function with far greater efficiency, giving it a propaganda victory, an ability to compete more heavily in world markets and a stronger economic base for its expansionistic political aims."[10] Specialized institutes for the study of automation were established in Kiev, Tallin, and Tbilisi. Several thousand mathematicians and physicists work solely on advanced theoretical problems, a much larger effort than in the United States, where only about 600 scientists, according to J. E. Ward of M.I.T., are engaged in theoretical work of control systems. The situation may be even worse, said L. A. Zadek of the University of California; he estimates that there are no more than thirty professors engaged in "noteworthy" theoretical work on control systems. Furthermore, whereas the Soviet Union produces about 5,000 engineers a year with undergraduate degrees in automatic control, there is no comparable degree in the United States. The one consolation for Americans disturbed by the computer knowledge gap is the switchover of some 2,000 older engineers and scientists in the United States to the computer field each year, supplementing the 2,000 annual output of new graduates in the field. Soviet work in this field is impressive: World-wide attention was attracted by A. A. Lyapunov's theories on the optimum mix of variables in a production process to enhance speed, economy, and quality. In November 1961 a computer in Kiev transmitted commands over a forty-eight-hour period to a soda plant in Slavyansk, 290 miles away, performing over a billion mathematical operations to determine the best blend of materials. Devices have been developed that employ pneumatic computing elements without any moving parts; the pneumatic controls now used in petrochemical plants could be easily hooked into such a computer to attain greater efficiency.

Not that the Soviets have caught up to us in computer technology: Their M-20 operates at a pedestrian speed of 50,000 additions a second, compared to an IBM 7030, which performs 667,000 additions a second. But they appear determined to make advances, if only to utilize networks of computers to feed economic data to central planning agencies and to retain control over the economy as a whole. The computer would enable the planners to determine rates of growth of major sectors of the economy, allocate capital outlays, and regulate over-all wage and price policies more effectively than has been hitherto possible. To supplement their own equipment the Soviets have not hesitated to buy machines in the West. Some American equipment has been reaching Russia by transshipment. (United States companies self-consciously state that they have sold the Soviets only old, small computers, but they do demand payment in cash.) In 1964 the Soviet government announced that 119 major industrial plants would be converted to a system of production management using electronic computers, with the object of ensuring speedy access to data necessary for decision making. Automated systems were to be introduced in both heavy industry and in consumer-goods production. Among the plants listed were the Gorky automobile factory, the Yaroslavl engine plant, an aluminum plant at Krasnotarsk, a steel mill in Novokuznetsk, and a machinery installation in Sverdlovsk. *Pravda* commented in January 1965 that automated systems of reporting, planning, and managing were completely attainable in the Soviet system. According to Soviet estimates, completely automatic planning would take no more than twenty years to achieve. More than 100 computer centers for this purpose were already in operation by the middle of 1964, with another 300 scheduled to open in the following year.[11]

When one examines the urge to automate among the Soviets, the potentialities for absolute control of man are underscored even more starkly than in the West. The

394

Soviets openly acknowledge the control potentials of the computer. Russia has given automation the same priority it gave to missile development in the early 1950s, and its achievements in the next decade may prove equally startling. For, as J. H. Bunzel, a Stanford University political scientist has said, automation for the Soviets represents only the latest technological development, which will lead not only to the control of nature but also to a rigorous conditioning of man. The work of such Soviet computer scientists as Academician A. I. Berg is supplemented by that of psychologists and physiologists studying instruments of control that may be used to examine the central nervous system and total patterns of behavior as well. People are viewed as predictable automatons, who, in the hands of men of knowledge and power, can be molded at will. When man has been conditioned to perfect self-control, his identity with the collective will have become absolute and irrevocable. The ideal of the Soviets—and perhaps of many computer specialists as well—is the construction of a giant machine whose answer to the first question fed to it, "Is there a God?" will be "*Now* there is."

Of course, those of a more optimistic persuasion insist that the machine can do only what man tells it to do. The major task of automation is to free man from degrading jobs, making him a skilled technician able to direct the machine and maintain it. In essence, the more automatic work becomes, say the optimists, the more human it really is, for then men have time to engage in creative and artistic work. It is a grand future that is depicted but a flawed one nevertheless, for it is based on the assumption that work has no other function than to produce material goods and that everyone can write poetry if given the opportunity.[12] On the technical side, the optimists know that a heavy investment in equipment requires continuous operation, but they fail to face up to the havoc this demand plays with the normal rhythms of work. They further assume that those who remain in automated plants will all become executives of sorts, indispensable staff officials discharging responsibilities once reserved to the front office. In effect, the worker would be converted from proletarian to technician. All this optimism is predicated on the notion that the computer is merely an extension of man's senses. Sir Leon Bagrit, for example, asserts that automation permits man to work at his own pace because the machine reacts to man, who indeed is the master.[13] He insists that we are approaching a golden age in which there will be an ample flow of material goods and opportunities to develop mind and body matched only by Periclean Athens. With all the work done by machines, everyone would be engaged in a task he wanted and preferred. Sir Leon contends that "opponents" of automation are pessimists who will not trust human beings with riches.

SUCH VACUOUS notions represent a form of belief in secular salvation; they assume that progress as embodied in technical advance is a natural phenomenon, expected and essential. Furthermore, such progress is said to be inherent in society and nature; it moves always upward and is self-sufficient. Progress is the history of man, as evident in evolution. Adherents of these views seem unaware that they offer an egocentric doctrine rooted in the belief that middle-class careers always move in rising spirals. So fervently are these ideas held that they are transmuted into religious faith[14] with a hope that the future will be kind to the middle class. As there has been advance in the past, why not expect the same in the future, for do not men make their own future? Indeed, if ideas possess demiurgic power, then why not impose the idea of progress?[15] The tragedy of these illusions, however, stems from the patent fact that technology possesses a power quite its own, capable of destroying the best plans of man. Furthermore, the idea of progress bears within it an ideological pressure, for it suggests that we accept a tendency that makes the future predictable and certain. The factory system in the eighteenth century may have represented gains in the accumulation of material goods, but, as Robert Heilbroner has said, when entrepreneurs looked to their fellow men what they wanted were *hands*. There is no reason to assume, as do believers in the idea of progress, that history is beneficent; surely this view is utterly parochial.

For the idea of evolution *cum* progress is false. Evolution is merely change, and in no way should it suggest perpetual wholesomeness. Unfortunately, the optimists who foresee a golden age in an automated society equate change and progress; any change is adjudged worthwhile as long as it can be directed toward an upward movement. In such a philosophy there is no climax, no apogee—only continuity. The advocates of progress in this sense are unprepared to suggest boundaries to man's search for knowledge or to indicate the point at which he might halt and contemplate what he has thus far gathered. They ignore the obvious fact that, as science and technology makes the world tractable, it is also necessary, in the name of progress, to make man tractable. As Roderick Seidenberg has said, the keynote for the optimist is identification rather than identity, administration rather than spontaneity.[16]

Quite simply, the idea of progress, especially as developed during the nineteenth century, makes puppets of men, happy victims of a kindly history. They learned from the French Revolution that politics might be controlled and from the Industrial Revolution that both technology and the economy could be shaped at will. But it was not long before the belief in progress degenerated into a kind of totalitarianism, for with this notion society became central and the individual only an agency. The consequence was that science and technology superseded the fundamental drives and wishes of man. There were dissenting voices—de Tocqueville and Burckhardt—but they were ignored, for the material benefits of a latter day cornucopia were too diverting to make men pause.[17]

Progress, then, came to mean technological and scientific gain. It meant order and sequence and perfectibility. Advancement through knowledge became a standardized slogan, and the optimists still give it voice. As Erich Kahler remarks, one had merely to know nature, and progress would automatically be established. Consciousness or individual fulfillment meant little as man was sucked into the impersonal milieu of a collective existence.[18] And nowhere were these views more firmly established than in the United States, for here the idea of progress was hospitably received and the climate conducive to an exquisite flowering. For example, in the eighteenth century Joel Barlow argued that progress was possible if only men gave

397

themselves to effort, science, democracy, and rationalism. Furthermore, America had been designated by Divine Providence to open the floodgates of unlimited good. America, said Barlow, would know no poverty and no war.[19] Even those who had some doubts — Franklin wondered whether or not resources would last, and Jefferson distrusted the proletariat of the cities — expressed the hope that in the end progress would prevail.

And as the burgeoning nation moved across virgin land, progress was confused with power, a state of mind that has not yet been overcome. America's destiny was progress, and American patriotism, parochial as it was, became the embodiment of human advancement. Timothy Walker asserted in 1831 the need for unlimited and unhampered expansion. For him technology created no problems; the machine was a way to improve nature. It could be comprehended by man and was the prime way to achieve the objectives of equality implicit in the American faith. The machine, argued Walker, was a liberator.[20]

Yet doubts arose. During the First World War an era of equilibrium had become unbalanced. For a brief spell after 1918 it was thought that normality would prevail. Then came the Great Depression of the 1930s, when the idleness of millions proclaimed the collapse of middle-class achievement. Society had failed to control for rational human needs the self-same technological order that had previously formed the cornerstone of the idea of progress. And after that shock humanity was involved in a war that everyone expected, to be succeeded by a sequence of unparalleled nationalistic rivalries and upheavals. And much of this nationalism in the last analysis represents a drive for the products of man's technology. Reason has been superseded by the new insanities of a technicized world. Little wonder that belief in the idea of progress is subjected to some question.

In short, the idea of progress is a nineteenth-century notion with little relevance for an era that moves from one point in time to another by happenstance. Yet within the sequence of accidents we have been forced to witness in the last half-century there have been forces that lend to history some decipherable meaning, the most significant of which is the set of constraints imposed upon man by his own technology. The central question of our time is: Can man divest himself of his role of victim and assert his control over the machine? As long as we delude ourselves that everything represents an upward spiral of advancement, this question will really lack a suitable answer. For it is just possible that material progress and the problems of an affluent society may be as burdensome, at more subtle levels of meaning, as are the problems of an economy of scarcity.[21]

There are those who argue that the idea of progress has a political dimension as well.[22] The Establishment would prefer a society without opposition: As power today is secured through technology, the idea of progress, which sustains the pressures toward further advances, becomes infused with ideological content. The system becomes totalitarian without terror, one that is self-programmed, establishing its own output. The justification of the underlying technology cannot therefore be neutral, and its semblance of rationality is fundamentally political. Technology in fact, can be employed and is employed to restrict the prospects of altering the structure of power in society. In the main, this end is achieved by absorbing society's members into an "administered population,"[23] involving all the apparatus of public relations, advertising, and social pressure. "The technological *a priori* is a political *a priori* inasmuch as the transformation of nature involves that of man. . . . Nature, scientifically comprehended and mastered, reappears in the technical apparatus of production and destruction which sustains and improves the life of individuals while subordinating them to the masters of the apparatus."[24]

The history of modern times, therefore, is basically a ". . . history of diverse parting, ramifying and specializing human functions, among which the *complex of economy, science and technology has come to predominate and determine the course of events*, actual and conceptual. Today, we witness the final stage of the long process of growing together, of increasing interaction and interpenetration, almost to a point of unity, of the three . . ."[25] And within this history, automation represents the climax of an earlier development, which had employed taxonomy to abstract characteristics and qualities. In time, the ability to abstract became so refined, generalized, and quantified that with the computer these qualities could be transferred to the machine.

IN ESSENCE, man began to act through the machine rather than through his own nature. He accommodated himself to the organization that this process demanded, and whatever crises were apt to occur became matters of adjustment to the organization rather than of opposition to it.[26] The general trend of society and technology was accepted not only because it was progress but also because it was practical and so fulfilled the destiny of nature. The relationships between men that ensued were thought to be the perfect means to an undefined end. But as organization in this sense requires standardized behavior and integration within the organization, it followed that spontaneity and deviance were to be eliminated. The whole process was so "scientific" that it acquired the character of a categorical imperative. Individuality as a public expression was frowned upon, and the only escape was the secrecy of one's own soul, hidden in an age of urbanization and statistics in the privacy of a high-rise apartment.

The technology suitable to such an age is precisely what we are getting—automation—for only in the patterns of action established by today's technique can the mass of men be handled expeditiously. The machine, typified by the computer, is an ideal instrument for such purposes, for it demands order, deliberate relationships among its constituent elements, and an inescapable loyalty to its own rhythms.[27] As Seidenberg has said, social forces become processes, transition becomes direction, cohesion becomes unification, freedom becomes compulsion. All this distortion severs man from nature, dispossesses him of whatever primal drives he may once have had, and deprives him of an awareness of consciousness. For the last derives its luminous quality from tension, a condition that is anathema to organization. The likely prospect in the future is an ice age of perfect social functioning, which will leave mankind sealed in a utopia of changelessness. Man will have reached "... the impasse of his existence as a species ... he learns to be perfect and to be blindly proud of the machinery of self-destruction."[28]

Yet as Paul Goodman has said, the centralization implicit in such a development can become wasteful and stultifying. It functions well for its own internal administrative purposes, but its application to all aspects of life seems dubious. Goodman illustrates the argument by reference to the computer in a library that selects books according to preordained standards, thus suppressing the educational values of individual selection.[29] It is this sort of thing that converts people into personnel, into individuals engaged in activity without commitment. Personal loyalties are attenuated, for personnel merely render service and await the moment of retirement. Existence is broken into particular functions, so that reality, even as it is conquered by technology, is irrevocably lost. Yet there is no responsibility that can be assigned for the changes that occur — there is no devil theory of history to which one may appeal.[30] It is simply a case, says Michael Harrington, of man revolutionizing everything except himself and in the process losing the capacity to dream the dreams that make men human. As Erich Kahler has said:

Modern technology, the product and achievement of Western civilization, has functionally contracted the world into a single unit, not only extrinsically, by its various instruments of mass communication, but also intrinsically, by spreading everywhere its daily proliferating machinery of life-preservation and life destruction, of comforts and atrocities, which will soon be the common property of a standardized world. So the technical developments change human conditions, and even the very foundations of human life. But man, human individuals and established communities do not keep pace with these rapid changes. This is easily understandable: organic processes, psychic processes, are slow, having to overcome inertia, habits, traditions, and inhibitions of all kinds; they need time, their natural time, their historical time of action and reaction, advance and recession. But mechanical developments, especially when a whole civilization sets all its pride and energy in their promotion, proceed quite unimpeded, in an almost automatic consecution. Our whole modern apparatus of human existence, including the apparatus of ideologies, took on dimensions appropriate only to vast collective units. But man, in his aspirations and volitions, has remained a narrow, however nationally inflated, self. The discrepancy, the clash, and the interaction of these two tendencies have brought about the present unprecedented anarchy. It is unprecedented precisely because it comes into friction with, and is, on the other hand, functionally aided by, the technical unity. The political world has always been anarchical, but today, for the first time, this anarchy surges against a technical counterforce.[31]

Kahler adds that this condition is not unlike that of the Roman Empire at its zenith.

As Lewis Mumford has said, we overstress man's tool-making capacity. Indeed, if tools played the greatest role in forming man, asks Mumford, why then do we propose to leave to the residual mass of workers the trivial task of watching dials and pressing buttons? And what is the logic of severing man from his tools so that he becomes a creature without function, a being without work, conditioned to accept what the machine offers, condemned to compulsory consumption, as he was condemned in earlier centuries to compulsory production? What remains of existence if human activity is taken over by the machine? The tragedy, says Mumford, is that our society has allowed a fraction of man's life — toolmaking — to dominate the larger part, suppressing or distorting play, ritual, sport, and fantasy. And toolmaking has become in our own time grotesque; it is now "the condition of scientific and technical advance," if not the main purpose of life.[32]

THE WORLD IS more a predicament than a spectacle. Paul Goodman argues rather cogently that there could not have been a worse time in history or a worse place than the United States for automation to have flourished. He may very well be right, for we are beginning to be dimly aware what the new technology has in store for us, or rather what the programmers and others who control the computer have in store for us. And as these changes occur, we stand by unable to respond, because we can think only of the economy and efficiency of it all.[33] In essence, we have allowed arithmetic to replace conscience. Given this situation, the victor will be he who breathes the ethic of efficiency — and it is he who controls the machine.

402

The consequence, as we have repeatedly argued, is a lopsided world in which human personality is set aside because it does not meet technological criteria. The latter demand specialists, but they know little outside their own spheres. They are the systems men, the computer experts, the programmers chillingly described by Robert Boguslaw as the "new utopians."[34] They design new ways to achieve objectives that transcend the present situation. But in contrast to the gentle dreamers of the past, these men are on the verge of making their fantasies come true. The idols of efficiency lead them to disdain the consequences of their science; humans *qua* humans are not part of their purview. All they seek is reliability of operations for the units of their systems. Unfortunately, humans are unreliable, notoriously so, and it is this quality that lends joy to existence. Reliability is useful in a spaceship, but, when rigidly applied to a factory without concern for the fact that workers are more than simply pairs of hands, it tends to make men less than human. One saving grace appears: The essential complexity of the human personality may yet confound the technicists and their cohorts. For even Stalin's Russia could not create a new Soviet type, and in Orwell's *1984* there is always the lingering suspicion that O'Brien's torture rack did not completely cleanse the soul of Winston Smith.

Of course, the new utopians can always destroy unreliable units. In this manner they can be assured that their goals are attainable. This possibility presupposes a disbelief in the uniqueness of the inefficiency of human beings. In the end there would be no special qualities in units that sensed and received data, compared information, measured, and actuated feedbacks. Society would be completely utilitarian, for at long last we should enjoy a guarantee that the behavior of each redounds to the benefit of all. Humanity would have been cleansed of all human attributes. There is indeed more in the ways of the new utopians than has been dreamt of in all the philosophies of the world.

"Critics" of automation are frequently accused of being reactionary or of recreating the myth of the noble savage. That is hardly the point, for what the critics seek is balance. For when "... men have grown 'mechanical' in head and heart ... they over-value those aspects of life which are calculable and manipulable, and by the same token ... they neglect the whole sphere of the spontaneous, the imaginative — all that springs from the inner resources of the psyche ..."[35] The balance between the imaginative and the mechanical is awry, and the weights are heaviest on the latter's side. The machine has no ethics, and when we speak of the ethics of technology we mean the actions of those who control the machine. There is nothing in the computer to ensure its use for the health of society, that is, to ensure its ethical use. The specialists who operate and control the new technology have their own vested concerns; balance and autonomy have no room in their realm. With the victory of the machine — a most notorious victory — the attainment of human autonomy is at best moot.

1 At first the wheel

1. C. E. Ayres, *The Theory of Economic Progress*, Chapel Hill, 1944, p. 105.
2. Cf. W. F. Ogburn, *Social Change*, New York, 1922.
3. R. B. Lindsay, *The Role of Science in Civilization*, New York, 1963, p. 199.
4. Karl Jaspers, *The Origin and Goal of History*, New Haven, 1953, p. 102.
5. Lewis Mumford, *Technics and Civilization*, New York, 1934, p. 53.
6. V. Gordon Childe, "A Prehistory of Science," in G. S. Métraux and F. Crouzet, eds., *The Evolution of Science*, New York, 1963 (paperback), pp. 34 ff.
7. S. Giedion, *Mechanization Takes Command*, New York, 1948, p. 46.
8. A. P. Usher, *An Introduction to the Industrial History of England*, London, 1921, p. 271.
9. S. Lilley, *Men, Machines and History*, London, 1965.
10. Giedion, *op. cit.*, p. 34.
11. Cf. P. Mantoux, *The Industrial Revolution in the 18th Century*, rev. ed., New York, 1961, pp. 230 ff.
12. Cf. H. G. Barnett, *Innovation: The Basis of Cultural Change*, New York, 1953, p. 71; and Ayres, *op. cit.*, pp. 133 ff.
13. N. J. Smelser, *Social Change in the Industrial Revolution*, London, 1959.
14. Cf. M. Beard, *A History of the Business Man*, New York, 1938, p. 487.
15. Cf. M. Peckham, *Beyond the Tragic Vision*, New York, 1962, pp. 230 ff.
16. Ibid., p. 233.
17. E. J. Hobsbawm, *The Age of Revolution*, New York, 1962, p. 207; *cf.* also E. P. Thompson, *The Making of the English Working Class*, New York, 1964, pp. 244 ff., 360; and J. Ellul, *The Technological Society*, New York, 1964, p. 112.
18. Cf. Mumford, *The City in History*, New York, 1961, pp. 460 ff.
19. Ibid., p. 461.
20. Cf. J. Schmookler, "Determinants

of Industrial Invention," in National Bureau of Economic Research, *The Rate and Direction of Inventive Activity*, Princeton, 1962, pp. 195 ff.
21. The 1955 Ford assembly plant in Cleveland was a splendid illustration of such display: The plant it displaced was still quite useful, according to the United Auto Workers Union. In conversation with me on July 5, 1963, Professor James Bright of Harvard agreed that "keeping up with Jones" is a powerful motive in present-day automation. *Cf.* H. J. Habakkuk, *American and British Technology in the 19th Century*, Cambridge, Eng., 1962, pp. 56 ff.
22. Cf. K. Wittfogel, *Oriental Despotism*, New Haven, 1957.
23. Mumford, *Technics and Civilization*, p. 89.
24. Cf. I. B. Cohen, "Science in the 19th Century," in A. M. Schlesinger, Jr., and M. White, eds., *Paths of American Thought*, Boston, 1963, p. 171. Robert Merton argues that science exhibited practical aims as early as the seventeenth century. The applications to which he refers, however, were mainly military and naval rather than industrial. *Cf.* Merton, *Social Theory and Social Structure*, rev. ed., New York, 1957, pp. 607 ff. *Cf.* also Alexander King, "Science and Technology in the New Europe," *Daedalus*, Winter, 1964, p. 435; and especially Ellul, *op. cit.*, pp. 7 ff.
25. Lindsay, *op. cit.*, pp. 212 ff. *Cf.* also J. K. Finch, *The Story of Engineering*, New York, 1960 (paperback).
26. The New York Times, October 4, 1963, noted that a "retirement" ceremony was held by the Department of Commerce. A bystander wondered if UNIVAC I would be given a gold watch.
27. Cf. H. Hart, "Acceleration in Social Change," in F. R. Allen, *et al.*, ed., *Technology and Social Change*, New **405**

York, 1957, pp. 27 ff; Hart, *The Technique of Social Change*, New York, 1931; B. S. Sanders, "Some Difficulties in Measuring Inventive Activity," in N.B.E.R., *op. cit.*, pp. 53 ff.; and W. O. Baker, "The Dynamism of Science and Technology," in E. Ginzberg, ed., *Technology and Social Change*, New York, 1964, pp. 82 ff.

28. Cf. J. L. Enos, "Invention and Innovation in the Petroleum Refining Industry," in N.B.E.R., *op. cit.*, pp. 304 ff.

29. Ayres, *op. cit.*, pp. 120–121. Italics added.

30. Mantoux, *op. cit.*, pp. 367 ff.

31. Ibid., p. 375.

32. J. A. Schumpeter, *Business Cycles*, II, New York, 1939, 768. Mumford, *Technics and Civilization*, pp. 143 ff., argues that, in the process of parallel and differential growth, the humanistic requirements of guild regulation were forgotten.

33. K. Marx, *Capital,* C. H. Kerr, ed., Chicago, 1909, I, 431; *cf.* also Smelser *op. cit.*, pp. 86, 186 ff.; Habakkuk, *op. cit.*, p. 148; and Thompson, *op. cit.*, pp. 269 ff.

34. For a more detailed analysis, see my article "Disarmament and The Economy," *Commentary*, May 1963.

35. S. Kuznets, "Inventive Activity: Problems of Definition and Measurement," in N.B.E.R., *op. cit.*, p. 19 ff.

36. Usher, *A History of Mechanical Inventions*, Cambridge, Mass., 1929 (paperback), 1959, p. 68.

37. Cf. S. C. Gilfillan, *Inventing the Ship*, Chicago, 1935.

38. Mumford, *Technics and Civilization*, pp. 14, 197.

39. A. Wolf, *A History of Science, Technology and Philosophy in the 16th and 17th Centuries*, II, New York, 1959 (paperback), 552; *cf.* also E. S. Ferguson, "The Origins of the Steam Engine," *Scientific American*, January 1964, pp. 98 ff.

40. Mantoux, *op. cit.*, p. 338.

41. On papermaking, *cf.* L. T. Stevenson, *American Papermaking*, New York, 1940.

42. Giedion, *op. cit.*, pp. 77 ff.

43. A. Nevins and F. E. Hill, *Ford, The Times, The Man, The Company*, New York, 1954, p. 471.

44. Ibid., p. 467.

45. Giedion, *op. cit.*, p. 118.

46. Enos, *op. cit.*, p. 319.

47. Herbert Marcuse, *One Dimensional Man*, Boston, 1964, p. xv.

2 A babel of calculators

1. A. Wolf, *History of Science, Technology and Philosophy in the 16th and 17th Centuries*, New York, 1950, pp. 556 ff.

2. Wolf, *History of Science, Technology and Philosophy in the 18th Century*, New York, 1952, pp. 656 ff.

3. For a fascinating account of Babbage's career, see Jeremy Bernstein, "The Analytical Engine," *The New Yorker*, October 19, 1963.

4. Charles Babbage, *On the Economy of Machinery and Manufactures*, London, 1835 (reprinted New York, 1963), pp. 315 ff.

5. Bernstein, *op. cit.*

6. G. R. Stibitz and J. A. Larrivee, *Mathematics and Computers*, New York, 1957, pp. 59–60.

7. The New York Times, December 2, 1962.

8. Bernstein, *op. cit.*, October 26, 1963.

9. Cf. M. Gardner, *Logic Machines and Diagrams*, New York, 1958, pp. 127 ff.

10. A. M. Hilton, *Logic, Computing*

Machines and Automation, Washington, D.C., 1963, pp. 156 ff., and 306 ff.

11. John von Neumann, *The Computer and the Brain*, New Haven, 1958, pp. 26 ff.

12. E. L. Harder, "Computers and Automation," *Electrical Engineering*, May 1959, p. 517.

13. Cf. R. M. Roesti, "The American Semiconductor Industry in World Trade," *Quarterly Review of Economics and Business*, Winter 1963, pp. 49 ff.

14. Cf. G. A. W. Boehm, "Electronics Goes Microminiature," *Fortune*, August 1962; and *The Wall Street Journal*, January 4, 1964.

15. Business Week, April 4, 1964, May 16, 1964, and April 17, 1965; *The Wall Street Journal*, July 6, 1964; *The New York Times*, October 30, 1964, December 6, 1964, May 23, 1965, and June 19, 1965; and *News Front*, November 1964.

16. Boehm, *op. cit.*, p. 102.

17. Business Week, December 8, 1962, and October 30, 1965; *cf.* also *The Wall Street Journal*, November 14, 1962.

18. The New York Times, November 2, 1962.

19. Boehm, *op. cit.*, p. 176; *Scientific American*, February, 1964, p. 105; M. A. Arbib, *Brains, Machines and Mathematics*, New York, 1964, pp. 56 ff; and W. H. Pierce, "Redundancy in Computers," *Scientific American*, February 1964, p. 103.

20. Automation, May 1964; *The New York Times*, June 29, 1965; *Business Week*, April 11, 1964, and May 1, 1965; and *The Wall Street Journal*, April 8, 1964, April 19, 1964, November 20, 1964, April 26, 1965, and April 28, 1965.

21. Business Week, September 23, 1961.

22. Ibid.

23. M. R. Wessel, "Legal Protection of Computer Programs," *Harvard Business Review*, March–April 1965.

24. Cf. Harold Borko, ed., *Computer Applications in the Behavioral Sciences*, New York, 1962, pp. 126 ff.

25. The New York Times, December 9, 1963.

26. Boehm, *op. cit.*, p. 99.

27. Business Week, August 31, 1963, and December 19, 1964; and *The Wall Street Journal*, December 15, 1964.

28. U.S.D.L. Manpower Report No. 7, *Reading Machines for Data Processing: Their Prospective Employment Effects*, June 1963.

29. The New York Times, November 23, 1963; *cf.* also *Proceedings*, American Federation of Information Processing Societies, 24, Baltimore, 1963, p. 27 ff.

30. U.S.D.L., *op. cit.*, p. 11.

31. Business Week, June 8, 1963.

32. Francis Bello, "The War of the Computers," *Fortune*, October 1959, p. 129.

33. Business Week, February 2, 1963.

34. Bello, *op. cit.*, p. 130.

35. The New York Times, December 3, 1963; *Business Week*, February 2, 1963, February 16, 1963, and December 7, 1963; *The Wall Street Journal*, October 12, 1962, and January 17, 1963; and *Sales Management*, January 3, 1964.

36. The Wall Street Journal, November 26, 1963.

37. Business Week, April 28, 1962; and *The New York Times*, February 14, 1965.

38. Fortune, July, 1964, and September, 1964; *The Wall Street Journal*, July 24, 1964, and September 1, 1964; *The New York Times*, July 24, 1964, and September 1, 1964; and *Business Week*, August 15, 1964, and September 12, 1964.

39. Time, November 2, 1962; *Business Week*, November 16, 1963, and January 25, 1964; *The Wall Street Journal*, November 26, 1963, September 9, 1964, and December 17, 1964; and *The New York Times*, April 12, 1964.

40. Business Automation, March 1965;

Business Week, July 25, 1964; *The New York Times*, February 14, 1965, and July 4, 1965; and *The Wall Street Journal*, August 4, 1965.

41. *The New York Times*, November 4, 1962; and *New Society*, December 10, 1964.

42. *The New York Times*, July 25, 1962, and February 16, 1965.

43. *Dun's Review*, December 1961; Cf. also *The New York Times*, April 4, 1965.

44. *Business Automation*, March 1965; *Dun's Review*, September 1964;

Business Week, December 19, 1964, March 13, 1965, and June 26, 1965; *The Wall Street Journal*, December 14, 1964, and March 25, 1965; *The Washington Daily News*, December 10, 1964, and *Automation Reports*, September 28, 1965.

45. *Sales Management*, June 1963.

46. *New Society*, December 19, 1963. *The Wall Street Journal* (February 28, 1966) reports that "speedy office machines [now] pour out enough paper to bury their users."

3 The programming of Minerva

1. *Cf.* M. Polanyi, *Personal Knowledge*, Chicago, 1958, p. 261; and A. Rapoport, "An Essay on Mind," in J. Scher, ed. *Theories of the Mind*, New York, 1962, p. 291.

2. *Cf.* D. E. Wooldridge, *The Machinery of the Brain*, New York, 1963, *passim*.

3. John von Neumann, "The General and Logical Theory of Automata," in J. R. Newman, ed., *The World of Mathematics*, IV, New York, 1956, 2080.

4. S. W. Angrist, "Fluid Control Devices," *Scientific American*, December 1964, pp. 81 ff; *Business Week*, November 7, 1964; *The Wall Street Journal*, August 25, 1964; and *Dun's Review*, June 1965.

5. Neumann, *The Computer and the Brain*, New Haven, 1958, p. 58.

6. *Cf.* W. R. Adey, "Computer Applications at the Frontiers of Biomedical Research," in *Proceedings of the American Federation of Information Processing Societies*, Fall 1963, pp. 603 ff.

7. T. D. Truitt, "An Introduction to Hybrid Computer Simulations," paper delivered at the Eastern Simulation Council, December 4, 1963.

8. Wooldridge, *op. cit.*, p. 29.

9. *Ibid.*, p. 189; *cf.* also *Fortune*, October 1964.

10. Wooldridge, *op. cit.*, p. 62; *Cf.* also Neumann, *The Computer and the Brain*, pp. 50 ff; and N. Wiener, *God and Golem, Inc.*, Cambridge, Mass., 1964, p. 72.

11. Quoted in S. Beer, *Cybernetics and Management*, New York, 1959, p. 2; also *cf* W. R. Ashby, "Simulation of a Brain," in H. Borko, ed., *Computer Applications in the Behavioral Sciences*, New York, 1962, pp. 453 ff. and Ashby, *An Introduction to Cybernetics*, London, 1956.

12. J. T. Culbertson, "Nerve Net Theory," in Borko, *op. cit.*, p. 486.

13. Ashby, *Introduction to Cybernetics*, pp. 86 ff.

14. Rapoport, *op. cit.*, p. 282.

15. Wiener, *The Human Use of Human Beings*, New York, 1954, (paperback edition), pp. 32 ff; and Wiener, *Cybernetics*, New York, 1948.

16. *Cf.* W. B. Cannon, *The Wisdom of the Body*, New York, 1939.

17. A. M. Hilton, *Logic, Computing Machines and Automation*, Washington, D.C., 1963, p. 383; *cf.* also M. A.

Arbib, *Brains, Machines and Mathematics*, New York, 1964, pp. 41 ff.

18. Cf. H. Kelman, "Toward a Definition of Mind," in Scher, *op. cit.*, p. 243; *cf.* also, S. Hook, ed., *Dimensions of Mind*, New York, 1960; and E. L. Harder, in *The New York Times*, May 27, 1965.

19. Rapoport, *op. cit.*, p. 292; and Newman, *op. cit.*, IV, 2067.

20. P. Armer, "Attitudes Toward Intelligent Machines," in E. A. Feigenbaum and J. Feldman, eds., *Computers and Thought*, New York, 1963.

21. E. D. T. Calhoun, "Why Machines Will Never Think," in M. Philipson, ed., *Automation: Implications for the Future*, New York, 1962 (paperback edition), pp. 180 ff.

22. M. Taube, *Computers and Common Sense*, New York, 1961, p. 69.

23. Cf. Wooldridge, *op. cit.*, pp. 74 ff.

24. Cf. views that make use of Gödel's theorem in Taube, *op. cit.*, p. 13; J. Lucas, "Minds, Machines and Gödel," in K. M. Sayre and F. J. Crosson, eds., *The Modeling of Mind*, Notre Dame, 1963, pp. 255 ff.; and E. Nagel and Newman, "Gödel's Proof," in Newman, *op. cit.*, III, 1668 ff. But *cf.* also Arbib, *op. cit.*, pp. 119 ff. Taube defeats himself with numerous misquotations and misrepresentations.

25. Cf. M. Scriven, "The Mechanical Concept of Mind," in Sayre and Crosson, *op. cit.*, pp. 243 ff., 254.

26. Cf. A. M. Turing, "Can a Machine Think?" in Newman, *op. cit.*, IV, 2099; *cf.* also, Scriven, "The Compleat Robot: A Prolegomena to Androidology," in Hook, *op. cit.*, pp. 112 ff.

27. Turing, *op. cit.*, p. 2110.

28. Cf. Wiener, *Human Use of Human Beings*, pp. 16 ff.

29. The Wall Street Journal, October 8, 1963; *cf.* also *The Wall Street Journal*, August 19, 1965; and *The Washington Post*, June 13, 1965.

30. The New York Times, December 3,
1963; E. Adams, "Electronic Data Processing Aid to the Courts," Conference on State and Local Governments, September 30, 1964; *The Wall Street Journal*, August 14, 1962; *The Washington Post*, November 22, 1964; and *Business Week*, January 23, 1965.

31. Council of Library Resources, *Automation and the Library of Congress*, Washington, 1963; *cf.* also J. G. Kemeny, "A Library for 2000 A.D." in M. Greenberger, ed., *Management and the Computer of the Future*, Cambridge, Mass., 1962, pp. 139 ff; *The Wall Street Journal*, August 3, 1964; and *The Washington Post*, April 4, 1965.

32. Cf. W. S. Cooper, "Automatic Fact Retrieval," *Science Journal*, June 1965; H. A. Simon and A. Newell, "What Have Computers to Do with Management?" in G. P. Shultz and T. L. Whister, eds., *Management Organization and the Computer*, New York, 1960, p. 44; *The New York Times*, September 10, 1964, September 13, 1964, September 27, 1964, and January 24, 1965; and *Business Week*, July 18, 1964.

33. Arbib, *op. cit.*, pp. 105 ff.; *The Washington Post*, March 4, 1964; and Wiener, *God and Golem, Inc.*, p. 74.

34. L. Lessing, "The Transistorized M. D.," *Fortune*, September 1963.

35. On hospital routine, *cf.* R. L. Coser, "The Hazards in Hospitalization," *Hospital Administration*, May 1960, pp. 25 ff; also *cf. Business Week*, September 19, 1964, and May 15, 1965; *The New York Times*, May 23, 1965; and E. M. Bluestone, "Who Pays The Price of Automation?" *Hospitals*, October 16, 1965.

36. K. S. Ledley, "Advances in Biomedical Science and Diagnosis," in Borko, *op. cit.*, pp. 491 ff.; and *The New York Times*, July 7, 1964.

37. The New York Times, May 28, 1963.

38. The New York Times, November 4, 1962, September 22, 1963.

39. *Cf.* K. Menninger, *The Vital Balance*, New York, 1963, *passim*.

40. A. Newell, J. C. Shaw, and H. A. Simon, "Empirical Explorations with the Logic Theory Machine," in Feigenbaum and Feldman, *op. cit.*, pp. 113 ff.

41. J. Pfeiffer, *The Thinking Machine*, New York, 1962, p. 149.

42. *The New York Times*, May 28, 1963.

43. D. G. Hays, *Automatic Language Data Processing in Sociology*, RAND Corporation, 1959; Hays, *On the Value of a Depending Connection*, RAND Corporation, 1961; and D. G. Dubrow, "Syntactic Analysis of English by Computer" in *Proceedings of the American Federation of Information Processing Societies*, Fall 1963, pp. 369 ff.

44. Taube, *op. cit.*, pp. 21 ff.

45. L. A. Hiller, Jr. and L. Isaacson, "Experimental Music," in Sayre and Crosson, *op. cit.*, pp. 43 ff.

46. *Cf.* E. Wind, *Art and Anarchy*, New York, 1964, pp. 94 ff.

47. Hiller and Isaacson, *op. cit.*, p. 67.

48. J. A. Thie, "Computers in the Arts," *Computers and Automation*, September 1961, p. 24.

49. Newman, *op. cit.*, I, 509 ff.; and Newman, *op. cit.*, IV, 2437.

50. M. Gardner, *Logic Machines and Diagrams*, New York, 1958, pp. 80 ff.

51. H. Wang, "Toward Mechanical Mathematics," in Sayre and Crosson, *op. cit.*, p. 115.

52. J. R. Slagle, "A Heuristic Program That Solves Symbolic Integration Problems in Freshman Calculus," in Feigenbaum and Feldman, *op. cit.*, pp. 191 ff.

53. Newman, *op. cit.*, IV, 2124.

54. Newell, "The Chess Machine," in Sayre and Crosson, *op. cit.*, pp. 73 ff.

55. *The New York Times*, December 20, 1963.

56. *Cf.* Richard Bellman, *Dynamic Programming*, New York, 1957; and *The Wall Street Journal*, May 18, 1962, and July 13, 1964.

57. Newell and Simon, "GPS, A Program That Simulates Human Thought," in Feigenbaum and Feldman, *op. cit.*, p. 293.

58. M. Minsky, quoted in Taube, *op. cit.*, p. 85; and Minsky, "Steps Toward Artificial Intelligence," in Feigenbaum and Feldman, *op. cit.*, p. 447.

59. S. C. Rome and B. K. Rome, "Computer Simulation Toward a Theory of Large Organizations," in Borko, *op. cit.*, pp. 523 ff.

60. Feldman, "Computer Simulation of Cognitive Processes," in Borko, *op. cit.*, p. 355.

61. I. de Sola Pool, "Automation: New Tool for Decision Makers," *Challenge*, March, 1963.

62. M. Mogel, "Voting Simulation: The Manufacture of Consent," in Philipson, *op. cit.*, pp. 355 ff.

63. *Ibid.*, p. 364.

64. *The New York Times*, April 30, 1963, May 1, 1963, October 4, 1964, November 19, 1964, and August 25, 1965; and *The Wall Street Journal*, July 20, 1964, October 16, 1964, and August 25, 1965.

65. M. Epernay, *The McLandress Dimension*, Boston, 1963, pp. 59 ff.

66. A. S. Banks and R. B. Texter, *Cross-Polity Survey*, Cambridge, Mass., 1963; and *Science Journal*, June 1965.

67. *Cf.* Newman, *op. cit.*, II, 1240 ff.; *cf.* also O. Benson, "Simulation of International Relations and Diplomacy," in Borko, *op. cit.*, pp. 575 ff.

68. *The Wall Street Journal*, December 11, 1963; and *The New York Times*, Febuary 28, 1965.

69. *The New York Times*, January 5, 1964, and June 29, 1964; *Business Week*, November 14, 1964; *The Washington Daily News*, June 9, 1965; and J. Pfeiffer, "Machines That Man Can Talk With," *Fortune*, May 1964.

70. L. Fein, "Computer-Oriented Peace Research," *Proceedings of the American*

Federation of Information Processing Societies, Fall 1963, p. 631.

71. W. McPhee, F. Scalora, and F. Stanton, "What Contribution Can Communication Theory Make to Constructing and Evaluating an Advertising Campaign?" *8th Annual Conference Proceedings of Advertising Research Foundation*, New York, 1963.

72. W. D. Wells, "Computer Simulation of Consumer Behavior," *Harvard Business Review*, March–April 1963, p. 93; and *Business Week*, April 17, 1965.

73. Business Week, June 1, 1963, and April 18, 1964.

74. Cf. B. B. Seligman, *Main Currents in Modern Economics*, New York, 1962, p. 779 ff.

75. G. E. Clarkson, "A Model of the Trust Investment Process," in Feigenbaum and Feldman, *op. cit.*, pp. 347 ff.; *The Wall Street Journal*, December 2, 1964, April 26, 1965, May 3, 1965, and August 10, 1965; *The New York Times*, April 25, 1964; and *Business Week*, October 10, 1964; and November 14, 1964.

76. G. H. Orcutt, *et al.*, *Microanalysis of Socioeconomic Systems*, New York, 1961.

77. R. Stone and A. Brown, *A Computable Model of Economic Growth*, Cambridge, Eng., 1962; *cf.* also W. W. Leontief, "The Structure of Development," *Scientific American*, September 1963.

78. S. Ramo, "A New Technique for Education," in Philipson, *op. cit.*, pp. 428 ff; *cf.* also J. R. Murphy and I. A. Goldberg, "Strategies for Using Programmed Instruction," *Harvard Business Review*, May–June 1964.

79. Cf. F. W. Matson, *The Broken Image*, New York, 1964, pp. 69 ff.

80. Cf. B. F. Skinner, "The Science of Learning and the Art of Teaching," in W. I. Smith and J. W. Moore, eds., *Programmed Learning*, Princeton, 1962, pp. 18 ff.; and W. A. Deterline, *An Introduction to Programmed Instruction*, Englewood Cliffs, 1962.

81. H. F. Silberman and J. E. Coulson, "Automated Teaching," in Borko, *op. cit.*, p. 309.

82. The Christian Century, January 2, 1964.

83. Cf. J. L. Hughes, *Programmed Learning: A Critical Evaluation*, Chicago, 1963; and *Dun's Review*, May 1964.

84. Cf. The Journal of Educational Research, June–July 1962; *The National Education Association Journal*, December 1962; *The New York Times*, July 9, 1964; and *The Wall Street Journal*, July 9, 1964.

85. Cf. P. Goodman, *Compulsory Miseducation*, New York, 1964, pp. 99 ff.; and A. Curle, S. Davis, F. Sloan, *Some Education Implications of Technological Development*, report to Harvard University Program on Technology and Society, (mimeographed), 1965.

86. R. W. Christian, "Guides to Programmed Learning," *Harvard Business Review*, November–December 1962, pp. 36 ff.

87. T. F. Gilbert, quoted in *ibid.*

88. The New York Times, July 5, 1964.

89. G. Arnstein, "Who Will Counsel the Counselors?" *Audiovisual Instruction*, January 1963; and *The New York Times*, November 30, 1963.

90. Cf. J. Barzun, *Science: The Glorious Entertainment*, New York, 1964, p. 44.

4 Work without men

1. Cf. J. R. Bright, *Automation and Management*, Cambridge, Mass., 1958.

2. Cf. A. Bluemle, *Automation*, New York, 1963, pp. 85 ff.; *Electronics*, October 24, 1958; and U.S.D.L., *Employment Outlook and Changing Occupational Structure in Electronics Manufacturing*, Washington, D.C., 1963.

3. G. H. Amber and P. S. Amber, *Anatomy of Automation*, Englewood Cliffs, 1962, p. 100.

4. Cf. J. K. Finch, *The Story of Engineering*, New York, 1960; A. P. Usher, *A History of Mechanical Inventions*, Cambridge, Mass., 1929; and M. A. Hollengreen, "Automation in the Metal Working Industries," in H. B. Jacobson and J. S. Roucek, eds., *Automation and Society*, New York, 1959.

5. U.S.D.C., *Patterns and Problems of Technical Innovation in American Industry*, Washington, D.C., 1963, p. 97.

6. Business Week, April 20, 1963, and May 4, 1963; *News Front*, June 1964; and *Dun's Review*, May 1965.

7. Automation, May 1964; and *Dun's Review*, February 1965.

8. The New York Times, February 2, 1964; *Automation*, May 1964; and *Dun's Review*, May 1965.

9. The American Machinist, October 7, 1957; *Automation*, September 1954, and May 1957; and P. D. Tilton, *Numerical Control for Machine Tools*, Stanford, 1957.

10. Dun's Review, August 1958, and March 1964; *Iron Age*, April 17, 1958; *Automation*, July 1957; *Fortune*, March 1962; *Business Week*, March 30, 1963, October 24, 1964; and April 10, 1965; and U.S.D.L., *Outlook for Numerical Control of Machine Tools*, Washington, D.C., 1965.

11. Cf. R. A. Johnson, F. E. Kast, and J. E. Rosenzweig, *The Theory and Management of Systems*, New York, 1963, pp. 164 ff.; Amber and Amber, *op. cit.*, p. 164; and, on special grinding methods, *cf. Automation*, May 1964.

12. Fortune, March 1962; *Dun's Review*, March 1964; and *Automation*, July 1964, February 1965, and March 1965.

13. U.S.D.C., *op. cit.*, p. 105.

14. Business Week, December 8, 1962.

15. Business Week, February 8, 1964, and March 7, 1964.

16. Fortune, July 1962; *The New York Times*, January 10, 1964; *Business Week*, January 25, 1964, March 28, 1964, October 31, 1964, November 7, 1964; and May 29, 1965; *Dun's Review*, May 1964; *Automation*, July 1964; *Tool and Manufacturing Engineer*, July 1963; and *Automotive News*, January 11, 1965.

17. U.S.D.L., *Case Study of a Modernized Petroleum Refinery*, Washington, D.C., 1957.

18. Business Week, December 8, 1962, and October 6, 1963.

19. U.S.D.L., *Impact of Technological Change and Automation in the Pulp and Paper Industry*, Washington, D.C., 1962, p. 19.

20. Business Week, October 20, 1962, and August 31, 1963.

21. U.S.D.L., *Case Study of a Large Mechanized Bakery*, Washington, D.C., 1956.

22. Business Week, March 14, 1964; *Dun's Review*, December 1963; U.S.D.L., *Technological Trends in Major American Industries*, Washington, D.C., 1964; *The New York Times*, February 4, 1958, and October 29, 1958; and *Supermarket News*, October 6, 1958.

23. Business Week, July 23, 1960, and August 4, 1962; *The New York Times*, May 26, 1962; and *Automation*, July 1964.

24. Fortune, April 1965; *The New York Times*, November 22, 1964; *Business*

Week, May 19, 1962, October 3, 1964, January 2, 1965, and January 30, 1965; *Dun's Review,* August 1962; and *Automation,* July 1964, September 1964, November 1964, and January 1965.

25. L. V. Gallagher and B. S. Old, "The Continuous Casting of Steel," *Scientific American,* December 1963, pp. 75 ff.; *The New York Times,* November 17, 1963, and September 13, 1964; *Fortune,* August 1962, and January 1965; *Business Week,* May 1, 1965; *Steelways,* November 1964; and *Automation,* March 1965, and May 1965.

26. *Business Week,* February 29, 1964.

27. D. S. Halacy, Jr., *Computers,* New York, 1962, p. 187; *The New York Times,* June 5, 1963, and January 5, 1964; *Business Week,* December 14, 1963, February 29, 1964, and August 15, 1964; *The Wall Street Journal,* October 17, 1963; and *Automation,* June 1964.

28. *The Wall Street Journal,* May 27, 1963.

29. *The Wall Street Journal,* January 2, 1964.

30. *Dun's Review,* April 1964; *Business Week,* August 23, 1958; October 27, 1962.

31. *Business Week,* May 19, 1962; *The New York Times,* March 27, 1954; and *Automation,* May 1964, and January 1965.

32. *The New York Times,* November 4, 1962, November 19, 1962, May 19, 1963, October 14, 1963, November 20, 1963, November 24, 1963, December 29, 1963, January 16, 1964, January 17, 1964, April 23, 1964, April 28, 1964, May 14, 1964, July 8, 1964, August 27, 1964, November 12, 1964, November 17, 1964, January 15, 1965, and January 27, 1965; *The Wall Street Journal,* March 25, 1964; *Business Week,* January 25, 1964; *The International Transport Journal,* February 1964; and *The Economist,* December 12, 1964.

33. *Cf.* U.S.D.L., *Employment and Changing Occupational Patterns in the Railroad Industry,* Washington, D.C., 1963; *The New York Times,* October 10, 1963, October 29, 1963, January 18, 1964, May 3, 1964, August 23, 1964, December 6, 1964, and December 20, 1964; *The Wall Street Journal,* February 13, 1963; and *Business Week,* October 19, 1963, and April 10, 1965.

34. U.S.D.L., *Technological Change and Productivity in the Bituminous Coal Industry,* Washington, D.C., 1961; *The Wall Street Journal,* May 15, 1964; and *The New York Times,* February 16, 1964.

35. *The New York Times,* April 21, 1963, and July 21, 1963; *The Wall Street Journal,* July 12, 1963, and December 10, 1964; *Business Week,* January 5, 1963, January 19, 1963, December 14, 1963, March 7, 1964, April 25, 1964, and April 24, 1965; and *The Economist,* September 29, 1962, and May 22, 1965.

36. *Automation,* April 1964, p. 22.

37. *Cf.* R. A. Brady, *Organization, Automation and Society,* Berkeley, 1961, *passim.*

38. *Union Postal Clerk and Postal Transport Journal,* September 1965.

39. *Cf.* U.S.D.C., *op. cit.,* pp. 33, 55.

40. These paragraphs on retailing are based on B. B. Seligman, "Automation Comes to the Supermarket," *Challenge,* November 1962; and Seligman, "Impact of Automation in Retailing," *Voice of America Forum Lecture Series,* No. 14, 1963.

41. Quoted in *Automation,* June 1964.

42. *Cf.* S. Moos, "The Scope of Automation," *The Economic Journal,* March 1957.

43. *Cf.* S. Beer, *Cybernetics and Management,* New York, 1959, p. 142; J. F. Engelberger, "Role of Industrial Robots in Improving Production Operations," *Automation,* June 1964; *Dun's*

Review, March 1962, January 1963, and March 1964; and R. S. Mosher, "Industrial Manipulators," *Scientific American*, October 1964.

44. *Dun's Review*, March 1965; and

The Journal of Commerce, January 28, 1965.

45. N. Wiener, *Cybernetics*, 2nd ed., Cambridge, Mass., 1961, pp. 27–28 (italics added).

5 The automated filing cabinet

1. *The New York Times*, November 4, 1962; *Dun's Review*, October 1963; and *Business Week*, February 29, 1964.

2. *The New York Times*, February 9, 1964; and *Business Week*, February 1, 1964.

3. *Business Week*, May 4, 1963, and August 1, 1964.

4. *The New York Times*, July 21, 1963, June 30, 1964, July 2, 1964, and May 24, 1964; *Drug News Weekly*, July 4, 1962; and *The Wall Street Journal*, January 17, 1963, and June 3, 1963.

5. J. C. McDonald, *Impact and Implications of Office Automation*, Ottawa, Canadian Department of Labour, 1964; *Dun's Review*, September 1963, and September 1964; and *The New York Times*, December 17, 1963.

6. U.S.D.L., *A Case Study of an Automatic Airline Reservation System*, Washington, D.C., 1958; *Fortune*, April 1964; *The New York Times*, November 6, 1958, April 24, 1963, September 6, 1964, and September 16, 1964; *The Wall Street Journal*, May 27, 1963; and *Dun's Review*, September 1963.

7. R. K. Wiener, "Changing Manpower Requirements in Banking," *The Monthly Labor Review*, September 1962; *The London Economist*, February 3, 1962, and June 30, 1962; *The Wall Street Journal*, January 13, 1959, and February 7, 1962; *The New York Times*, March 14, 1962, and December 15, 1964; *Business Week*, October 17, 1964; *The Washington Post*, October 31, 1964; and McDonald, *op. cit.*, pp. 11 ff.

8. *The New York Times*, October 5, 1962, November 18, 1962, May 8, 1964, and May 11, 1964; *Prentice-Hall Executive Letter*, November 16, 1963; and *The Wall Street Journal*, April 27, 1964, June 29, 1964, July 27, 1964, August 3, 1964, and September 24, 1964.

9. *Business Week*, November 23, 1963; and *Supermarket News*, December 2, 1963.

10. Cf. J. W. Widing, Jr., and C. G. Diamond, "Buy by Computer," *The Harvard Business Review*, March–April 1964; *The Wall Street Journal*, June 23, 1964; and *Business Week*, July 11, 1964.

11. *The New York Times*, May 17, 1962. On data processing by computer, cf. also R. A. Johnson, F. E. Kast, and J. E. Rosenzweig, *The Theory and Management of Systems*, New York, 1963, Chapters 10, 11, 12, pp. 179 ff.; R. N. Schmidt and W. E. Meyers, *Electronic Business Data Processing*, New York, 1963, *passim*; *Dun's Review*, October 1963; *Stores*, November 1963; *Supermarket Merchandising*, April 1961, August 1963, and September 1963; *Drug News Weekly*, November 20, 1963; and *Sales Management*, September 15, 1961.

12. On PERT and related methods, cf. Johnson, Kast, and Rosenzweig, *op. cit.*, pp. 241 ff.; R. L. Eris and B. N. Baker, *An Introduction to PERT/CPM*, Homewood, 1964; *The London Economist*, July 28, 1962, and July 13, 1963; *Automation*, May 1964; *Business Week*,

July 7, 1962, and September 8, 1962; *Fortune*, April 1962; R. W. Miller, "How to Plan and Control with PERT," *The Harvard Business Review*, March–April 1962, pp. 93 ff.; F. K. Levy, G. L. Thompson, and J. D. Weist, "The ABC's of the Critical Path Method," *The Harvard Business Review*, September–October 1963, pp. 98 ff.; H. W. Paige, "How PERT Cost Helps the General Manager," *The Harvard Business Review*, November–December 1963, pp. 87 ff.; A. R. Dooley, "Interpretations of PERT," *The Harvard Business Review*, March–April, 1964, pp. 160 ff.; J. Dearden, "Can Management Information be Automated?" *The Harvard Business Review*, p. 128 ff.; E. S. Buffa, G. C. Armour, and T. E. Vollman, "Allocating Facilities with CRAFT," *The Harvard Business Review*, pp. 136 ff.; and *Dun's Review*, February 1962, and February 1964.

13. U.S.D.L., *Automatic Data Processing in the Federal Government—Its Manpower Requirements*, Washington, D.C., 1963; and *The Wall Street Journal*, December 30, 1964.

14. U.S.D.L., *Impact of Office Automation in the Internal Revenue Service*, Washington, D.C., 1963; *The New York Times*, September 14, 1960; and *Business Week*, February 8, 1964.

15. U.S.D.L., *Women Telephone Workers and Changing Technology*, Washington, D.C., 1963; I. R. Hoos, *Automation in the Office*, Washington, D.C., 1961, *passim*; *The Wall Street Journal*, June 30, 1964; *The New York Times*, June 30, 1964; J. Mersel, "The Computing Machine as Message and Control Center of a Cybernated System," Conference on the Cybercultural Revolution, New York, June 19, 1964, and U.S.D.L., *Changing Workforce Characteristics of an Automated Insurance Company*, Washington, D.C., 1964.

16. Cf. J. Stieber, "Automation and the White Collar Worker," *Personnel Magazine*, November–December 1957; *Statistical Abstract*, 1962, p. 226; U.S.D.L., *Adjustments to the Introduction of Office Automation*, Washington, D.C., 1960; Industrial Relations Counselors, *White Collar Restiveness*, New York, 1963; and *The Wall Street Journal*, May 7, 1963.

17. T. O'Toole, "White Collar Automation," *The Reporter*, December 5, 1963; *AFL-CIO Industrial Union Department Bulletin*, October 1959; *Dun's Review*, September 1963; *The Wall Street Journal*, February 13, 1962, and May 5, 1964; and U.S.D.L., *Automation and Employment Opportunities for Officeworkers*, Washington, D.C., 1958.

6 The trauma we await

1. P. Mantoux, *The Industrial Revolution in the 18th Century*, London, 1961, p. 409.

2. Cf. P. Taft, "Organized Labor and Technological Change: A Backward Look," in G. G. Somers, E. L. Cushman, and N. Weinberg, *Adjusting to Technological Change*, New York, 1963, p. 29; and A. A. Blum, "America's Reaction To Technological Change and Automation," *Management of Personnel Quarterly*, Fall 1964.

3. Cf. F. C. Mann and L. R. Hoffman, *Automation and the Worker*, New York, 1960, p. 192; and *The Monthly Labor Review*, June 1964.

4. *The New York Times*, April 7, 1961; and cf. W. Haber, L. A. Ferman, and J. R. Hudson, *The Impact of Technological Change*, Kalamazoo, 1963.

5. United Packinghouse Workers of America, *Facts and Figures*, August 7, 1964.

6. *Cf.* Haber, *et al.*, *op. cit.*, pp. 47–48.

7. *The Federal Reserve Bulletin*, September 1965; *The Wall Street Journal*, June 4, 1965, September 27, 1965, October 8, 1965; and October 13, 1965; and *The New York Times*, May 15, 1965.

8. U.S.D.L., *Employment Outlook and Changing Occupational Structure in Electronics Manufacturing*, Washington, D.C., 1963.

9. E. B. Jakubauskas, "Technological Change and Recent Trends in the Composition of Railroad Employment," *The Quarterly Review of Economics and Business*, November 1962; and *The Monthly Labor Review*, October, 1962.

10. *Cf.* H. L. Sheppard, Ferman, and S. Faber, *Too Old to Work — Too Young to Retire*, Senate Committee on Unemployment Problems, 86th Congress, Washington, D.C., 1959.

11. *Cf.* R. C. Wilcock and W. H. Franke, *Unwanted Workers*, New York, 1963.

12. *The New York Times*, February 16, 1964, March 13, 1964, August 10, 1964, August 16, 1964, and August 23, 1964; *The Wall Street Journal*, December 13, 1963, and December 14, 1964; *The Washington Post*, August 16, 1964; *John Herling's Labor Letter*, December 21, 1963; and *The National Observer*, September 6, 1965.

13. Wilcock and Franke, *op. cit.*, pp. 69 ff., 93. *Cf.* also C. V. Willie and W. E. Riddick, "The Employed Poor: A Case Study," in B. B. Seligman, ed., *Poverty As A Public Issue*, New York, 1965, pp. 139 ff; and for a more sanguine view, *cf. The Monthly Labor Review*, June 1964.

14. Ferman, *Death of a Newspaper: The Story of the Detroit Times*, Kalamazoo, 1963.

15. Wilcock and Franke, *op. cit.*, p. 122, (also see p. 95); *cf. The National Observer*, September 30, 1963; and Haber, Ferman, and Hudson, *op. cit.*, pp. 29 ff.

16. J. M. McCrea, "Labor Markets and Social Security," paper delivered at the Southern Economic Association Meeting, November 15, 1963; Wilcock and Franke, *op. cit.*, pp. 45, 54; and U.S.D.L., *Case Studies of Displaced Workers*, Washington, D.C. 1964.

17. *The Wall Street Journal*, August 21, 1962.

18. *Cf.* E. F. Denison, *Incidence of Unemployment by States and Regions: 1950 and 1960*, unpublished memorandum, Committee for Economic Development, 1963.

19. C. C. Killingsworth, "Automation in Manufacturing," *Industrial Relations Research Association Proceedings*, December 1958; *cf.* also Wilcock and Franke, *op. cit.*, p. 4.

20. *Automation*, April 1964; and *The New York Times*, April 15, 1963.

21. Leon Keyserling, *Two Top Priority Programs to Reduce Unemployment*, Washington, D.C., 1964; U.S.D.L., *Extent and Nature of Frictional Unemployment*, Washington, D.C., 1959; and U.S.D.L., *Unemployment: Terminology, Measurement and Analysis*, Washington, D.C., 1961.

22. Ewan Clague, Commissioner of Labor Statistics, testimony to the House Labor Committee, June 11, 1963.

23. A. Tella, "The Sensitivity of Labor Force to Employment: An Age-Sex Analysis," unpublished paper, Federal Reserve Board, April 1964.

24. Tella, "The Relation of Labor Force to Employment," *The Industrial and Labor Relations Review*, June 1964; *cf.* also L. Greenberg and E. Weinberg, "Automation: Nationwide Studies in the United States," paper delivered at The International Labor Organization Conference in Geneva, March 1964; Clague and Greenberg, "Employment," in J. T. Dunlop, ed., *Automation and*

Technological Change, Englewood Cliffs, 1962, pp. 114 ff; and *The New York Times*, May 5, 1962, and September 27, 1963.

25. Memorandum to the author by Nat Goldfinger, Research Director, A.F.L.-C.I.O., May 14, 1964.

26. U.S.D.L., *Employment Trends and Manpower Requirements in Government*, Washington, D.C., 1963; and B. B. Seligman, "Automation and the State," *Commentary*, June 1964.

27. United States Civil Service Commission, *A Study of the Impact of Automation on Federal Employees*, Washington, D.C., 1964.

28. I. R. Hoos, "Impact of Automation on Workers," *The International Labour Review*, October 1963, pp. 363 ff.; and J. R. Bright, *Automation and Management*, Cambridge, Mass., 1958.

29. *Cf.* Hoos, *Automation in the Office*, Washington, D.C., 1961; and *Time*, February 24, 1961.

30. *The New York Times*, July 12, 1964; *cf.* B. B. Seligman, "Disarmament and the Economy," *Commentary*, May 1963; *Product Engineering*, July 6, 1964; and U.S.D.L., *The Current Employment Market for Engineers, Scientists and Technicians*, Washington, D.C., 1965.

31. Seymour L. Wolfbein, Director of the Office of Manpower, Automation and Training, U.S.D.L., testimony before the Senate Select Committee on Small Business, June 1963; and *The Monthly Labor Review*, April 1965.

32. *Cf. The American Federationist*, October 1963; and D. E. Diamond, "The Shift to Services," *Challenge*, July 1962.

33. *Cf.* Bright, "Does Automation Raise Skill Requirements?" *The Harvard Business Review*, July–August 1958; *The Washington Post*, August 23, 1964; *Dun's Review*, January 1962; and *The New York Times*, October 24, 1965.

34. Greenberg, statement to the Senate Subcommittee on Employment and Manpower, September 26, 1963, reprinted in *Selected Readings in Employment and Manpower*, Senate Committee on Labor and Public Welfare, 88th Congress, p. 365; *cf.* also S. Fabricant, "Productivity and Economic Growth," in E. Ginsberg, ed., *Technology and Social Change*, New York, 1964; Fabricant, "Productivity: Its Meaning and Trend," *Challenge*, October 1962; J. W. Kendrick, *Productivity Trends in the U.S.*, Princeton, 1961; and National Bureau of Economic Research, *Output, Input and Productivity Measurement*, Princeton, 1961.

35. Greenberg, statement; *The Monthly Labor Review*, October 1963; and *cf. The Wall Street Journal*, October 15, 1965.

36. U.S.D.L., *Automation, Productivity and Manpower Problems*, Washington, D.C., 1964.

37. *Cf.* tabulation in *The American Federationist*, May 1964, with output data in U.S.D.L., *Technological Trends in 36 Major Industries*, Washington, D.C. 1964.

38. Columbia University Bureau of Applied Social Research estimate cited in *The American Federationist*, November 1963. This estimate assumed no change in the relationships that obtained during the 1950s.

39. World Health Organization, *Mental Problems of Automation*, 1959; Mann and Hoffmann, *op. cit.*, pp. 90–91; W. Buckingham, *Automation: Its Impact on Business and People*, New York, 1961; *The Washington Post*, June 4, 1963; *New Society*, November 19, 1964.

40. Hoos and B. L. Jones, "Office Automation in Japan," *The International Labour Review*, June 1963.

41. H. Swados, *On The Line*, Boston, 1957; Swados, "The Myth of the Happy Worker," in *A Radical's America*, Boston, 1962; *Newsweek*, August 10,

1964; and E. Chinoy, "Manning the Machine: The Assembly Line-Worker," in P. L. Berger, ed., *The Human Shape of Work*, New York, 1964, p. 57.

42. Floyd Mann in Foundation for Research on Human Behavior, *The Worker in the New Industrial Environment*, Ann Arbor, 1962, p. 21; *cf.* W. A. Faunce, "Automation in the Automobile Industry," *The American Sociological Review*, August 1958, p. 401; Faunce, "Automation and the Automobile Worker," in B. Rosenberg, I. Gerver, and F. W. Howton, eds., *Mass Society in Crisis*, New York, 1964, p. 446; F. C. Mann, "Psychological and Organizational Impact of Automation," in Dunlop, ed., *op. cit.*, p. 43; Hoos, "When Computers Take Over the Office," *The Harvard Business Review*, July–August 1960.

43. Hoos, "Impact of Automation on Workers."

44. Cf. R. Blauner, *Alienation and Freedom*, Chicago, 1964; L. E. Davis, "Effects of Automation on Job Design," *Industrial Relations*, October 1962; Mann and Williams, "Observations on the Dynamics of a Change to Electronic Data Processing Equipment," paper presented at the 13th International Congress of Applied Psychology,

Rome, 1958; C. R. Walker, "Life in the Automatic Factory," *The Harvard Business Review*, January–February 1958; and F. E. Emery and J. Marek, "Some Socio-Technical Aspects of Automation," *Human Relations*, Vol. 15, No. 1, 1962.

45. Cf. G. Friedmann, *Industrial Society*, New York, 1955; and J. Froomkin, "Jobs, Skills and Realities," *Columbia University Forum*, Spring 1964.

46. Cf. Hoos, *op. cit.*

47. Bright, "Some Effects of Automation Upon Wage Determination," in G. Friedrichs, ed., *Automation und Technischer Fortschritt in Deutschland und den USA*, Frankfurt, 1963, p. 139.

48. P. Sultan and P. Prasnow, "Skill Impact of Automation," in Senate Labor Committee, 88th Congress, *Selected Readings in Employment*, Washington, D.C., 1964, p. 548; and Bright, "Skill Requirements and Wage Aspects of Automation," paper delivered at the Labor Relations Council Conference, November 8, 1960.

49. W. W. Wirtz, *Labor and the Public Interest*, New York, 1964, p. 183. *Cf.* also Killingsworth, testimony to the Senate Labor Committee, June 15, 1960.

7 Slow road to Erewhon

1. Opinion Research Corporation, *What's Troubling Labor Leadership?* Princeton, 1963; *The Economist*, November 23, 1963; and *The Wall Street Journal*, November 15, 1963.

2. Cf. C. E. Silberman, "The Real News About Automation," *Fortune*, January 1965; *cf.* also response by C. C. Killingsworth, *Fortune*, March 1965; and B. B. Seligman, "Real News and Automated Villains," *Dissent*, Spring 1965.

3. The New York Times, April 7, 1963; *The Wall Street Journal*, April 7, 1959; *The Christian Science Monitor*, September 28, 1963; *cf.* also U.S.D.L., *Report on Manpower*, Washington, D.C., 1965.

4. Cf. J. J. Healy, ed., *Creative Collective Bargaining*, Englewood Cliffs, 1965.

5. The Wall Street Journal, January 19, 1962.

6. Healy, *op. cit.*, pp. 27 ff.; P. Jacobs, *The State of the Unions*, New York,

1963, pp. 264 ff.; B. S. Kirsch, *Automation and Collective Bargaining*, Brooklyn, 1964; and *The New York Times*, April 15, 1963.

7. *Cf*. B. B. Seligman, "The American Corporation: Ideology and Reality," *Dissent*, Summer 1964, pp. 316 ff.

8. *Dun's Review*, February 1963; Bureau of National Affairs, *Labor Relations Reporter*, September 23, 1963; "Abell Co. v. Typographical Union No. 12," U.S.D.C., Maryland, June 30, 1964.

9. *Fortune*, May 1962; *The New York Times*, March 29, 1964; *Challenge*, October 1964; R. L. Aronson, "Automation—Challenge to Collective Bargaining?" in H. W. Davey, H. S. Kaltenborn, and S. H. Ruttenberg, *New Dimensions in Collective Bargaining*, New York, 1959, pp. 52 ff.; and Seligman "Automation and the Unions," *Dissent*, Winter 1965, pp. 33 ff.

10. *The Wall Street Journal*, January 19, 1962.

11. G. Strauss, "The Shifting Power Balance in the Plant," *Industrial Relations*, May 1962; and R. C. Wilcock, "Fast Changing Technology—Its Impact on Labor Problems," *Pennsylvania Business Survey*, December 1959.

12. *Cf*. A. H. Raskin, "Automation: Road to Lifetime Jobs?" *Saturday Review*, November 28, 1964; and J. Seidman, "The Union Agenda for Security," *The Monthly Labor Review*, June 1963.

13. *Cf. Business Week*, February 27, 1965.

14. M. E. Segal, "Portable Pensions and Early Retirement: Are They Partial Solutions?" in C. Markham, ed., *Jobs, Men and Machines*, New York, 1964; *The American Federationist*, March 1965; *The New York Times*, April 22, 1963, and August 16, 1964; and *Segal Newsletter*, April 1963.

15. *The New York Times*, November 30, 1962; and *Business Week*, October 10, 1964.

16. T. Kennedy, *Automation Funds and Displaced Workers*, Boston, 1962, p. 340.

17. *Ibid*., p. 352.

18. *Cf*. C. E. Dankert, "Shorter Hours — In Theory and Practice," *Industrial and Labor Relations Review*, April 1962, pp. 307 ff.

19. *Cf*. W. J. Baumol and R. E. Quandt, "Rules of Thumb and Optimally Imperfect Decisions," *The American Economic Review*, March 1964, pp. 23 ff.

20. *Cf. The American Federationist*, October, November, and December 1962; T. Sowell, "The Shorter Work Week controversy," *Industrial and Labor Relations Review*, January 1965; M. L. Greenbaum, *The Shorter Work Week*, Ithaca, 1963; S. A. Levitan *Reducing Work Time as A Means to Combat Unemployment*, Kalamazoo, 1964; E. Ginzberg, statement to House Labor Committee, 88th Congress, pp. 217 ff.; E. Clague, statement to House Labor Committee, 88th Congress, pp. 58ff.; B. Graham, *The Flexible Work Year*, Santa Barbara, 1964; *The Nation*, December 7, 1963; *N.Y. Industrial Bulletin*, August 1963; *The New York Times*, May 24, 1962, May 25, 1962, May 15, 1963, and September 20, 1964; *Challenge*, March 1962, and November 1963; *Business Week*, October 20, 1962; *The Boston Globe*, August 25, 1963; and *Womens' Wear Daily*, June 20, 1962, and June 22, 1962.

21. A. A. Blum, "Fourth Man Out: The Background of the Flight Engineer Pilot Conflict," *The Labor Law Journal*, August 1962, pp. 649 ff.

22. *Cf*. H. S. Kramer, "Anatomy of a Lost Strike: The Eastern Airlines—Flight Engineers Dispute," *I.L.R. Research*, IX, 1964, 3; and Jacobs, *op. cit*., pp. 218 ff.

23. *The New York Times*, December

6, 1961; U.S.D.L., *Recent Collective Bargaining and Technological Change*, Washington, D. C., 1964.

24. Jacobs, *op. cit.*, pp. 198 ff. "Bogus" began in the Great Depression, but has been used as a defense against technological change.

25. *Cf.* A. L. Svenson, "An Augean Stable—the Case of Management Featherbeds," *California Management*, Summer 1963.

26. *The New York Times*, March 31, 1964, June 27, 1964, October 21, 1964, February 8, 1965, February 24, 1965, March 8, 1965, March 9, 1965, March 18, 1965, June 24, 1965, July 3, 1965, August 25, 1965, and October 11, 1965; *The Wall Street Journal*, August 6, 1963, August 12, 1963, November 13, 1963, February 24, 1965, September 15, 1965, October 1, 1965, and October 11, 1965; *Business Week*, August 31, 1963; and *Fortune*, March, 1965.

27. Healy, *op. cit.*, pp. 174, 165 ff.; *cf.* C. C. Killingsworth, "The Modernization of West Coast Longshore Work Rules," *Industrial and Labor Relations Review*, April 1962, pp. 297 ff.; H. Swados, *A Radical's America*, Boston, 1962, pp. 47 ff.; and *The New York Times*, October 21, 1959.

28. *Cf. Labor Law Journal*, July 1961, p. 664; and E. Kassalow, "Labor Relations and Employment Aspects After Ten Years," in M. Philipson, ed., *Automation: Implications for the Future*, New York, 1962, pp. 316 ff.

29. *The New York Times*, May 27, 1963; *Business Week*, May 26, 1962; *The Wall Street Journal*, November 20, 1964; *Time*, December 27, 1963; *The New Leader*, July 6, 1964; *The Washington Post*, November 10, 1964; *The Boston Globe*, August 29, 1963; *cf.* also *Union Democracy in Action*, September 1964.

30. U.S.D.L., *Manpower Utilization—Job Security in the Longshore Industry: Port of New York*, Washington, D.C., 1964; *The New York Times*, April 10, 1960, June 9, 1964, June 17, 1964, June 21, 1964, July 6, 1964, September 27, 1964, October 4, 1964, November 7, 1964, and November 8, 1964; *The Wall Street Journal*, June 26, 1964; and *Business Week*, December 12, 1959, and March 14, 1964.

31. *Cf.* Seligman, "Automation and the Unions"; *The New York Times*, November 19, 1962, May 19, 1963, October 14, 1963, October 5, 1964, November 20, 1963, January 17, 1964, April 23, 1964, August 21, 1964; September 4, 1964, October 10, 1964, November 18, 1964, January 2, 1965, March 28, 1965, April 6, 1965, and June 15, 1965; *Business Week*, January 25, 1964; *The Wall Street Journal*, March 25, 1964; and *Dun's Review*, December 1963.

32. Swados, *op. cit.*, pp. 24 ff.; *cf.* also H. M. Caudill, *Night Comes to the Cumberlands*, Boston, 1963; and *Automation*, April 1964.

33. *The Wall Street Journal*, March 15, 1963, August 30, 1963, March 23, 1964, March 24, 1964, December 11, 1964, September 13, 1965, and September 24, 1965; *Business Week*, March 28, 1964, and August 15, 1964; *The Economist*, April 11, 1964; and *The National Observer*, August 30, 1965.

34. Caudill, *op. cit.*; Dan Wakefield, "In Hazard," *Commentary*, September 1963; *The New York Times*, September 3, 1964; and *The Wall Street Journal*, February 7, 1964, April 9, 1964, May 15, 1964, September 2, 1964, September 4, 1964, October 10, 1964, and November 4, 1964.

35. *The Machinist*, September 8, 1960; and *The Wall Street Journal*, February 7, 1962, and January 22, 1963.

36. Healy, *op. cit.*, pp. 43 ff.; *The New York Times*, November 24, 1963, February 16, 1964, and September 20, 1964; *The Wall Street Journal*, March 18, 1964, March 27, 1964, June 5, 1964, June 16, 1964, October 28, 1964, and

March 26, 1965; *Business Week,* March 25, 1961, November 16, 1963, November 23, 1963, March 28, 1964, May 30, 1964, July 4, 1964, September 19, 1964, September 26, 1964, and October 17, 1964; *Fortune,* May 1965; *The Social Security Bulletin,* August 1964; and *The American Federationist,* March 1965.

37. Healy, *op. cit.,* p. 151; Kennedy, *op. cit.,* p. 155; Wilcock and W. H. Franke, *Unwanted Workers,* New York, 1963; *The Monthly Labor Review,* January 1964; *The New York Times,* May 18, 1961, and April 1, 1962; *The Wall Street Journal,* March 21, 1961, August 26, 1963, and September 4, 1964; *Business Week,* July 16, 1960, July 20, 1963, and June 27, 1964; and *The Economist,* September 21, 1963.

38. Report of the Presidential Railroad Commission, Washington, D.C., 1962, especially Appendix, Vol. II and III; P. Arnow, "Findings of the Presidential Railroad Commission," *The Labor Law Journal,* August 1963, pp. 677 ff.; E. B. Shils, "Transportation's Labor Crisis," *The Harvard Business Review,* May–June 1964, pp. 84 ff.; *The New York Times,* July 14, 1963, October 29, 1963, April 2, 1964, April 10, 1964, April 23, 1964, April 28, 1964, May 27, 1964, September 26, 1964, January 23, 1965, and April 1, 1965; *The Wall Street Journal,* January 3, 1963, February 13, 1963, March 18, 1963, April 9, 1963, April 28, 1964, May 7, 1964, April 15, 1964, June 12, 1964, February 9, 1965, March 1, 1965, and April 3, 1965; *The Congressional*

Quarterly, March 18, 1964, and April 24, 1964; *The Washington Post,* December 5, 1962, and September 26, 1964; *Challenge,* May 1963; *Business Week,* September 28, 1963, December 7, 1963, April 11, 1964, and April 25, 1964; *Time,* July 19, 1963; and *Dun's Review,* June 1963.

39. Joint Statement of Kaiser Steel Corporation and United Steelworkers, December 1962, amended, February 1964; *Joint Statement of Results During the First Year,* April 1964; U.S.D.L., *Recent Collective Bargaining and Technological Change;* D. L. Cole, "The Kaiser-Steelworkers Long Range Plan: Has It General Application?" in Markham, *op. cit.,* pp. 63 ff.; Bureau of National Affairs, *52 Labor Relations Reporter 35,* Washington, D.C., 1963; J. Stieber, "Work Rules and Practices in Mass Production Industries," *IRRA Proceedings,* Madison, 1962; *The Monthly Labor Review,* January 1963; *Challenge,* November 1963; *The New York Times,* April 26, 1964, December 6, 1964, and March 18, 1965; *The Wall Street Journal,* August 22, 1962, September 17, 1962, April 26, 1963, July 12, 1963, July 26, 1963, April 7, 1964, May 29, 1964, June 3, 1964, and December 2, 1964; *Business Week,* May 4, 1963, September 21, 1963, September 26, 1964, October 17, 1964, and October 24, 1964; *The Washington Post,* July 30, 1962, December 14, 1962, December 18, 1962, and June 14, 1964; *Dun's Review,* July 1964: and *The Economist,* April 14, 1962, and December 29, 1962.

8 Big brother tries

1. Time, April 2, 1965.

2. Joint Economic Committee, *Automation and Technological Change,* 84th Congress, Washington, D.C., 1955.

3. Report, President's Committee on Labor-Management Policy, January 11, 1962, Washington, D.C.; *cf.* also *Business Week,* January 20, 1962; and

The Monthly Labor Review, February 1962.

4. Cf. B. G. Hickman, *Investment Demand and U.S. Economic Growth*, Washington, D.C., 1965, pp. 177 ff.

5. Report of the Council of Economic Advisers, Washington, 1963, p. 41; *ibid.*, 1964, p. 87.

6. The New York Times, July 24, 1963.

7. United States Senate Committe on Labor, *History of Employment and Man-Power Policy in the United States*, Part IV, Washington, 1965; L. H. Keyserling, "Employment and Economic Progress," in H. L. Lurie, ed., *Encyclopedia of Social Work*, New York, 1965, pp. 283 ff.; and B. B. Seligman, "Economic Planning," in Lurie, *op. cit.*, pp. 262 ff.

8. Cf. C. McKinley, "The Valley Authority and its Alternatives," *The American Political Science Review*, September 1950.

9. Cf. W. H. Miernyk, "Area Redevelopment," in J. M. Becker, ed., *In Aid of the Unemployed*, Baltimore, 1965, pp. 158 ff.; and S. A. Levitan, *Federal Aid to Depressed Areas*, Baltimore, 1964.

10. Levitan, *op. cit.*, pp. 98 ff.; Levitan, *Programs in Aid of the Poor*, Washington, D.C., 1965; *Business Week*, April 21, 1962; *The Wall Street Journal*, October 30, 1963, and June 17, 1965; and *Challenge*, July 1963, November 1963, and April, 1964.

11. Levitan, *Federal Aid*, pp. 1 ff.; and Miernyk, *op. cit.*, pp. 164 ff.

12. Levitan, *Federal Aid*, pp. 251ff.

13. Miernyk, *op. cit.*, p. 161.

14. Levitan, *Federal Aid*, pp. 192–193.

15. K. Komatsu, "Black Christmas in South Bend," *New Politics*, Vol. III, No. 4; *The Wall Street Journal*, December 13, 1963; *The New York Times*, March 13, 1964; *The Washington Post*, August 16, 1964; and *Business Week*, November 7, 1964.

16. The New York Times, March 26, 1965.

17. Cf. H. M. Caudill, *Night Comes to the Cumberlands*, Boston, 1963.

18. The New York Times, November 13, 1963, March 29, 1965 and July 7, 1965; *The Wall Street Journal*, March 10, 1965, and April 28, 1965; *Business Week*, April 24, 1965; and October 9, 1965; *cf.* also J. McHale, "Big Business Enlists for the War on Poverty," *Trans-Action*, May–June 1965.

19. Cf. W. Haber and D. H. Kruger, *The Role of the U.S. Employment Service in a Changing Economy*, Kalamazoo, 1964; H. L. Sheppard, L. A. Ferman, and S. Faber, *Too Old to Work – Too Young to Retire*, Washington, D.C., 1959; and R. C. Wilcock and W. H. Franke, *Unwanted Workers*, New York, 1963, pp. 94 ff.

20. Cf. The Congressional Record, October 3, 1964; U.S.D.L., *Employer Attitudes Toward Advance Notice of Technological Change*, Washington, D.C., 1962; and E. E. Liebhafsky, "Improving the Operation of Labor Markets Through an Employment Service Advance Notice System," *The Southern Economic Journal*, April 1963.

21. The Wall Street Journal, April 22, 1965; and *Business Week*, October 3, 1964.

22. P. Goodman, *Growing Up Absurd*, New York, 1960, pp. 17 ff.; and G. Venn, *Man, Education and Work*, Washington, D.C., 1964.

23. A. A. Blum and C. T. Schmidt, Jr., "Job Training Through Adult Education: The Negro and the Community's Second Chance," unpublished paper, April 1965.

24. Venn, *op. cit.*, p. 29.

25. Cf. H. T. Smith, *Education and Training For the World of Work*, Kalamazoo, 1963; S. M. Miller, "Search for an Educational Revolution," in C. W. Hunnicutt, ed., *Urban Education and Cultural Deprivation*, Syracuse, 1965; Levitan, *Vocational Education and Federal Policy*, Kalamazoo, 1963; H. Rosen, "Vocational Education and

Manpower Needs," *Occupational Outlook Quarterly*, December 1964; G. E. Arnstein, "Vocational Education," *Bulletin of the National Association of Secondary School Principals*, November 1964; U.S.D.L., *Reports of Subcommittees of the President's Committee on Youth Employment*, Washington, D.C., 1963; and U.S.D.L., *Report on Manpower Requirements, Resources, Utilization and Training*, Washington, D.C., 1965, pp. 98 ff.

26. *Cf.* G. G. Somers, "Training the Unemployed," in Becker, *op. cit.*, pp. 227 ff.; U.S.D.L., *Training for Jobs in Redevelopment Areas*, Washington, D.C., 1962; U.S.D.L., *Occupational Training: Pathway to Employment*, Washington, D.C., 1963; and Levitan, *Federal Manpower Policies and Programs to Combat Unemployment*, Kalamazoo, 1964.

27. *The National Observer*, September 30, 1963; *The New York Times*, May 24, 1964; and *Fortune*, May 1962.

28. *Cf.* S. M. Miller and M. Rein, "The War on Poverty: Perspectives and Prospects," in Seligman, ed., *Poverty as A Public Issue*, New York, 1965, pp. 272 ff.

29. N. Kellgren, "An Active Labor Market Policy," Memorandum to the Secretary of Labor, 1963, p. 61; U.S.D.L., *Occupational Mobility Through MDTA Training*, Washington, D.C. 1964; *The Wall Street Journal*, March 25, 1963; and *The New York Times*, April 14, 1962, and December 1, 1962.

30. W. F. Brazziel, *Factors in Workers' Decisions to Forego Retraining Under MDTA*, Washington, D.C., 1964; *The New York Times*, June 24, 1963; *The Washington Post*, June 22, 1964; and *The Wall Street Journal*, April 29, 1964.

31. *Cf.* U.S.D.L., *Manpower Research and Training*, Washington, D.C., 1964, pp. 6 ff.; and *The New York Times*, November 11, 1962.

32. *Cf.* M. K. Freedman, *et al., Getting Hired, Getting Trained*, New York, 1964, pp. 6 ff.; United States Department of Health, Education and Welfare, *Education and Training: The Bridge Between Man and His Work*, Washington, D.C., 1965; U.S.D.L., *Manpower Research and Training*, Washington, D.C., 1965; and U.S.D.L., *MDTA Fact Sheet*, February 16, 1965.

33. *New Society*, March 19, 1964.

34. *Ibid.*

35. U.S.D.L., *Industrial Retraining Programs for Industrial Change*, Washington, D.C., 1963.

36. Blum and Schmidt, *op. cit.*; and *The Wall Street Journal*, August 4, 1964.

37. *The New York Times*, December 6, 1964; *cf.* also *Challenge*, November 1963.

38. Blum and Schmidt, *op. cit.*; *The Washington Post*, April 28, 1965; *The Nation*, May 25, 1963; and J. Froomkin, "Jobs, Skills, and Realities," *Columbia University Forum*, Spring 1964.

39. M. L. Gordon, "U.S. Manpower and Employment Policy," *The Monthly Labor Review*, November 1964; J. K. Galbraith, *The Affluent Society*, Boston, 1958; Galbraith, "Economics and the Quality of Life," *Science*, July 10, 1964; and Galbraith, statement to Joint Economic Committee, February 24, 1965.

40. *Cf.* K. Polanyi, *The Great Transformation*, New York, 1944; and Gordon, *The Economics of Welfare Policies*, New York, 1963, pp. 3 ff.

41. Gordon, *The Economics of Welfare Policies*, pp. 24 ff.

42. *Ibid.*, p. 35; and C. D. Long, *The Labor Force Under Changing Income and Employment*, Princeton, 1958, p. 163.

43. *Cf.* H. L. Sheppard, "The Poverty of Aging," in Seligman, *Poverty as a Public Issue*.

44. Gordon, *The Economics of Welfare Policies*, p. 57.

45. U.S.D.L., *Handbook of UI Financial Data*, Washington, D.C., 1964.

46. *Cf.* Galbraith, *The Affluent Society*, pp. 292 ff.; R. A. Lester, *The Economics of Unemployment Compensation*, Princeton, 1962, p. 301; M. G. Murray "Unemployment Insurance: Risks Covered and Their Financing," in *Becker, op. cit.;* and J. M. Becker, "The Adequacy of Benefits in Unemployment Insurance," in Becker, *op. cit.*

47. R. Theobald, *Free Men and Free Society*, New York, 1963; Theobald, ed., *The Guaranteed Income*, New York, 1966.

48. Ferman, J. L. Kornbluh, and A. Haber, eds., *Poverty in America*, Ann Arbor, 1965, pp. 443 ff.

49. M. Friedman, *Capitalism and Freedom*, Chicago, 1962, pp. 190 ff.

50. J. Tobin, "On Improving The Economic Status of the Negro," *Daedalus*, Fall 1963, pp. 878 ff.

51. R. Lampman, "Negative Rates Income Taxation," Office of Economic Opportunity, Washington, D.C., n.d. (mimeographed).

9 Scientists, engineers and archons

1. *Cf.* F. L. Nussbaum *The Triumph of Science and Reason*, New York, 1953; W. Letwin, *The Origins of Scientific Economics*, London, 1963, especially Chapter 5, pp. 114 ff.; and E. A. Burtt, *The Metaphysical Foundations of Modern Science*, 1932 (reprinted, New York, 1954), pp. 104 ff.

2. *Cf.* J. Bronowski, *The Common Sense of Science*, New York, n.d. (paperback), p. 48.

3. A. N. Whitehead, *Science and the Modern World*, New York, 1925; and L. Marx, *The Machine in the Garden*, New York, 1964, pp. 169 ff.

4. *Cf.* Bronowski, *Science and Human Values*, New York, 1956, p. 73; *cf.* also Bronowski and B. Mazlish, *The Western Intellectual Tradition*, New York, 1960; and J. H. Randall, Jr., *The Making of the Modern Mind*, Boston, 1940.

5. *Cf.* B. Russell, *An Inquiry into Meaning and Truth*, New York, 1940; Russell, *Human Knowledge*, New York, 1948; Ludwig Wittgenstein, *Tractatus Logico-Philosophicus*, New York, 1961; Bronowski, *Science and Human Values*, p. 48; on positivist rejection of values, *cf.* R. von Mises, *Positivism*, New York, 1956; and P. Bridgman, *The Way Things Are*, Cambridge, Mass., 1959.

6. M. Merleau-Ponty, *The Primacy of Perception*, Evanston, 1964, pp. 159–160; *cf.* Whitehead, *op. cit.*, p. 59; F. G. Juenger, *The Failure of Technology*, Chicago, 1949; and E. Kahler, *The Meaning of History*, New York, 1964, pp. 132 ff.

7. *Cf.* Juenger, *op. cit.*

8. J. Barzun, *Science: The Glorious Entertainment*, New York, 1964, p. 5.

9. P. Valéry, *The Outlook for Intelligence*, New York, 1962, p. 77.

10. *Cf.* J. Ellul, *The Technological Society*, New York, 1964, *passim*.

11. *Cf.* K. E. Boulding, *The Organizational Revolution*, New York, 1953; and B. B. Seligman, "The American Corporation: Ideology and Reality," *Dissent*, Summer 1964.

12. *Cf.* Congressional Hearings on Atomic Energy, 79th Congress, 1946, cited by H. S. Hall in B. Barber and W. Hirsch, *The Sociology of Science*, New York, 1962, pp. 269 ff.

13. *Cf.* J. S. Dupre and S. A. Lakoff, *Science and the Nation*, Englewood Cliffs, 1962, pp. 81 ff.

14. *The New York Times*, November 16, 1964.

15. K. Mannheim, *Ideology and Utopia*, New York, 1936, pp. 155 ff.; and

Mannheim, *Essays in the Sociology of Culture*, London, 1956, pp. 117 ff.

16. M. Lerner, *America as Civilization*, New York, 1957, p. 236.

17. R. M. Hutchins, *et al.*, *Science, Scientists and Politics*, Santa Barbara, 1963; *cf.* also the furious attack on science and experts by J. Ortega y Gasset, *The Revolt of the Masses*, New York, 1932 (paperback, 1950), pp. 78 ff.; and *The New York Times*, November 20, 1964, December 28, 1964, and December 31, 1964.

18. *Cf.* K. Denbigh, *Science, Industry and Social Policy*, London, 1963; Bridgman, *op. cit.*; and N. Wiener, *God and Golem Inc.*, Cambridge, Mass., 1964.

19. *Cf.* Burtt, "Value Presuppositions of Science," in P. C. Obler and H. A. Estrin, eds., *The New Scientist*, New York, 1962.

20. W. A. Faunce and D. A. Clelland, "The Professional Society," *New Society*, November 7, 1963.

21. *Cf.* E. Ashby, *Technology and the Academics*, London, 1958.

22. R. Graves, "900 Iron Chariots," lecture at M.I.T. reprinted in *The Saturday Review*, December 7, 1963; *cf.* also G. Friedmann, *The Anatomy of Work*, New York, 1961, pp. 146 ff.

23. Ashby, *op. cit.*, p. 88.

24. *Cf.* H. S. Becker and J. Carper, "Elements of Identification with an Occupation," in Barber and Hirsch, *op. cit.*, pp. 288 ff.

25. *Cf.* W. M. Evan, "On the Margin — The Engineering Technician," in P. L. Berger, ed., *The Human Shape of Work*, New York, 1964, pp. 83 ff.

26. U.S.D.L., *Employment of Scientific and Technical Personnel in Industry*, Washington, D.C., 1964.

27. *Cf.* W. H. Whyte, Jr., *The Organization Man*, New York, 1956, pp. 205 ff.; C. B. Randall, *The Folklore of Management*, New York, 1962; and R. Presthus, *The Organizational Society*, New York, 1962, pp. 290 ff.

28. S. Marcson, *The Scientist in Industry*, Princeton, 1960, pp. 51 ff.; and *cf.* N. Kaplan, "Organization: Will It Choke or Promote the Growth of Science?" in K. Hill, ed., *The Management of Scientists*, Boston, 1964, p. 116.

29. Wiener in *The Bulletin of the Atomic Scientists*, November 1948, quoted in L. S. Feuer, *The Scientific Intellectual*, New York, 1963, p. 399.

30. F. L. Polak, *The Image of the Future*, II, New York, 1961, 185 ff.

31. *Cf. New Society*, January 2, 1964.

32. *Fortune*, August 1964.

33. H. A. Simon, "New Developments in the Theory of the Firm," *Papers and Proceedings of the American Economic Association*, May 1962, p. 6.

34. I. R. Hoos, "When the Computer Takes Over the Office," *The Harvard Business Review*, July–August 1960.

35. *Business Week*, September 21, 1963; and *The Wall Street Journal*, September 19, 1963.

36. *Cf.* H. M. Wriston in J. T. Dunlop, ed., *Automation and Technological Change*, Englewood Cliffs, 1962, pp. 169 ff.

37. *Fortune*, March 1964; *Automation*, May 1964, June 1964, August 1964, September 1964, November 1964, March 1965, and June 1965; and *Dun's Review*, September 1964, and October 1964.

38. L. R. Fiock, Jr., "Seven Deadly Dangers in EDP," *The Harvard Business Review*, May–June 1962; *cf.* also J. R. Bright, "Opportunity and Threat in Technological Change," *The Harvard Business Review*, November–December 1963; *Dun's Review*, February 1963; *Data Processing*, September 1962; and *Home Furnishings Daily*, October 2, 1964.

39. H. J. Leavitt and T. L. Whisler, "Management in the 1980's," *The Harvard Business Review*, November–December 1958; and G. P. Shultz and Whisler, eds., *Managment Organization and the Computer*, New York, 1960, pp. 3 ff.

40. Simon, "The Corporation: Will It Be Managed by Machines?" in M. L. Anshen and G. L. Bach, eds., *Management and the Corporation*, New York, 1960, pp. 17 ff.

41. Cited in *Fortune*, August 1964.

42. Dun's Review, July 1964; *cf.* also F. E. Emery and J. Marek, "Some Socio-technical Aspects of Automation," *Human Relations*, 15, No. 1, 1962, 17.

43. Women's Wear Daily, September 30, 1964.

44. Hoos, *op. cit.*; *Dun's Review*, July 1963, and September 1964; T. D. C. Kuch, "Managers and Machines,"

Dissent, Spring 1963; and J. Diebold, "ADP: The Still Sleeping Giant," *The Harvard Business Review*, September–October 1964.

45. Cf. Diebold, *op. cit.*

46. Business Week, June 21, 1958, and February 29, 1964.

47. Cf. Whyte, *op. cit.*, pp. 243 ff.; *Business Week*, June 12, 1965; and *Business Automation*, February 1965.

48. Hoos, *op. cit.*; *The Wall Street Journal*, June 29, 1964; *Dun's Review*, September 1963; and *Business Week*, November 10, 1962.

49. Quoted by C. R. Bowen in *The Bulletin of National Association of Secondary School Principals*, November 1964, p. 13.

10 Conventional wisdoms

1. Cf. A. Gourvitch, *Survey of Economic Theory on Technological Change and Employment*, Philadelphia, 1940; and P. Douglas, "Technological Unemployment," *The American Federationist*, August 1930.

2. Douglas, *op. cit.*, p. 929.

3. Cf. S. R. Sen, *The Economics of Sir James Steuart*, Cambridge, Eng., 1957, p. 135.

4. T. R. Malthus, *Principles of Political Economy*, 1836 (reprinted, New York, 1951), p. 360.

5. D. Ricardo, *Principles of Political Economy* 1821 (Sroffa edition, Cambridge, Eng., 1951), p. 388.

6. Cf. B. B. Seligman, *Main Currents in Modern Economics*, New York, 1962, pp. 477 ff., 730 ff.

7. G. D. H. Cole and R. Postgate, *The British Common People: 1746–1938*, New York, 1939, pp. 263 ff.; *cf.* also R. Lekachman, "Automation is Nothing New," *Challenge*, April 1963; and E. P. Thompson, *The Making of The English Working Class*, New York, 1963, pp. 359, 565.

8. Automation, November 1964.

9. J. Diebold, *Automation: Its Impact on Business and Labor*, Washington, D.C., 1959, p. 24.

10. Ibid.

11. J. R. Bright, *Research Development and Technological Innovation*, Homewood, 1964, p. 2.; and P. Einzig, *The Economic Consequences of Automation*, New York, 1957.

12. D. A. Laird and E. C. Laird, *How to Get Along with Automation*, New York, 1964.

13. The New York Times, March 22, 1964.

14. W. H. Ferry, address to San Diego, California, forum, November 8, 1964.

15. Research Institute of America report, December 27, 1963.

16. Automation, April 1964.

17. R. Solo, "Automation: Technique, Mystique, Critique," *The Journal of Business*, April 1963.

18. R. M. Solow, "Investment and Technical Progress," in K. J. Arrow, S. Karlin, and P. Suppes, eds., *Mathematical*

Methods in the Social Sciences: 1959, Stanford, 1960, pp. 89 ff.

19. Einzig, *op. cit.* pp. 48 ff.; and *The Wall Street Journal*, April 15, 1963.

20. Survey of Current Business, Washington, D.C., April 1963; and Economic Statistics Bureau, *Basic Economic Statistics*, Washington, D.C., May 1964.

21. Cf. Diebold, *op. cit.*, pp. 42 ff.

22. Automation, April 1964.

23. R. A. Beaumont and R. B. Helfgott, *Management, Automation and People*, New York, 1964, p. 26.

24. Statement of R. S. Weinberg, IBM Advanced Systems Division, to author, October 1, 1964.

25. S. P. Sobotka and T. A. Domencich, *Profile of Michigan—Economic Trends and Paradoxes*, New York, 1963.

26. D. Fusfeld, in review of *ibid.*, *The American Economic Review*, June 1964, p. 445.

27. Automation, November 1964; *cf.* also W. A. Wallis, "Some Economic Considerations," in J. T. Dunlop, ed., *Automation and Technological Change*, Englewood Cliffs, 1962, pp. 103 ff.

28. Statistical Abstract, Washington, D.C., 1964, p. 499; *Business Statistics*, Washington, D.C., 1963, p. 9; and *The American Federationist*, July 1964.

29. K. Wicksell, *Value, Capital and Rent* 1893 (reprinted, London, 1954), p. 137; and Wicksell, *Lectures on Political Economy*, I, 1901 (reprinted, New York, 1934), pp. 269 ff., 291 ff.

30. Cf. J. Robinson, *Collected Economic Papers*, II, Oxford, 1960, p. 185.

31. Robinson, *The Accumulation of Capital*, London, 1956, p. 78.

32. Ibid., p. 79.

33. Ibid., p. 94.

34. Cf. Y. Brozen, "The Economics of Automation," *The American Economic Association Proceedings*, May 1957, pp. 339 ff.; and Brozen, *Automation: The Impact of Technological Change*, Washington, D.C., 1963.

35. H. J. Habakkuk, *American and British Technology in the 19th Century*, Cambridge, Eng., 1962; N. J. Simler, "The Structural Hypothesis and Public Policy," *The American Economics Review*, December 1964; and E. R. F. W. Crossman, "Automation, Skill and Manpower Predictions," Office of Manpower, Automation and Training Seminar, Washington, D.C.; April 1965.

36. Statistical Abstract, Washington, D.C., 1964, p. 541; and *Historical Statistics of the U.S.*, Washington, D.C., 1960, pp. 613–614.

37. The Wall Street Journal, November 13, 1964.

38. Cf. G. J. Stigler, *Capital and Rates of Return in Manufacturing Industries*, Princeton, 1963, p. 5; and S. Kuznets, *Capital in the American Economy*, Princeton, 1961.

39. A. J. Jaffee, testimony to Senate Labor Committee, September 26, 1963; and *Business Week*, September 14, 1963.

40. U.S.D.L., *Indexes of Output per Man-Hour: Selected Industries, 1939 and 1947–62*, Washington, D.C., 1964; and U.S.D.L., *Indexes of Output per Man-Hour: Primary Aluminum Industry, 1947–62*, Washington, D.C., 1964.

41. M. J. Ulmer, *Capital in Transportation, Communication and Public Utilities*, Princeton, 1960, pp. 179 ff.; D. Creamer, S. P. Dobrovolsky, and I. Borenstein, *Capital in Manufacturing and Mining*, Princeton, 1960; and E. D. Domar, "The Capital Output Ratio in the United States: Its Variation and Stability," in F. A. Lutz and D. C. Hague, eds., *The Theory of Capital*, London, 1961, pp. 95 ff.

42. The New York Times, January 16, 1964.

43. Silberman, in *The American Child*, November 1964, p. 8.

44. Automation, April 1964; *The New York Times*, September 25, 1962,
427

October 4, 1963, and March 22, 1964; *The Wall Street Journal*, November 20, 1963; *Dun's Review*, December 1963; *The American Child*, November 1964; and Bureau of National Affairs, *The Daily Labor Report*, October 28, 1963.
45. *Cf.* S. Moos, "Automation and Employment," *The Political Quarterly*, January–March 1964; *The Washington Post*, September 29, 1963; *The New York Times*, November 18, 1963; and

March 22, 1964; J. P. Lewis, "The Unemployment Problem," address to the Southern Economic Association, November 14, 1963; and W. W. Heller, testimony to Senate Labor Committee, October 28, 1963; and C. C. Killingsworth, testimony to Senate Labor Committee, September 20, 1963.
46. R. L. Heilbroner, "The Impact of Technology: The Historic Debate," in Dunlop, *op. cit.*, p. 22.

11 Time on our hands

1. T. Veblen, *Essays in Our Changing Order*, New York, 1934, pp. 78 ff.
2. Veblen, *The Instinct of Workmanship*, New York, 1914, *passim*.
3. P. Schrecker, *Work and History*, Princeton, 1948.
4. S. Diamond, *The Search For the Primitive*, Washington, D.C., n.d., p. 90; R. Seidenberg, *Post-Historic Man*, Boston, 1957; and P. Radin, *Primitive Man as Philosopher*, New York, 1927.
5. G. Friedmann, *Où va la travail humaine?* Paris, 1950, p. 37.
6. Schrecker, *op. cit.*, p. 13.
7. R. S. Weiss and D. Riesman, "Social Problems and Disorganization in the World of Work," in R. K. Merton and R. A. Nisbet, eds., *Contemporary Social Problems*, New York, 1961, pp. 455 ff.
8. *Cf.* K. Marx, "Alienated Labor," from *Economic and Philosophical Manuscripts* (1844), in E. Fromm, *Marx's Concept of Man*, New York, 1961, pp. 93 ff; H. Arendt, *The Human Condition*, Chicago, 1958, p. 140; and R. Tucker, *Philosophy and Myth in Karl Marx*, London, 1961, pp. 123 ff.
9. Schrecker, *op. cit.*, p. 123.
10. *Ibid.*, p. 133; and Arendt, *op. cit.*, pp. 8, 94.
11. Schrecker, *op. cit.*, p. 140; *cf.* also F. W. Howton, "Work Assignment and

Interpersonal Relations in a Research Organization: Some Participant Observations," *The Administrative Science Quarterly*, March 1963, p. 502.
12. S. Giedion, *Mechanization Takes Command*, New York, 1948, p. 715.
13. *Ibid.*, p. 720.
14. Schrecker, *op. cit.*, p. 212.
15. *Ibid.*, p. 254, 259; *cf.* also K. Löwith, *From Hegel to Nietzsche*, New York, 1964, pp. 263 ff.; and R. Dubin, "Industrial Workers' Worlds," *Social Problems*, January 1956.
16. S. Freud, *Civilization and Its Discontents*, (paperback), New York, 1958, pp. 20–21.
17. J. A. Hobson, *Work and Wealth*, London, 1914, pp. 44 ff.
18. *Ibid.*, p. 62.
19. *Cf.* Weiss and Riesman, *op. cit.*, p. 473; C. W. Mills, *White Collar*, New York, 1951, p. 221; and Riesman, *The Lonely Crowd*, New Haven, 1950, pp. 133 ff.
20. Arendt, *op. cit.*, p. 84; and S. de Grazia, *Of Time, Work, and Leisure*, New York, 1962, pp. 37 ff.
21. *Cf.* F. R. B. Godolphin, ed., *The Greek Historians*, I, New York, 1942, p. 597.
22. Arendt, *op. cit.*, p. 32.
23. Mills, *op. cit.*, pp. 218 ff.; *cf.* also K. Jaspers, *The Origin and Goal of*

History, New Haven, 1953, p. 107.
24. Cf. R. H. Tawney, *Religion and the Rise of Capitalism*, New York, 1926; and A. Tilgher, *Work: What It Has Meant to Men Through the Ages,* New York, 1930.
25. Cf. Fromm, *op. cit.*, especially reprint of Marx's early paper "Alienated Labor," pp. 93 ff.; Jaspers, *op. cit.,* p. 114; and K. Polanyi, *The Great Transformation*, New York, 1944.
26. Mills, *op. cit.*, p. 200.
27. Arendt, *op. cit.*, pp. 4, 46; Schrecker, *op. cit.,* p. 270; *cf.* also E. Chinoy, "Manning the Machines – The Assembly Line Worker," in P. L. Berger, ed., *The Human Shape of Work,* New York, 1964, pp. 51 ff.
28. De Grazia, *op. cit.*, pp. 299 ff.; and S. Weil, "Factory Work," *Politics*, December 1946.
29. H. Swados, *A Radical's America*, Boston, 1962, p. 115; W. G. Dyer, "Family Reactions To The Father's Job," in A. B. Shostak and W. Gomberg, *Blue Collar World*, Englewood Cliffs, 1964, p. 86; and D. Caplovitz, "The Problems of Blue Collar Consumers," in Shostak and Gomberg, *op. cit.*, pp. 110 ff.
30. Cf. B. Karsh, "The Meaning of Work in an Age of Automation," *Current Economic Comment*, August 1957; R. S. Weiss and R. L. Kahn, "Definitions of Work and Occupation," *Social Problems*, Fall 1960; N. C. Morse and Weiss, "The Function and Meaning of Work and the Job," *The American Sociological Review*, April 1955; E. H. Friedmann and R. J. Havighurst, *The Meaning of Work and Retirement*, Chicago, 1954; A. S. Tannenbaum, ed., *The Worker in the New Industrial Environment*, Ann Arbor, 1962; R. W. Hodge, P. M. Siegel, and P. H. Rossi, "Occupational Prestige in the United States, 1925–63," *The American Journal of Sociology*, November 1964; and H. J. Loether, "The Meaning of Work and Adjustment to Retirement," in Shostak and Gomberg, *op. cit.*, pp. 517 ff.
31. L. Mumford, *The Condition of Man*, New York, 1944, p. 5, (italics in original).
32. D. Bell, *Work and Its Discontents*, Boston, 1956; and H. Marcuse, *One-Dimensional Man*, Boston, 1964.
33. Cf. Freud, *op. cit., passim*; and J. Ellul, *The Technological Society*, New York, 1964, p. 320.
34. Cf. G. Friedmann, *Industrial Society*, New York, 1955, pp. 291 ff.; and Ellul, *Propaganda: The Formation of Men's Attitudes*, New York, 1965, pp. 140–141.
35. Quoted by E. Kahler, *The Tower and the Abyss*, New York, 1957, p. 24.
36. Marx, *op. cit.*, p. 95.
37. New Society, February 2, 1964; and *cf.* K. Keniston, *The Uncommitted*, New York, 1965.
38. R. Blauner, *Alienation and Freedom*, Chicago, 1964.
39. Cf. Chapter 6; *cf.* also H. L. Wilensky, "Varieties of Work Experience," in H. Borow, ed., *Man in a World of Work*, Boston, 1964, pp. 138 ff.
40. L. Feuer, "What is Alienation?: The Career of a Concept," *New Politics*, Spring 1962, p. 116.
41. C. R. Walker and R. Guest, *Man on The Assembly Line*, Cambridge, Mass., 1952, p. 54; and Wilensky, *op. cit.*, pp. 146–148.
42. Cf. R. Williams, *The Long Revolution*, London, 1961, p. 77; Williams, "Prelude to Alienation," *Dissent*, Summer 1964, pp. 303 ff.; and M. Merleau-Ponty, *Signs*, Evanston, 1964, p. 242.
43. Merleau-Ponty, *op. cit.*, p. 33; and Williams, *The Long Revolution*, p. 88.
44. Ellul, *op. cit.*, p. 321.
45. Cf. W. H. Whyte, Jr., *The Organization Man*, New York, 1956; and J. R. Seeley, R. A. Sim, and E. W. Loosley, *Crestwood Heights*, New York, 1956.
46. Kahler, *op. cit.*, p. 9.
47. F. Tönnies, *Community and Society*, 1887 (paperback, New York, 1963).

48. Kahler, *op. cit.*, p. 207.

49. M. Buber, *Pointing the Way* (paperback), New York, 1963, p. 8.

50. Jaspers, *op. cit.*, p. 97.

51. De Grazia, *op. cit.*, pp. 63 ff.; *cf.* also S. Pieper, *Leisure, The Basis of Culture*, New York, 1952.

52. Cf. P. Radin, *Primitive Religion*, New York, 1937; M. Herskovitz, *Man and His Works*, New York, 1948, pp. 286 ff.; and *Encyclopaedia of Social Sciences*, II, New York, 1930, 89, 100, and IX, New York, 1930, 402.

53. Cf. Mumford, *The City in History*, New York, 1961, pp. 269 ff.; and J. Gassner, *Masters of the Drama*, New York, 1940, pp. 144 ff.

54. Cf. Riesman, *Abundance for What?* New York, 1964, pp. 147–148; and N. Anderson, *Work and Leisure*, New York, 1961, p. 2.

55. W. E. Moore, *Man, Time, and Society*, New York, 1963, p. 35.

56. R. Callois, *Man, Play and Games*, New York, 1961, p. 32.

57. Cf. J. Huizinga, *Homo Ludens* (paperback), Boston, 1955.

58. Outdoor Recreation Resources Review Committee, *Trends in American Living and Outdoor Recreation*, Washington, D.C., 1962; D. N. Michael, "Free Time – The New Imperative in Our Society," *Vital Speeches*, August 1, 1963, p. 616; and *The Wall Street Journal*, February 3, 1965.

59. Wilensky, "The Uneven Distribution of Leisure," *Social Problems*, Summer 1961, p. 33.

60. Ibid., p. 36.

61. Ibid., pp. 51–52; *cf.* also G. A. Lundberg, M. Komarovsky, and M. A. McInerny, *Leisure: A Suburban Study*, New York, 1934; and M. W. Clawson, "How much Leisure, Now and in the Future," in J. C. Charlesworth, ed., *Leisure in America: Blessing or Curse?* Philadelphia, 1964.

62. Mills, *op. cit.*, p. 238.

63. Cf. C. K. Brightbill, *The Challenge of Leisure*, Englewood Cliffs, 1960, pp. 16 ff.

64. Swados, *op. cit.*, p. 129.

65. Ibid., p. 102; *The New York Times*, March 8, 1965; and the Rockefeller Brothers' Panel, *The Performing Arts*, New York, 1965.

66. Cf. Charlesworth, *op. cit.*, pp. 30 ff.; Faunce, "Automation and Leisure," in H. B. Jacobson and J. S. Roucek, eds., *Automation and Society*, New York, 1959, p. 304; Friedmann, *The Anatomy of Work*, New York, 1961, pp. 104 ff.; R. Hoggart, *The Uses of Literacy*, London, 1957; Ellul, *op. cit.*, pp. 400 ff.; Marcuse, cited in H. Collins, "The Sedentary Society," in E. Larrabee and R. Meyersohn, eds., *Mass Leisure*, New York, 1958, p. 23; and H. Levin, "Semantics of Culture," *Daedalus*, Winter 1965.

67. Levin, *op. cit.*, p. 13.

12 Ice age of perfection

1. The Washington Post, May 24, 1965.

2. Automation: Research Report No. 2, Manpower Research Council, Milwaukee, 1965.

3. News Front, April 1965.

4. Cf. J. E. Meade, *Efficiency, Equality and the Ownership of Property*, London, 1964, pp. 22 ff.

5. Automation, November 1964; *Business Week*, April 28, 1962, and December 22, 1962; F. Pollack, *Automation: Materielen zur Beurteilung ihrer Ökonomischen und sozialen Folgen*, Frankfurt, 1964, pp. 357 ff.; and *The New York Times*, July 21, 1963.

6. The New York Times, October 20, 1963, and January 15, 1965.

7. *The New York Times*, January 10, 1964, and October 12, 1964; Pollack, *op. cit.*, pp. 360, 367, and G. Friedrichs, ed., *Automation und Technischer Fortschritt in Deutschland und den USA*, Frankfurt, 1963.

8. *T.U.C. Releases*, New Series, No. 114, 137; *Canadian Labour*, April 1964; and *Data Processing*, September 1962.

9. *The New Society*, January 16, 1964.

10. *The Wall Street Journal*, August 2, 1962.

11. Pollack, *op. cit.*, pp. 391 ff.; *The New York Times*, January 18, 1965, March 12, 1965, and June 27, 1965; *The Wall Street Journal*, August 2, 1962; and June 18, 1965; and *The Washington Post*, June 21, 1964.

12. *Cf.* S. Demczynski, *Automation and the Future of Man*, London, 1964, p. 66.

13. L. Bagrit, *The Age of Automation* (paperback), New York 1965.

14. *Cf.* E. Gellner, *Thought and Change*, Chicago, 1964, pp. 3 ff.

15. *Cf.* R. L. Heilbroner, *The Future as History*, New York, 1959, pp. 17 ff.

16. R. Seidenberg, *Post-Historic Man*, Chapel Hill, 1950, pp. 64 ff.

17. *Cf.* A. Solomon, *The Tyranny of Progress*, New York, 1955; J. L. Talmon, *The Rise of Totalitarian Democracy*, London, 1952; and Talmon, *Political Messianism*, London, 1960.

18. E. Kahler, *The Meaning of History*, New York, 1964, pp. 145, 173–174.

19. *Cf.* M. Curti, *The Growth of American Thought*, New York, 1943, p. 174.

20. *Cf.* L. Marx, *The Machine in the Garden*, New York, 1964, pp. 181 ff.

21. *Cf.* Kahler, *op. cit.*, pp. 21 ff.; Heilbroner, *op. cit.*, p. 203; and M. Harrington, *The Accidental Century*, New York, 1965.

22. *Cf.* H. Marcuse, *One Dimensional Man*, Boston, 1964.

23. *Ibid.*, p. 26.

24. *Ibid.*, pp. 154, 166.

25. Kahler, *op. cit.*, p. 135 (italics in original).

26. Seidenberg, *op. cit.*, pp. 1 ff.

27. *Ibid.*, p. 29.

28. E. H. Erikson, *Insight and Responsibility*, New York, 1964, p. 104.

29. P. Goodman, *People or Personnel*, New York, 1965, p. 11.

30. Harrington, *op. cit.*, p. 41.

31. Kahler, *op. cit.*, pp. 215–216.

32. *The Washington Post*, September 19, 1965.

33. *Cf.* N. Calder, "The Control and Use of Technology," *The Nation*, January 4, 1965.

34. R. Boguslaw, *The New Utopians*, Englewood Cliffs, 1965.

35. Marx, *op. cit.*, p. 175.

Index

Index

Index

435

Index

436

Index

Index